Ferries 20

Europe's leading guide to the
UK & Northern European ferry

Europe's **leading** guide to the ferry industry

Contents...

Produced and designed by Ferry Publications trading as Lily Publications Ltd
PO Box 33, Ramsey, Isle of Man, British Isles, IM99 4LP.
Tel: +44 (0) 1624 898446 Fax: +44 (0) 1624 898449
www.ferrypubs.co.uk e-mail: info@lilypublications.co.uk
ISBN: 978-1-911268-28-4

Europe's **leading** guide to the ferry industry

Introduction...

This is the thirty-second edition of this book, which first appeared in 1983 as the 24-page 'home published' *'Car Ferries from Great Britain and Ireland'*. The book aims to list every passenger/vehicle ferry in Great Britain and Ireland, ro-ro freight vessels which operate regular services between Great Britain and Ireland and to nearby Continental destinations and major passenger/vehicle ferries in other parts of Northern Europe. The coverage of Northern Europe is not fully comprehensive (to make it so would probably triple the size of the book) and does not include freight-only operations and vessels - although freight-only vessels have been included where the operators also run passenger services. Where operators use a mixture of ro-ro and container ships, I have only included the ro-ro ships. Exceptionally I have included the *Arx* of CLdN/Cobelfret Ferries and the *Elisabeth* of P&O as they operate to provide additional container capacity on ro-ro routes.

Each operator is listed alphabetically within sections - major operators, minor operators, freight-only operators, chain, cable and float ferries, passenger-only ferries, other North European passenger operators and vehicle/passenger vessels owned by companies not currently engaged in operating services. After details relating to each company's management, address, telephone numbers, email, website and services, there is a fleet list with technical data and then a potted history of each vessel with previous names and dates.

Nick Widdows
Whitstable, Kent
August 2019

Pearl Seaways *(Rob de Visser))*

Foreword...

In seeking to provide a fresh overview of developments in the northern European ferry industry for this issue, one is reminded of how slow the passage of history can be. Too many of the issues raised previously have made glacial progress in the twelve months since the last edition of this book was published. Principal amongst these is the implementation of the UK's decision to leave the European Union (EU), which has fundamental consequences for all international ferry services around the UK.

The UK government's support to Brittany Ferries and DFDS (and the nascent Seaborne Freight) in anticipation of a 'no-deal' UK exit from the EU on 31 March 2019 proved unnecessary, forcing a change of travel plans for many, as schedules were altered to meet the government's needs to provide additional freight capacity away from the choke-point of Dover. But this provided a useful boost in ferry company income at a time when domestic uncertainty in the UK forced a pause in bookings, and a collapsing pound cast shadows on the industry's prospects for the peak summer season. The great British hope was Seaborne Freight and its ongoing ambitions to re-open services from Ramsgate to Oostende; the company was allocated £13.8m in support, but this was subsequently withdrawn when it became apparent there was little short-term prospect of the company's ambitions being fulfilled, despite the confidence and backing from the UK Department of Transport. A company with no track record, no ships, with proposals to introduce services from a port which required significant investment seemed an odd government focus to many observers. The process of allocation of funds was successfully challenged by Eurotunnel, which secured £35m in compensation to be invested in terminal improvements on the basis of their short-lived involvement in MyFerryLink. To make matters worse for the government, this out of court settlement was then contested by P&O Ferries, who cited their competitive disadvantage against Eurotunnel in their challenge. The outcome of this is awaited at the time of writing.

All of this highlights the decline of UK interests in the vital ferry services around its shores. At a time when the nation is seeking to 'take back control' by leaving the EU, it is totally dependent on overseas-owned interests to provide the passenger links with Europe, and the majority of freight traffic is shipped under similar ownership. Only domestic ferry services within UK waters remain strongly operated by UK interests. What a change from the UK-dominance of European business by Sealink, Townsend Thoresen and P&O Ferries when the previous UK referendum on EU membership was held in 1975...

One of the key Brexit stumbling points remains the Irish border question, which will remain as the only land border between an independent UK and the EU. Both Brittany Ferries and Irish Ferries increased capacity of their direct 'by-pass' links between Ireland and the EU in 2018/19 with the addition of the *Connemara* and *W.B. Yeats* respectively. The *W.B. Yeats* slipped quietly into service in January 2019 without the fanfare her arrival might have precipitated if she had been delivered in summer 2018 as planned, but this muted introduction should not detract from her being the first new large ferry for UK waters since the *Spirit of France* in 2012. The *W.B. Yeats* has been hoovering up awards and customer plaudits despite these setbacks, indicating the success of her dual-purpose design to serve both the short Dublin-Holyhead crossing and the longer links from Dublin to Cherbourg, where her 22.5kt speed allows for a reduction in crossing time.

The late arrival of the *W.B. Yeats* was embarrassing for both Irish Ferries, which was forced to reschedule the vital summer and autumn season, and builder Flensburger Schiffbau-Gesellschaft of Fensburg, Germany. The impact on the Yard had a knock-on effect on delivery of Brittany Ferries' *Honfleur,* which has now missed her planned July 2019 introduction. But Irish Ferries remain on course to take a second new cruise ferry from the yard for the Dublin-Holyhead route - the largest cruiseferry in the world - in late 2020. Modern ship construction is frequently planned to achieve heroic relative compared to comparable land investment, and

Stena Estrid *(Stena Line)*

Glen Sannox *(Mark Nicolson)*

Visborg *(John Bryant)*

Color Hybrid *(Color Line)*

these problems are a reminder that it doesn't take much to stall delivery and face the consequences.

Similar issues thwarted the ambitions of Polferries to introduce the chartered *Nova Star* as the company's flagship on the Nynäshamn-Gdansk route, with the vessel delayed from June to September 2018 during her extensive refit at Gdansk. 'Just in time' is a sound management philosophy when it works, particularly when enhanced summer market capacity can be delivered at the right moment, but the reputational and financial fallout when a company fails to deliver outweighs any additional cost of bringing in capacity before the main season and bedding it in slowly.

Delivery problems of a more protracted nature continue to befall the *Glen Sannox* and the second vessel, *Hull 802*, commissioned by Caledonian Maritime Assets (CMAL) for Caledonian MacBrayne (CalMac) services, and being built at Ferguson's Marine shipyard on the River Clyde, in Port Glasgow. The battle between the two - over alleged additional costs of £61m incurred as a result of design changes - has cast doubts over the future of Scotland's small shipbuilding sector, and fuelled concerns about the reliability of island ferry services. CalMac's ageing 31-vessel fleet has a number of vessels on lifeline routes more than three decades old. The 100m dual-fuel *Glen Sannox*, which is due to operate on Arran services, was intended to enter service in 2018, but is now not expected to sail until the middle of 2020 at the earliest. The second vessel will serve the far-western Outer Hebrides but remains under construction at the Ferguson yard. Both vessels were ordered under a fixed-price design-and-build contract. Whilst the parties prolong their argument, the real losers are the passengers, deprived of much-needed additional modern capacity.

Despite these problems the order book for new ferry capacity remains buoyant, with a healthy volume of new tonnage expected to keep the authors of *Ferries 2021* (and beyond!) busy. Foremost amongst the new builds are the nine orders for the Stena Ro-Ro E-Flexer design – with options for a further two. They are fast becoming a flexible design of choice across the northern European ferry market, with Brittany Ferries agreeing to long term charter three vessels, a further three destined for Stena's Irish Sea operations, and DFDS bringing one to the short sea Dover-Calais crossing, breaking an unprecedently long void of orders for that sector. All nine vessels will be delivered between 2020 and 2023.

The Brittany Ferries commitment to E-Flexers is part of a €550m fleet renewal and investment programme, a substantial stake in the post-Brexit British market for a French company whose revenues are predominantly generated in sterling. The company remains committed to the employment of French seafarers, and will see the investment as protection of its western Channel monopoly on all UK routes west of Newhaven-Dieppe. Whether the company will consolidate this position with a bid for the Condor Channel Island business, or see competition on its doorstep in St Malo from another operator such as DFDS, remains to be seen.

New fast craft have been added to the north European fleet with the arrival of *Express 4*, a 109m Austal catamaran design with a 40kt service speed and capacity for 1,000 passengers and 425 cars for Molslinjen's Sjællands Odde-Århus service. Amongst domestic service operators, *Victoria of Wight* and *Red Kestrel* represent multi-purpose and freight investment by competitors for the Isle of Wight business. Elsewhere differing power sources are to the fore as *Tycho Brahe* and *Aurora af Helsingborg* usher in a new era of battery power to the Helsingør-Helsingborg route, LNG is the fuel of choice for *Huftarøy* and Samnøy on the Norwegian Halhjem-Sandvikvåg service, and diesel-electric propulsion is favoured by FosenNamsos Sjø with the *Lagatun* and *Munken* on their new Flakk-Rørvik route.

A glance through this volume will illustrate that there is plenty more in the offing, with new vessels ordered for Fjord1, Havilen Kystruten, Kvarken Link, Norled, Polferries Tallink, TT Line, and Viking Line. Driven by easier vessel-financing options, this cumulative pattern of investment represents not just the highest tonnage of new vessels on record, but a confidence in the long-term future of ferry travel despite the political uncertainties of the modern era. Coupled with a drive for sustainability and a move towards innovative fuel sources, the industry is gearing up to meet future environmental challenges. An exciting time indeed!

Richard Kirkman, Editor of Ferry & Cruise Review

IRISH FERRIES NEW CRUISEFERRY - W.B. YEATS

The *W.B. Yeats* is a significant ferry in many ways. Foremost the €144 million and 51,388 gt ferry is the first large new build to operate in UK Waters since 2012 when the *Spirit of France* was delivered to P&O Ferries. The *W.B. Yeats* is the largest and most luxurious ferry to sail on the Irish Sea but is also significant in terms of flexibility and efficiency being purposely designed to operate for Irish Ferries in two very different formats; as an Ireland - France overnight cruise ferry during the spring and summer and as an Ireland to Wales short sea ro-pax during the autumn and winter.

Although built with a significant cabin capacity to primarily to serve Irish Ferries' Ireland to France sailings, now relocated to Dublin and with a 22.5 knot service speed to provide an accelerated crossing time, the new cruise ferry, which in the words of Irish Ferries represents "a game changer" for Ireland - France sailings is cleverly configured for her dual purpose role. With the vessel scheduled to operate up to four departures per week between Dublin and Cherbourg across the summer peak, the vessel will provide a major boost to trade and tourism between France and Ireland. Meanwhile in the quieter autumn and winter period the *W.B. Yeats* is deployed between Holyhead and Dublin where her passenger capacity has allowed the previously year round fast craft sailings to become seasonal.

Shortly after ordering the vessel, Irish Ferries began actively marketing the new build using the strap line BIG SHIP BIG NAME and through a dedicated website ran a naming competition with the winner receiving free travel for life. The company sought an Irish literary name in keeping with their vessel naming policy and that conveyed a sense of Ireland and the country's literary past to have a proud and emotional appeal to Irish people, tourists and freight customers. The name *W.B. Yeats,* which was chosen from 100,000 entries, firmly achieves that objective. William Butler Yeats (pronounced Yates) is acclaimed as one of Ireland's greatest poets and foremost literary figures having contributed to Irish society, theatre and arts. Born in Dublin in 1865 and educated in Ireland and London, W.B. Yeats studied poetry from an early age. He was a recipient of a Nobel Prize in Literature, he helped found The Abbey Theatre, now the national theatre of Ireland, and is remembered for his poem 'The Lake Isle of Innisfree'. Yeats' life and career are celebrated through the vessel and the writers work is featured on décor, the facilities are named after aspects of his life and there is also a walking tour on-board, charting his work.

The first section of steel for *W.B. Yeats* was cut at Flensburg in April 2017 prior to the keel laying ceremony which took place on 11 September 2017 when Irish Ferries Managing Director, Andrew Sheen presented builders FSG with a specially commissioned ceremonial coin that was placed in the keel to bring the vessel good luck and calm seas. Construction of the hull and superstructure was undertaken separately with FSG constructing the hull themselves and sub-contracting superstructure construction to Marine Projects and Holm Construction of Gdansk, Poland.

On 2 January 2018, just over a week before the launch of the *W.B. Yeats* at the Flensburg yard, Irish Ferries parent Irish Continental Group announced they had placed a further order with FSG for a €165.2 million 67,300 gt new cruise ferry. Scheduled for delivery in 2020 the vessel will serve on the Holyhead - Dublin route in replacement of the *Ulysses*. The new vessel will be fitted with scrubbers and will have four engines providing 33,600 KW of power and offering 22.8 knots. It will be the largest cruise ferry in the world in terms of vehicle capacity, accommodating 5,610 lane metres and carrying 1,500 cars or 330 freight units to be carried over five vehicle decks. 3 tier loading for freight will be provided at the bow to ensure efficient loading and port turnaround times. Freight capacity represents almost a 50% increase on that carried by the *Ulysses* which is expected to be redeployed to the schedule of the *Epsilon* allowing the *W.B. Yeats* to be deployed to the Ireland - France route year-round. Passenger capacity is for 1,800 and includes 152 cabins with passenger leisure catering and retail facilities similar in specification to those of the *W.B. Yeats.*

The competed hull of the *W.B. Yeats* was formally launched in a ceremony at Flensburg on 19 January 2018 and named by Ms. Rikki Rothwell, daughter of Irish Continental Group Chief Executive Eamonn Rothwell. Meanwhile the superstructure, built in 3 pre-assembled blocks, 2 by Marine Projects and 1 by Holm Construction at separate Gdansk shipyards was towed in separate sections on barges to FSG. The blocks comprising fore section including bridge, mid-ship section

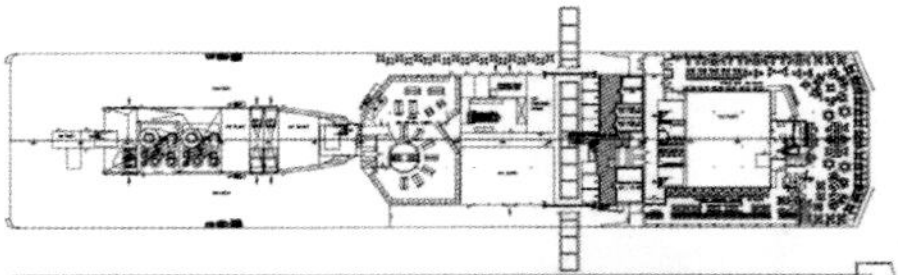

IRISH FERRIES

DECK 11

DECK 10

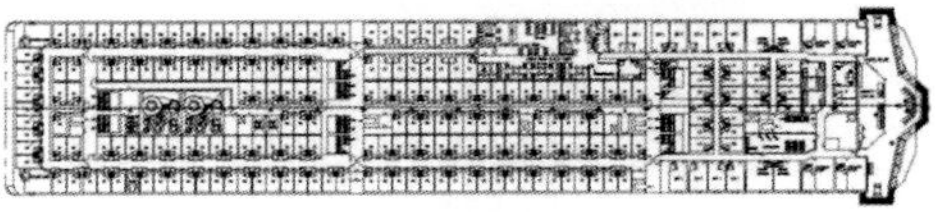

DECK 9

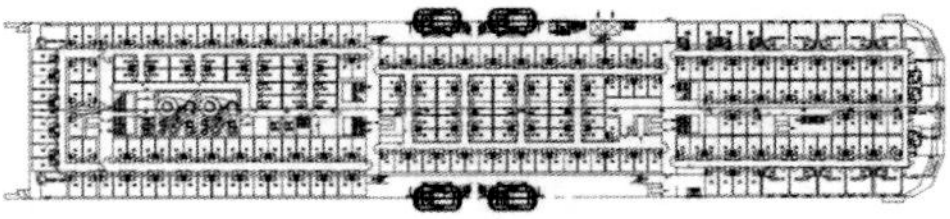

DECK 8

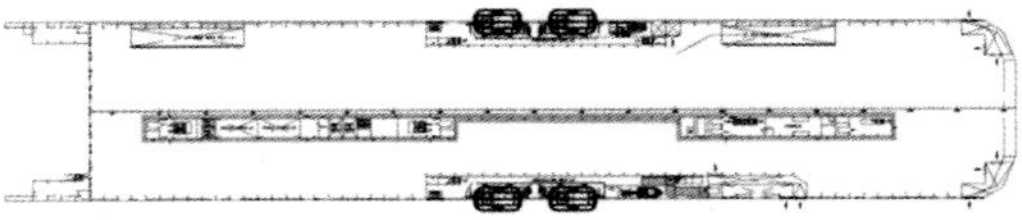

DECK 7

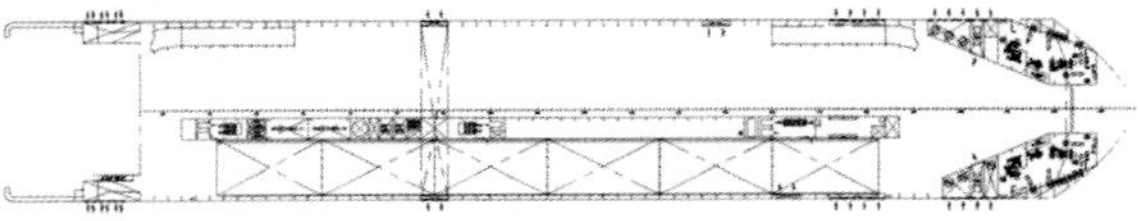

DECK 6

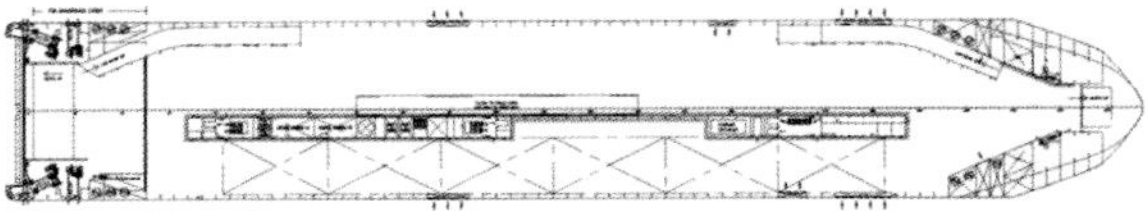

DECK 6

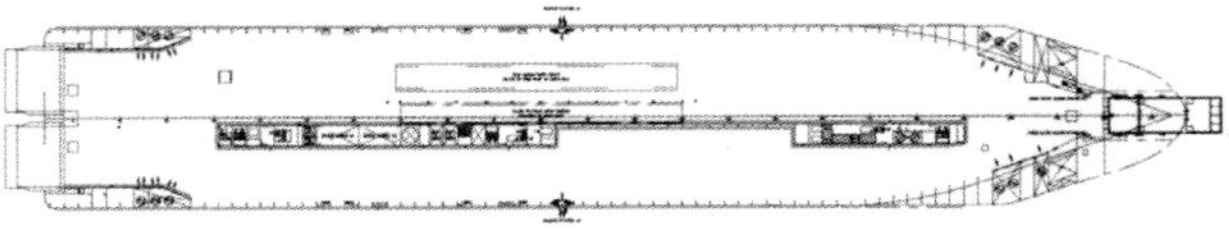

DECK 5

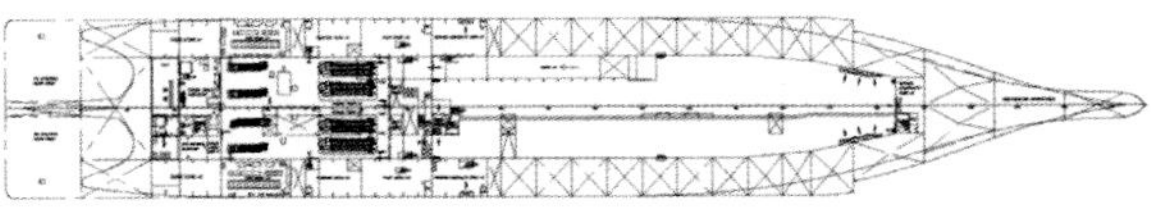

DECK 4

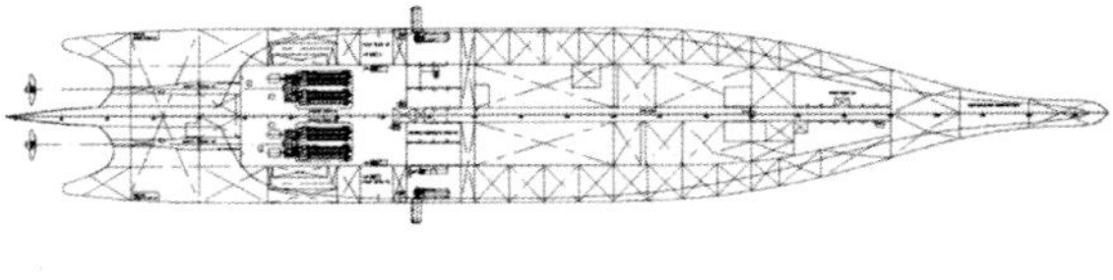

DECK 3

and an aft section including the funnel were each around 70% complete with floors, ceilings and wall panels fully installed. On the bridge, the consoles were installed and connected into the cabling systems and elsewhere air conditioning and ventilation systems were fitted and even the engine casings to the funnel were complete. The three sections were lifted into position one at a time and connected to the hull by heavy lift cranes between 8 and 9 February 2018. Work then continued on fitting out with technical and operational equipment, décor, furnishing and facility equipment fitted.

In April 2018 FSG informed Irish Ferries that they would not be able to meet the intended May delivery and 12 July 2018 was confirmed. Consequently, Irish Ferries reluctantly took the decision to cancel the vessel's scheduled sailings until 30 July 2018 leaving time to prepare the *W.B. Yeats* for service with berthing trials, crew training and storing. Subsequently, in June FSG informed Irish Ferries of further delays and new earliest delivery of September. Faced with the loss of the vessel for the summer season, Irish Ferries contracted brokers to search the charter market for cover. With few suitable vessels available one could not be found. As a result, the whole summer schedule of Dublin - Cherbourg sailings by the *W.B. Yeats* was cancelled and Irish Ferries worked hard to rearrange around 8,500 bookings with around 88% of them accommodated on the Ireland - France sailings of the *Oscar Wilde* and *Epsilon* or routed overland via Wales and England for an onward ferry to France.

Fortunately, Irish Ferries had decided to retain the *Oscar Wilde* for the first season of the *W.B. Yeats* with the intention to operate both vessels between Ireland and France between June and September with the former sailing from Rosslare to Cherbourg or Roscoff and return on the alternate days to the *W.B Yeats* sailing from Dublin, thereby providing a daily sailing between Ireland and France. The plan to operate the *Epsilon* seven days a week between Holyhead and Dublin was shelved so that the vessel could continue to operate a Dublin - Cherbourg weekend round trip.

In late August Irish Ferries announced that they hoped to take delivery of the *W.B. Yeats* towards the end of the year and in their trading statement it was confirmed that FSG was liable for financial penalties arising from delivery beyond September. Unfortunately, for FSG the late delivery almost resulted in their bankruptcy and owners the Siem Group, have sought additional capital resulting in a 76% share of FSG being acquired by Dutch investor Sapinda Holding. The difficulties at the yard have resulted in knock on delays to Brittany Ferries newbuilding the 42,500 gt *Honfleur* which was due for delivery in summer 2019 and is not expected until spring 2020 at the earliest.

In October 2018 the *W.B. Yeats* left Flensburg for the first time to conduct the first of several sea trials which continued through November. The vessel was handed over to Irish Ferries on 14 December and left the yard the next day for Cherbourg where she arrived on 18 December 2018 and conducted berthing trials. Further trials followed in Rosslare and Holyhead before she made a maiden arrival in Dublin on 20 December 2018. After spending a month alongside whilst undertaking storing, crew training and obtaining the necessary certification, the *W.B. Yeats* was quietly put into service without fanfare on 22 January 2019 making her maiden voyage with the 08:05 Dublin to Holyhead sailing in the place of the *Ulysses* which was released for dry docking. The maiden sailing of the *W.B. Yeats* from Ireland to France took place on 14 March 2019 when the vessel switched to the Dublin - Cherbourg route for the summer season, swapping places with the *Epsilon* which returned to the Holyhead - Dublin route to sail opposite *Ulysses* with additional support from the fast craft *Dublin Swift* which resumed twice daily seasonal sailings. The return sailing, which coincided with the St Patrick's Day weekend, was specially marked to commemorate the occasion with Cherbourg Port lit up in emerald green.

Irish Ferries have decided not to continue with the proposal to operate two vessels between Ireland and France across the summer peak. Instead the *Oscar Wilde* was sold to MSC in April 2019 for service with GNV as *GNV Allegra* after completing winter refit cover at both Holyhead and Pembroke Dock. For the 2019 season the *W.B. Yeats* has been scheduled for 3 departures a week on the Dublin - Cherbourg route between March and the end of May, sailing from Dublin at 16:00 on Saturdays, Tuesdays and Thursdays arriving in Cherbourg at 11.00 the next day with return crossings from Cherbourg at 17:00 on Sundays, Wednesdays and Fridays arriving in Dublin at 10:15 the following morning. From late May until the mid-September the schedule

The *W.B. Yeats* under construction in Germany. *(Uwe Jakob)*

Part of the Innisfree Club Class Lounge. *(Andrew Wood)*

The Maud Gonne Lounge and Bar. *(Andrew Wood)*

The entrance to Maud Gonne Lounge and Bar, with a 'Yeats' quotation on the wall. *(Andrew Wood)*

The Boylan's Brasserie servery area. *(Miles Cowsill*

The Cafe Lafayette bar and seating on Deck 10. *(Miles Cowsill)*

intensified to 4 crossings a week by stepping up to sail from both ports on alternate days. In late September the vessel switches back to the Holyhead – Dublin route partnering the *Ulysses* and providing additional passenger capacity once the *Dublin Swift* seasonal service is finished. The *Epsilon* moved back to the Dublin – Cherbourg route undertaking three weekly round trips each way until spring 2020, when the vessels swap back.

Despite the late delivery, the *W.B. Yeats* appears to have been worth the wait and Irish Ferries now have an impressive and well-appointed vessel that will serve their route network well. The vessel which can carry 1,800 passengers is 51,388 gt, 194.8 metres long and 31.6 metres wide and offers 2,800 lane metres for vehicles is quite unusual in appearance. At the bow the forecastle is very short and the bridge is located low, below the twin decks of passenger accommodation, Aft the superstructure is squared off before the stern to create an open section of upper vehicle deck. Overall the appearance is angular but striking. This design is function over form and a result of months of computational modelling and towage tank tests to ensure good seakeeping abilities which has been born out by her performance through unseasonal conditions over the summer.

On the vehicle deck, many elements of the design of the *Ulysses* have been employed. There are three full height freight decks, served via double deck loading with a hoist-able ramp also available between them and ramp access to the lower hold. In total 165 freight units can be carried on the three decks. At the lowest level, forward of the engine room on decks 1 and 2 is a lower hold for 12 trailers accessed by a fixed ramp. At deck 7 above the upper vehicle deck is a segregated car deck for 300 cars accessed by fixed curving ramps located at both bow and stern. Without freight in full car mode a total of 1,216 cars can be carried; slightly less than the impressive capacity of the 50,938gt and 4,076 lane metre *Ulysses* which can carry 1,342 cars. Power comes from 4 Caterpillar MAK 9M43C engines which provide 33600kW driving twin 5 metre diameter variable pitch propellers at 127 rpm giving a service speed of 22.5 knots, though on trials in light ship mode the *W.B. Yeats* exceeded 25 knots.

The interior was designed OSK Shiptech's subsidiary Steen Friis Design in conjunction with Irish interior design consultant Helen Kilmartin of Minima. She selected the furniture, finishes and designed the showcase a la carte restaurant, and she has worked with Irish Ferries for 20 years in a relationship dating back to her having a shop close to Irish Ferries offices. Kilmartin has previously designed ICG's foyer and boardrooms and opted to use dark greys and blacks interspersed with neutral blues, reds and dark oranges, to give a minimalist contemporary feel not uncommon with boutique hotels. Heavily patterned abstract carpets in beige, grey or black feature throughout along with grey walls, chosen to ensure that they don't date or stain and look contemporary.

The public areas on the *W.B. Yeats* are located on decks 8 to 11 with the lowest two decks consisting entirely of cabins. In total there are 440 cabins with berths for 1774. Forward on deck 8 are the luxury cabins and suites designed by Kilmartin featuring double beds with deeply sprung mattresses, bedside cabinets with table lamps, sofas, two LCD televisions in each cabin (one to watch from the bed and the other from the sofa), Foxford rugs, floor to ceiling wave curtains and heavily patterned woven carpets inspired by the artwork of Damien Hirst. There are 10 luxury cabins; five on each side of the vessel and 3 luxury suites overlooking the bow. The Coole Park and Lissadel both have a corner balcony recessed into the superstructure, whilst the Thoor Ballylee suite which lies in-between is to the same standard but without. Within each is a mini bar and tea and a coffee pod machine as well as selection of reading materials by *W.B. Yeats*. On deck 9 the bridge is located forward in its unique low position, with accommodation behind for crew and remainder of the deck is made up of more passenger cabins.

Three colour coded stairwells connect the passenger decks – the Blue Stairs (aft), the Purple Stairs (mid-ships) and the Grey Stairs (forward). The majority of facilities are located on deck 10 and the public areas are largely open allowing a free flow walkthrough as one facility dissolves into another. 21 further cabins are located aft adjacent to the Hazelwood Quiet Lounge on the port side with lightly toned reclining seats and the Café Lafayette which features a mix of fixed stools and tables with chairs. In the same area on the starboard side can be the found the Abbey and Peacock Cinemas, with a retro style glass ticket booth that also sells popcorn and ice slush drinks and black and grey toned reclining seating alongside the windows. Linking the area to the

Access to the upper freight deck from the bow, with ramp access to Deck 7 for exclusive parking for passengers vehicles . *(Miles Cowsill)*

The main freight deck is located on Deck 3. *(Miles Cowsill)*

IRISH FERRIES
W.B. YEATS

***W.B. Yeats* leaving Dublin.** *(Gordon Hislip)*

Café Lafayette is the walkthrough Salley Gardens Kids Room furnished in orange, red, beige and black with plastic tub chairs designed by Vondom, video screens, soft padded kids play area and an optical illusion light box mirror on the wall.

Mid-ship is the focal point of the *W.B. Yeats*, a large open plan walkthrough lounge spanning the vessel's full width and containing various seating styles, with stools around counters, long curving boardroom style tables, fixed seating and freestyle seating. In the centre is an atrium with skylight and a stylish glass staircase providing access to The Shop on deck 11 above. Forward and in the centre of the lounge is Boylans Brasserie from where the food purchased is taken back to the expansive seating area in the lounge behind. To the starboard side is the Reception which features a large neon sign with the quote "I have sailed the seas" from W.B. Yeats which shimmers and changes colour. Moving forward beyond the Grey Stairs is the impressive Lady Gregory Restaurant to port and the twin level Wild Swans Freight Drivers Lounge to starboard.

The Lady Gregory Restaurant is a waiter served restaurant and is furnished in overwhelmingly contemporary décor. It is an attractive and opulent space with deep velour carpets and a textured and mirrored metal ceiling designed by Kilmartin to resemble waves. In the adjacent Wild Swans lounge, freight drivers and car passengers are treated to a touch of luxury too. Spread over two levels the downstairs section on deck 10 features a food servery counter and red and grey seating around tables with a staircase leading up to a seating lounge with reclining seats lining the floor to ceiling height windows. Located forward above the bridge overlooking the bow and accessed by a walkway past the Wild Swan is the Innisfree Club Class Lounge which offers really impressive views. The lounge contains a mix of sofa, bucket style seating around tables and recliners in grey, black and dark orange tones with a mix of carpet and marble tiled flooring.

Above on the highest level at deck 11, also located forward and offering a bow view is the L-shaped Maud Gonne Bar and Lounge which also covers the port side. It is named after the English Heiress and Irish Nationalist with whom *W.B. Yeats* had a famous affair. With full height windows it offers impressive sea views. Stylised on the wall is the legend "Tread softly because you tread on my dreams" - another quote from the poet. The décor comprises grey stripped walls with tiled floors bordered by back, grey and beige zig zagged striped carpeting and a range of bucket and booth seating styles in an orange and grey whilst over on the starboard side of the lounge colours used change to blue, black and cream. There is also a magnificent replica fire place as would be found in a country house and wording on the wall from W.B. Yeat's The Cloths of Heaven. Moving aft behind the Maud Gonne Bar and Lounge, the starboard section contains the upper section of the Wild Swans Freight Driver Lounge and a small video games area called Crazy Janes. Beyond are the Grey Stairs and more crew accommodation with The Shop located on the other side but accessed from the main lounge on deck 10 below. The remainder of deck 11 is given over to the funnel casing and a large outside open deck space which is branded as the Drumcliffe Promenade and features fixed stool and table seating along the port side walkway.

The interior of the *W.B. Yeats* is contemporary, stunning and innovative, so much so that the vessel was recognised by the International Shipping World in scooping up both the Ferry Concept Award and the Interior Architecture Award at the March 2018 Shippax Industry Awards. The judges commented that the vessel has a contemporary design that employs understated elegance and natural tones throughout. The cabins and luxury suites, as well as public areas including the 'Innisfree' Club Class Lounge and the 'Maud Gonne' Bar & Lounge, were highly acclaimed as was the use of energy efficient LED lighting systems and the general design with separate vehicle decks for freight and cars and the vessel's flexibility in being suited for both long and short sea routes".

Matt Davies

WELCOME TO THE ROALD AMUNDSEN – THE JOURNEY BEGINS!

Hurtigruten's first hybrid powered expedition ship

At 13.01 local time on 29th June 2019, under the command of Captain Kai Albrigtsen, the *Roald Amundsen*, the world's first hybrid cruise ship, departed from the shipyard at Kleven Verft, Ulsteinvik bound for Tromsø. From there on 3rd July she would begin her maiden voyage, a year later than originally planned.

The occasion had been a long time coming with numerous delays on the way. Some of this was early on as a result of the shipyard experiencing financial problems. Equally, as befits any revolutionary new vessel with its innovative fuel efficient propulsion technology enabling it to sail more quietly and cleanly than anything else before, both construction and technical issues also played their part in the delay.

First moves

The background story to this new era can be traced as far back as 2012 when Daniel Skjeldam, took over as CEO of Hurtigruten. The company immediately announced a fresh focus on the hotel and restaurant sectors as well as looking to markedly expand the existing and successful explorer programme. A second major turning point came in October 2014 when the company was sold to Silk Bidco AS Norway (owned by British buyout fund TDR Capital), with original investors Trygve OBI and Petter Stordalen retaining 5% each. TDR Capital were quick to stress that it would continue with Norwegian management in order to preserve its unique history and quality. They envisaged investing up to NOK 5.5 billion into the business, geared towards expanding expedition experiences, with the promise of building up to four new ships. It is this investment which has now manifested itself in the construction of Hurtigruten's first hybrid powered expedition ship, *Roald Amundsen* with a second (*Fridtjof Nansen)* in service in the spring of 2020 and a third scheduled for 2021.

The first firm news of an expansion in the explorer programme came in June 2015 with the announcement that their flagship *Midnatsol*, after modifications to make her more suited to such voyages, would join the *Fram* in Antarctica for the 2016/17 season. The focus would be on polar science and nature with the ship carrying her own team of scientists including a 'science laboratory' on board. In addition, they purchased the small Portuguese car ferry ms *Ferry Atlântida,* totally rebuilding her as their *Spitsbergen*, to provide cover for the *Midnatsol* whilst she was on Antarctic duties as well as offering fresh explorer cruises in the summer months.

Going green

Hurtigruten and its predecessors have long been sensitive to the need to ensure an environmentally sustainable means of travel along both the Norwegian coastline and the polar territories. The conventional power plants on six of their coastal voyage ships will be replaced with natural liquefied gas-powered engines (LNG) together with the installation of large battery packs by 2021 using climate-neutral liquefied biogas (LBG) made from fish and other organic waste. Hurtigruten has already embarked on a programme of reducing ship emissions whilst in port by using on-shore power, a process known as 'cold ironing'. On 28th February 2018 the *Spitsbergen* became the first in the fleet to use this technology at Bergen, where ships are berthed from between 5½ hours to 8 hours depending on the season. It is estimated that by doing so nitrogen oxide emissions would be reduced at the port by 1,600 tonnes per year, with the CO2 reduction even greater. Additionally, both the *Fram* (2020) and *Finnmarken* (2021) will receive 'keel-to-mast' makeovers, emerging as brand new expedition ships, the latter along with the *Trollfjord* and *Midnatsol*, will be upgraded to hybrid power with the installation of battery units. At the same time these three ships will be renamed *Otto Sverdrup* (one of Norway's most notable polar heroes), *Maud* (after *Roald Amundsen*'s famous 1917 polar vessel) and *Eirik Raude* (Erik the Red, the great Viking chief) respectively.

Increasingly stringent directives coming into force are aimed at drastically reducing the main pollutants from the ships' emissions, i.e. carbon dioxide (CO^2), nitrogen oxides (NOx) and sulphur oxides (SOx). It is these gases which adversely affect the ozone layer in the troposphere resulting

Launching of ***Roald Amundsen*** **at Kleven Shipyard, Ulsteinvik - 17th February 2018.** *(Oclin/Hurtigruten)*

A three generation meet up at Trondheim: ***Lofoten***, ***Trollfjord*** **and** ***Roald Amundsen*** **- 15th July 2019 .**
(Tor Arne Aasen/Samferdselsfoto)

in the greenhouse effect and consequent global warming.

The company has already drawn up plans to replace the conventional power plants on six of their coastal voyage ships with natural liquefied gas-powered engines (LNG) together with the installation of large battery packs by 2021. As part of a multi-year deal with Biokraft (Norway) using climate-neutral liquefied biogas (LBG) these ships will be powered by fuel made from fish and other organic waste. Hurtigruten had already embarked on a programme of reducing ship emissions whilst in port by using on-shore power, a process known as 'cold ironing'. On 28th February 2018 the *Spitsbergen* became the first in the fleet to use this technology at Bergen, where ships are berthed from between 5½ hours to 8 hours depending on the season. It is estimated that by doing so nitrogen oxide emissions would be reduced at the port by 1,600 tonnes per year, with the CO_2 reduction even greater. Additionally, both the *Fram* (2020) and *Finnmarken* (2021) will receive 'keel-to-mast' makeovers, emerging as brand new expedition ships with upgraded low emission propulsion units.

An order is placed

Back In early April 2016, Hurtigruten announced an order for two new (with an option for two more) hybrid powered ice strengthened expedition ships, scheduled for delivery in 2018, which could sustain operation on battery power of up to two hours before switching to algae-based fuels.

Announcing the names of the ships Hurtigruten CEO Daniel Skjeldam said, *'It is exactly 105 years since Roald Amundsen became the first person in the world to plant his flag on the South Pole; 128 years since Fridtjof Nansen skied across Greenland; and 125 years since Richard With, Hurtigruten's founder, first started exploration tourism in the Arctic. What could be more natural and appropriate than to name our new ships after these inspiring trailblazers.'*

The ships designed by Rolls-Royce, in collaboration with the highly respected Norwegian yacht designer Espen Øino, would also have the capability to operate on the classic service route along the Norwegian coast. Each ship would measure 20,890gt, be 143m in length, with a beam of 24m, draft of 5.3m and service speed of 15 knots. Her accommodation would be for around 530 guests served by a crew of 150.

On 24th February 2017 construction of the main superstructure officially started at the Kleven Shipyard, Ulsteinvik, which had previously built three of the current Hurtigruten fleet, *Nordkapp, Nordnorge* and *Finnmarken.* Hurtigruten's CEO Daniel Skjeldam assisted by Kleven's CEO Ståle Rasmussen pressed the button to activate the welding robots to begin the fabrication of the steel section which would house the *Roald Amundsen's* revolutionary hybrid engines.

Other sections for the *Roald Amundsen* were simultaneously being built at the Montex Shipyard Dębowski Wasiołek Sp. J., Gdansk, Poland, partners in the Kleven Group, who would also construct similar elements for the *Fridtjof Nansen.*

On 24th October 2017, the first hull segments of the *Roald Amundsen*, comprising the bow block, two bottom sections, the stern section (with aft overhang and transom) and a three-storey section of the superstructure including the wheelhouse, were dispatched by Montex on a barge-pontoon and towed to Ulsteinvik arriving there on Thursday 2nd November. The bow section was immediately manoeuvred into place on the slipway in front of the main pre-constructed superstructure block, and as a result the *Roald Amundsen* was began to look more like a ship. Such is the pace at which ships are constructed today that the *Roald Amundsen* was able to take to the water at noon on 17th February 2018, fittingly to be greeted by the classic 1964 built *Lofoten*, Hurtigruten's oldest member of the fleet which was on her northbound service. However, owing to the new complex technology involved, her rather ambitious original completion date of May 2018 was put back to the spring of 2019.

Four Rolls-Royce Bergen B33:45 engines, each with an output of 3,600*kW, used in* combination with batteries are at the heart of the innovative hybrid solution onboard these two vessels. This new technology enables the ships to sail with electric propulsion under ideal conditions for around 45 to 60 minutes, the main gain being a reduction in fuel consumption and reduced CO_2 emissions by at least 20%. The batteries are then recharged whilst the ship's main engines are running. This technology for the *Roald Amundsen* and *Fridtjof Nansen* is planned for delivery in two phases. In phase one, auxiliary battery power will enable large reductions in fuel consumption and this is being installed on the first expeditionary ship.

For phase two, larger battery packs will be installed, with twice the capacity of those installed in the *Roald Amundsen*, enabling fully electric sailing across greater distances and over longer periods of time. This will be used when sailing into fjords, at port and in vulnerable areas so allowing silent and emission free sailing. Rolls-Royce aims to install this newer technology firstly in the *Fridtjof Nansen* (now due to take up service in Spring 2020) and then to furnish the *Roald Amundsen* with the newer technology at later date. Hurtigruten are of the opinion that the future of shipping is for silent and emission free operation and are using these new expeditionary ships as ground breakers to show the world that hybrid propulsion on large ships is possible and particularly pertinent when sailing in the Arctic and Antarctic.

A third vessel is ordered

On 25th October 2018 it was announced that Hurtigruten had ordered a further hybrid cruise vessel from Kleven Verft, scheduled for delivery in the second quarter of 2021. Based on the two previously ordered this vessel will have even bigger battery packs, which should further increase zero-emission sailing capabilities. The three ships will run on marine diesel oil when not operating on batteries, as opposed to the LNG-battery configurations that the company will install on its six retrofitted coastal cruise ferries as the limited availability of LNG currently prevents the deployment of the gas fuel on the wider ranging expedition cruise ships.

On board

With the *Roald Amundsen*, Hurtigruten has set new standards in interior layout, much of which comes from the world class Tilburg Design Associates stable, the décor mirroring the breath-taking waters and landscapes in which the expedition ships sail. Materials are predominantly Norwegian, with a typically Scandinavian approach using granite, oak and birch and wool amongst other mediums.

Guests on excursions will embark/disembark on the Tender Deck (Deck 3), where the large inflatable explorer boats, kayaks and underwater drones are stored. The Pharmacy and Medical Centre is also to be found on this deck. Deck 4 (on which the main passenger gangway is located) and Deck 5 are given over almost entirely to cabin accommodation.

Deck 6 is the main passenger facilities deck with, aft on the starboard side, the Aune Dining Room (named after Norwegian ship chandler and polar expedition supplier Tinus Aune), the prime venue for breakfast, lunch and dinner. On the adjacent portside is the exclusive international kitchen, Fredheim Restaurant (which also acts as the ship's informal and social meeting place), named after a 1900s hunting station on Svalbard.

The midships area of Deck 6 is where the Compass Service Centre (Reception) and Shop are sited, whilst further forward towards the bow is the Amundsen Science Centre, the base for the ship's expedition team. This area is packed with state of the art technology, sophisticated gadgetry and plenty of interactive touch screens. The facility features lecture spaces, a small library, and speciality areas for workshops in photography, biology and more. From this area a covered outdoor explorer deck leads right up to the bow and is one of several large observation platforms on the ship. Specially designed underwater drones will stream live images to the ship's TV screens further enhancing the experience.

High quality artwork has always been a feature on board Hurtigruten ships and almost 600 unique works by young Norwegian artists, chosen by HM Queen Sonja herself through her art foundation's award scheme, are featured throughout the *Roald Amundsen*.

At the bow on Deck 7 is an open explorer deck, whilst midships, can be found the Fitness Centre and Wellness Room. The remainder of this deck, together with the whole of Deck 8, is given over to cabin accommodation. Moving further upwards, Deck 9 contains much of the de-luxe cabin accommodation, together with a third dining option, the speciality Lindstrøm Restaurant, named after Adolf Lindstrøm the favourite chef of Norwegian polar heroes.

The cosy Explorer Lounge and Bar is to be found on Deck 10 together with the heated outdoor pool and sauna. Finally, on Deck 11 is another open Explorer Deck overlooking the bridge which offers guests outstanding views of nature and wildlife.

Roald Amundsen **on her first sea trials - 23rd February 2019.** *(Tor Erik Kvalsvik/Hurtigruten)*

Roald Amundsen **preparing to berth at Hammerfest - 18th July 2019.** *((Jonathan Jaeger)*

ROALD AMUNDSEN
TROMSØ
HURTIGRUTEN

Cutaway profile of *Roald Amundsen*'s starboard side - note the tender deck arrangements. *(Hurtigruten)*

Roald Amundsen **southbound, traversing the Tjeldsundet, Ofotens - 6th July 2019.** *((Frode Adolfsen)*

Roald Amundsen **berthed at the Cruise Terminal, Tromsø on 2nd July 2019.** *(Odd Roar Lange/Hurtigruten)*

The ship also boasts the tallest LED (4K ultra-HD+) screen at sea, 17.5m (57.4ft) high, spanning no less than seven decks. This spectacular and technically difficult installation, which faces the three glass lifts, is designed to operate in both polar and exotic waters and in conditions that can be rough and without a stable internet connection. The video wall will show live images of the scenery and wildlife as the vessel passes by. It will also feature live presentations and lectures and pre-scheduled external content triggered by the ship's location and GPS. For the remainder of the time it will have the ability to create 'special mood atmospheres' from around the ship.

Cabin accommodation

Every cabin is outside facing, a first for Hurtigruten, each with large windows which enable guests to immerse themselves in the views outside. All can accommodate two to four guests with a choice of either double or twin beds. The accommodation is divided into three major categories; namely Expedition Suites, Arctic Superior Class cabins, and Polar Outside cabins.

Expedition Suites are exclusively in upper and mid deck locations, large and well-appointed, with expansive windows and most having secluded balconies. Some even have their own private outside Jacuzzi. The suites feature flexible sleeping arrangements with comfortable sofas, sitting areas and TV, an amenity kit, espresso maker and much more.

Arctic Superior Class cabins are also comfortable and roomy. Those on the higher decks have balconies. The Arctic Superior concept too includes an amenity kit, kettle, tea and coffee provision. Sleeping arrangements can be varied, generally with sofa beds which has made this grade the popular choice.

The Polar Outside cabins are primarily on the middle decks, all with windows and are surprisingly spacious. Some may have restricted views, but they do offer an excellent standard of accommodation with TV as standard in every cabin.

Appointment of the captain

On the 26th December 2018, Hurtigruten officially named 54 year old Norwegian Kai Albrigtsen as captain of the *Roald Amundsen*. Having been with Hurtigruten throughout his whole working life, starting at the age of 17 as a galley assistant, he has a wealth of sailing experience behind him. He has, over the years, worked on more than ten of the vessels in the fleet in various capacities and so knows the company's needs well. His first expedition to Antarctica was in 2003, later rising to the rank of captain in 2006. Very much an outdoor enthusiast, Kai Albrigtsen spends much of his free time with his family hiking or fishing around Norway's Vesterålen and Lofoten Islands. For the past two years, he has held the position of Master on the company's flagship, *Midnatsol*, which currently dovetails its summer Norwegian coastal voyage commitments with winter expeditions to Antarctica.

He says *'taking command over such a unique vessel is a great honour and a big responsibility and is without a doubt the highlight of my career. But most of all, working for Hurtigruten is an adventure which I look forward to every day, as no two days at 'the office' are ever the same'.*

Sea trials

On Saturday 23rd February 2019, a year after her launch, the *Roald Amundsen* began her first sea trials in the fjords adjacent to Ulsteinvik with the famous Sunnmøre Alps as the backdrop. After the ship's return to the shipyard on the following Monday morning, Kleven CEO Olav Nakken remarked that he was very pleased with the results of the sea trial. Project Director at Kleven, Asbjørn Vattøy, added that *'with the number of innovations and this being a highly technically complicated ship, it was important to verify that all the systems worked as planned. The next stage was to get the interior completed.'* Rather prophetic words as it turned out.

The construction and fitting out issues had already caused the *Roald Amundsen's* inaugural 'shakedown' cruises in the spring of 2019 to be cancelled. These had been set to begin in the Caribbean, followed by visits to the Azores, Madeira and the Canary Islands before cruising along the north west coast of Europe, with calls at various ports in Portugal, Spain, France, Belgium and the Netherlands along the way prior to basing herself at Hamburg.

After further sea trials a planned maintenance dry docking at the Westcon Group facility in Florø

The fine dining Fredheim Restaurant is located on Deck 6 of the *Roald Amundsen*. *(Agurtxane Concellon/Hurtigruten)*

One of the luxurious Expedition Suites on board the *Roald Amundsen*. *(Agurtxane Concellon/Hurtigruten)*

followed, returning to the Kleven shipyard on 30th May. There, final preparations were undertaken in readiness for the rescheduled official first voyage, a round trip to begin from Hamburg on 27th June 2019. This cruise would be along the Norwegian coastline, mirroring the existing classic coastal service from Bergen to Kirkenes which the 'hurtigrute' has operated since 1893, including a special call at Reine, one of the jewels of the Lofotens. Even then this new deadline had to be missed owing to unfinished interior work.

The inaugural season

However, the ship did finally sail from the shipyard on 29th June bound for Tromsø where her maiden voyage would now begin, using the remaining sea days in order to get any outstanding internal work completed. The upshot of this latest delay and re-jigging of her itinerary meant Hurtigruten had the costly exercise of having to offer passengers booked on the original voyage from Hamburg a transfer to this new maiden voyage at a heavily discounted price, including covering all extra hotel costs, expenses and flights. Many passengers were less than impressed at the timing of the announcement being so close to the sailing date, feeling that the company should have known well in advance whether the ship would be ready or not.

As the ship sailed from northwards to Tromsø, the navigation systems were further tested in open waters with the seagoing capability and manoeuvrability being reported by Captain Kai Albrigtsen as 'fantastic'. In addition, the *Roald Amundsen* was able to sail stints both purely on battery power as well as in conjunction with its diesel engines which can at peak loadings help to reduce fuel consumption and emissions by about 20%. Using the dual hybrid option is also is a much safer way to sail in sensitive areas as it mitigates the risk of blackouts.

After a call at Bodø on 1st July, the *Roald Amundsen* sailed around the western coastline of the Lofotens and Vesterålen arriving at Tromsø the following evening. Shortly after 1430 on Wednesday, 3rd July she began her maiden voyage being welcomed at the port by the arriving northbound coastal voyage ship *Nordkapp*. Only 211 passengers were on board, reflecting the difficulties caused by the ship's belated entry into service. Making an unusual detour around the west side of Tromsøya (the island on which most of Tromsø is located) she headed northwards via Lyngenfjord making no further calls until Kirkenes (on the Russian border) was reached the following day at 16.15. Each day she was noisily greeted by passing members of the Hurtigruten coastal fleet.

Leaving Kirkenes soon after 20.00 the *Roald Amundsen* began to retrace its steps with extended calls at *Honningsvåg* (stop-off port for the North Cape), Hammerfest, Reine, Brønnøysund, Kristiansund, Molde and Florø. After a brief visit to Cuxhaven at the mouth of the River Elbe in the evening of 10th July she arrived early the next morning at Hamburg, her final destination.

One of *Roald Amundsen*'s spacious middle deck Polar Outside Cabins. *(Tillburg Design/Hurtigruten)*

The *Roald Amundsen's* second 'Norwegian Coastal Highlights' cruise on 11th July from the German port was fully booked with 530 passengers. The ship called briefly at a very soggy Esbjerg before sailing on to Bergen, the southern terminal of the Hurtigruten coastal service. Here she moored at the cruise terminal on the north side of the harbour before setting out once more northwards along the Norwegian 'long coast' including a planned meet up at Trondheim with fleetmates, *Lofoten* and *Trollfjord*). However, this time the return leg from Kirkenes would terminate at Tromsø.

The delay into service meant that both these cruises would be the only opportunity for quite some considerable time for those in Norway wanting to take a look at the *Roald Amundsen*. Recognising this Hurtigruten did publish a detailed timetable of the ship's calls at the various ports along the way. However, despite having extended stops owing to 'capacity considerations', disappointingly it wasn't possible for members of the public to board her for a visit.

The ship's arrival at Tromsø marked the beginning of the *Roald Amundsen* momentously circuitous journey to Antarctica via the west coastline of the Americas. The first leg which began on 21st July involved sailing northwards to Svalbard. Having called once more at *Honningsvåg*, the *Roald Amundsen* set off in an anticlockwise direction around Magerøya in order to give guests the opportunity to view Skarsvåg (with its claim to be the world's northernmost fishing village) and the North Cape itself from the sea.

At this point the *Roald Amundsen* officially bid farewell to the European mainland until at least 2021 as she set course for Bjornøya (Bear Island), the southernmost island in the Svalbard Archipelago with its eight semi-permanent inhabitants, before sailing onto Longyearbyen (Spitsbergen). A fresh journey from Svalbard's administrative centre would then enable guests to explore the eastern coastline of Greenland ending at Reykjavik (Iceland). The last leg in this trio of 'arctic expeditions' took the *Roald Amundsen* from the Icelandic capital along the southern and western coastlines of Greenland with Kangerlussuaq as the final port of call.

The *Roald Amundsen's* arrival at Kangerlussuaq would be of great significance as on 20th August she would begin 'the big one'; traversing the whole of the famous North West Passage to Nome in Alaska. This exciting 24 day exploration cruise would make Hurtigruten the first company in the world to sail the route using battery pack and hybrid propulsion, more than 100 years after Roald Amundsen himself had become the first person to sail through this famous and notorious passage from the Atlantic Ocean to the Pacific in his polar boat *Gjøa*. But where it took Amundsen three years to achieve, the Hurtigruten ship will take three weeks.

Upon leaving Nome the *Roald Amundsen* would sail southwards along Canada's famous 'inside passage' to Vancouver for a late September arrival. From there she travels lightship along the west coastline of the United States and Mexico to begin her next set of cruises on 10th October from Puntarenas in Costa Rica. These will take her southwards along the Andean coastline via Ecuador and Peru (Land of the Incas, Machu Picchu, Galápagos Islands etc) before arriving in late October at the Chilean port of Punta Arenas in time to begin her Antarctic 2019/2020 season.

Many thought that the *Roald Amundsen* would have her official naming ceremony on 'home ground' either at Tromsø or Bergen or even possibly in Hamburg (as with the *Midnatsol* in 2003). However, in homage to the man after whom the ship is named, this will now take place in Antarctica in late 2019 (something never done before), not by using the traditional bottle of champagne but with a chunk of ice, copying a ritual invented by Amundsen himself when christening his famed expedition ship *Maud* in 1917. When doing so Roald Amundsen stated:

'It is not my intention to dishonour the glorious grape, but already now you shall get the taste of your real environment. For the ice you have been built, and in the ice, you shall stay most of your life, and in the ice, you shall solve your tasks'.

Roald Amundsen and Hurtigruten are wished well in this new and exciting phase in the company's exploration voyage concept programmes. With sister ship *Fridtjof Nansen* scheduled now to begin service in Spring 2020 and a third about to begin construction this represents a massive investment for Hurtigruten. Hopefully they will be more than well rewarded and the initial fitting out delays quickly become a distant memory. The journey has begun!

John Bryant

STEAM PACKET MOVING INTO THE NEXT DECADE

The Isle of Man Steam Packet Company began operating in 1830, when the population of the Island was in the region of 40,000 and is now the oldest continually operating shipping company in the world. Today it is owned by the Isle of Man Government and serves the Island and its population of 83,000. The Company carry over 600,000 passengers annually and conveys 170,000 cars and motorcycles. Since beginning operations, the Company has owned 72 different vessels, ranging from steamships to today's fastcraft.

Under Government Ownership

The Company had in January 2016 produced, at the request of the then IOM Government Minister for Infrastructure, a Strategic Sea Services document outlining its proposals for an extension to the existing linkspan user agreement. A second offer came in March 2017. This potential agreement was voted on by the IOM Government in July 2017 and rejected but instructing the Department to continue discussions with the Steam Packet in the hope of arriving at a deal that offered a greater benefit to the Island.

Following that vote, confidential negotiations between the Government and the then owners of the Steam Packet took place, with the result that on 8 May 2018, the Government announced that it had agreed terms to purchase the Company, and that the proposal would be debated at the next sitting of the Government. The purchase price was to be £124 million.

The sitting was held on Tuesday 18 May and members of the Government voted overwhelmingly to approve the purchase. The process was concluded on Tuesday 25 May, the cost broken down to; £48.3 million for the purchase of the parent company MIOM Ltd and a £76 million loan to the Company. A report by Park Partners had been commissioned to value the Company and a separate report by Braemar to assess the condition of the two vessels. Both vessels received a 'Good' score of 5 out of 7, the report noting that both had been well maintained.

Following the purchase, the Government stated that the Company would continue to operate at arms-length from Government. A new agreement would be drawn up and discussed in due course. Shortly after the completion of the purchase, adverts were placed for applications to become non-executive directors of the Company. On 16 January 2019, the IOM Government Treasury Minister Alfred Cannan MHK announced that Philip Dearden, Captain Simon Pressley and David Oldfield would be joining the Board, the new directors bringing experience in accountancy, shipping and the maritime industry.

New Sea Services Agreement

Following the purchase of the Isle of Man Steam Packet Company by the Isle of Man Government in 2018, the opportunity was taken to enter into a new Sea Services Agreement with the Company.

The Isle of Man Government published its proposed new Sea Services Agreement in early March 2019. The extensive document was debated at the sitting of Tynwald, the Island's Government, on Wednesday 20 March 2019 and was approved. The new agreement will come into force on 1 January 2020 and stand for 25 years.

The complete document is well over 100 pages, and very detailed, the text that follows is a brief resume of the primary points of the document. The entire document, it is available at: http://www.tynwald.org.im/business/opqp/sittings/20182021/2019-GD-0009.pdf?fbclid=IwAR1xb_bxLDUn_tMK-7ekduAkrGlFCL3qiKk3xlbt1Uh_OCq0y2BGgOZwHw8

The Isle of Man Government first intervened in the ferry services, to and from the Island, in 1995 when it entered into a user agreement with the Steam Packet Company. The Government built the new King Edward Pier linkspan for virtually exclusive use by the Steam Packet, the new agreement outlining the conditions associated with the use of the new linkspan.

The Steam Packet had changed hands several times during recent years and there was growing concern that a future owner might adopt an aggressive operational approach, with

The *Ben-my-Chree* arriving at Heysham. *(George Holland)*

The *Manannan* maintains the Liverpool, Belfast and Dublin services from to March to October each year. *(Miles Cowsill)*

profitability becoming the focus, over and above service levels.

In drafting the new Sea Services Agreement, the Government has been able to secure a service level that best suits the needs of the Island for the next 25 years, while ensuring that the Steam Packet is able to provide renewal of ships and other benefits to its customers.

In compiling the agreement, the Government conducted workshops with local interested parties and undertook a public survey to gauge satisfaction or otherwise with current services. Unusually but, perhaps not surprisingly, in the 16 days that the survey was open, just short of 5000 responses were received, mainly from Island residents.

Steam Packet Vessels

Perhaps the most significant part of the agreement, in particular from an enthusiast's point of view, is the replacement of the *Ben-my-Chree*, with a new vessel by the end of 2021. The *Ben-my-Chree* is 125.2meters long, the longest capacity at Douglas is 136m while Heysham and the new Liverpool Ferry Terminal are 142m.

Approval has already been granted separately to increase the maximum capacity at Douglas to match Heysham and Liverpool to 142m, allowing the replacement for the *Ben-my-Chree* to be 17m longer if required. The *Ben-my-Chree*, *Manannan* and *Arrow* all date from 1998 and are therefore all 21 years old this year.

The replacement Ro-Pax must be designed to provide enhanced passenger accommodation, differing from the *Ben-my-Chree* that was designed primarily as a freight vessel and has subsequently been extended to increase passenger capacity to 630. The new vessel is to have a passenger capacity of 800. The vessel must be capable of operating on either diesel or liquefied natural gas and comply with the 2020 International Maritime Organisation Regulation. Freight meterage will need to be 1250m against the current 1235m with greater capacity for high or double deck trailers.

When the new vessel is delivered and is in service, the *Ben-my-Chree* will be retained and become the back-up vessel, and the MV *Arrow* will be returned to its owners.

In addition to the new Ro-Pax, there is a requirement to replace the fastcraft *Manannan* by the end of 2026, and to complete a £250,000 refurbishment of the vessel by the end of 2021.

At this stage there is no decision regarding the type of ship that will replace *Manannan,* so there is opportunity for either a new fast craft or a faster Ro-Pax vessel.

The new agreement requires the back-up vessel to be available for both the TT and Festival of Motorcycling periods and that it should be able to be deployed on Island routes within 96 hours of a need occurring. All vessels operated by the Company must be registered in the Isle of Man.

Routes

The surveys and workshops, undertaken ahead of the new agreement being drafted, provided a great deal of feedback regarding sailing frequency and destinations. As a result, the current requirement for Liverpool sailings will increase by one per week, the total sailings to the North West of England is increased from 936 to 947 per annum.

The 02.15 nightly sailing from Heysham is considered very important in the provision of fresh products to the food outlets around the Island. Transit times are not given as much priority by freight users as the importance of regular sailings giving the opportunity for 'just in time' delivery, to shops, businesses and private addresses.

While the number of sailings to the North West of England increase, those to Ireland (Dublin and Belfast), are reduced from the current 69 return sailings to 52.

There is some discussion around the opportunity to provide freight capacity from either Irish port but neither berth can currently accommodate larger size vehicles. With the *Ben-my-Chree* becoming the back-up vessel, the potential opportunity for freight and indeed Irish coach operators bringing tours to the Island, could be investigated further in the future.

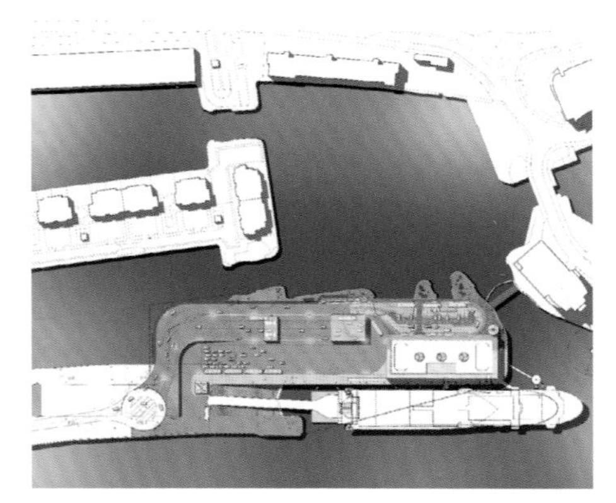

Left: An overview of the new terminal and berth at Liverpool. Right: An artist's impression of the new terminal building at Liverpool. *(Isle of Man Government))*

Strategic Re-Set

The new agreement allows for a revisit every five years to allow for any modifications that may be required as the result of changes affecting the overall services required.

Additionally, there is a reset provision for Irish services with 12 months of the UK formally leaving the European Union.

Terminal facilities and Linkspans

On the signing of the agreement the Victoria Pier linkspan at Douglas will be transferred to the Government. The new Liverpool terminal will also be Isle of Man Government owned.

Considerable criticism came from passengers using the 02.15 service from Heysham, many of whom arrive several hours before sailing time, that the facilities at Heysham need improvement.

The agreement gives the Steam Packet until the end of 2019 to bring about improvements at Heysham, including the provision of wifi. Clearly, any improvements will also enhance the experience of passengers travelling on daytime sailings.

Additionally, the Government will refurbish the baggage and customer areas at Douglas.

New Liverpool Terminal

The Isle of Man Steam Packet has for many years operated to and from the Pier Head in Liverpool. The berth is on a floating pontoon that is becoming life expired. Over recent years various discussions have been undertaken by both the Steam Packet and the Isle of Man Government with authorities in Liverpool and the ports owner Peel Holdings.

Additionally, Liverpool City Council want to close the Pier Head site to enable it to expand its cruise ship terminal and so it will be necessary for the Steam Packet to move.

On Friday 7 September 2018 the IOM Government announced that it had completed negotiations with Peel Holdings for a long-term leasehold ownership of a new site at Princes Half Tide Dock, about 675 metres down river from the Pier Head. The new site would provide the opportunity for a modern terminal building along with improved road access to be available to passengers. The linkspan would be capable of accommodating loads of 120 tonnes, enabling the terminal to be used for freight during the winter weekends. The cost to the IOM Government would be in the region of £31.5 million, while £20 million will be made available locally to upgrade and provide the new road access.

New Ships for the Island

The first design images were made available in late October 2018, ahead of the formal planning application being made.

On Tuesday 9 April 2019 the IOM Government announced that planning permission for the new terminal had been approved and that construction would start this summer. Completion is anticipated in late 2020, and so it might be hoped that services will start from the new terminal at the start of the 2021 fastcraft season. Unlike the current Pier Head berth, both the *Ben-my-Chree* and *Manannan* would be able to use the new facility, as would any new ro-pax vessel in the future. The facility will be capable of handling vessels up to 142 metres.

Perhaps not surprisingly, in recent days, it has been announced that the cost has risen to £37 million but, as yet no reason has been given.

What should replace the *Ben-my-Chree* and *Manannan*? As mentioned earlier, the new Sea Services agreement requires a replacement vessel for the *Ben-my-Chree* by the end of 2021, or at the very latest, the end of 2022 and a replacement for the Manannan by the end of 2026.

Improvements at Douglas Harbour will increase the permissible length of vessels to around 142m, matching that of Heysham and the new Liverpool terminal. The current maximum is 136m.

The agreement specifies that the new vessel must be capable of carrying 800 passengers, an increase of 170 over the *Ben-my-Chree*. Interestingly the agreement also specifies that no replacement vessel should be more than 10 years old. It seems unlikely that the Company would consider purchasing secondhand ships to replace the current fleet, unless it sees a short-term secondhand option as giving some time to decide what should replace the *Manannan*, and the potential for two identical ships.

The advantage of the fast craft on the Liverpool route, will need to be seriously evaluated, when the replacement vessel is considered.

There must be considerable advantages to ordering two identical ro-pax ships, capable of up to around 25 knots, with the added possibility of a third vessel to replace the Condor Ferries *Commodore Clipper*, being built at the same time.

While this would increase the crossing times to Liverpool, in comparison with the *Manannan*, the increase would likely only be in the region of 30 minutes but, would not be so susceptible to weather conditions, and therefore more reliable. Crossing times to Heysham would be reduced.

In terms of maintenance, spares, engineer knowledge and crew training having two identical ships would have clear advantages in terms of operating costs.

Barry Edwards

RED FUNNEL FERRIES' RED KESTREL

The Southampton Isle of Wight and South of England Royal Mail Steam Packet Company Limited (better known as Red Funnel Ferries Limited) was formed in 1861 and proudly states that it is the original operator to the Isle of Wight.

The company took delivery of the Solent's very first freight-only newbuild in April 2019, which received the name *Red Kestrel*. The ship was ordered on 14th February 2018 from Cammell Laird of Birkenhead, Merseyside, as a solution to easing capacity on the vehicle ferries. Western Ferries' 2013 built *Sound of Seil* and *Sound of Soay* formed the basis for the *Red Kestrel*'s design but the Clyde ferries differ in terms of length (49.95m), beam (15.01m) and also have a lower gross tonnage of 497gt. They have capacity for 40 cars/194 lanemetres of freight and 220 passengers. Whilst the Western Ferries vessels have passenger capacity for their mixed traffic role at deck level, and a small offset wheelhouse over the car deck, the *Red Kestrel* boasts a full width accommodation area above the freight deck and a full-size bridge above that.

The keel laying ceremony for Yard No. V1393 took place on 31 May 2018 and the construction process included the use of 564t of steel, 94,000m of welding, 12,000m of cabling and 9,404 litres of paint. The float out took place on 19 February 2019 from the tidal basin. As with the keel laying, the launch ceremony was conducted by Karen George, wife of Red Funnel Chairman Kevin George. After sea trials were completed, the *Red Kestrel* was towed to Southampton by the Williams Shipping tug Willpower, departing from Birkenhead on 11 April after the newbuild had been handed over. The ensemble reached Southampton on 18 April after a bad weather stop at Milford Haven.

The ship was named on 25 April during a ceremony held in Ocean Dock, adjacent to the Ocean Cruise Terminal at Southampton. A bottle of English sparkling wine (Rose Brut) was used to officially christen the ship, supplied by the IoW's Rosemary Vineyard. Mrs Karen George pressed the red button to send the bottle smashing against the hull, completing her variety of roles as Godmother to the *Red Kestrel*. The first visit to the East Cowes berth and new layover berth built for the vessel took place on 9 May and, after trials, the *Red Kestrel* entered full revenue earning service on 24 May, departing Southampton at 09.25.

With a layover berth at both terminals, the ship can wait at either port upon arrival at the layby and then move to the berth when the vehicle ferry is clear to unload, load and vacate the berth again ahead of the following vehicle ferry's arrival (a 30-minute window generally at peak times). Timings are variable depending on traffic, but this new asset to Red Funnel can also carry other wheeled cargo whenever necessary. For example, on 23 July an abnormal load destined for the Isle of Wight Steam Railway was carried to East Cowes.

The Ro-Ro ferry is 74.25m long with a 17m beam, 2.82m draught and deadweight of 541dwt. The 1,102gt vessel consists of 5 deck levels with the lowest being the tank top and machinery spaces. Two spacious areas house a Cummins QSK38-M1 969kW diesel engine that operates at 1800rpm. The combined power output is 1,938kW and each main engine is accompanied by a Cummins KCD2 80kW 3 Phase auxiliary unit that operates at 1500rpm. The main engines each drive a Rolls Royce US 155-P12 Azimuthing Fixed Pitch Shrouded Propeller. These 10t units feature a 1.6m diameter propeller that runs at 1800rpm, power input is 1,000kW and the units are driven via a shaft from the gearbox that extends around 9 metres in to each propeller compartment from the engine rooms. The service speed is 12.5 knots @ 85% MCR (ideal for the 55-60-minute crossing time). Above the machinery spaces is the weather deck that forms the 1,021sqm vehicle deck. This is accessed at either end by hydraulically operated doors that open outwards. The ferry's true bow faces Southampton and bestowed upon the bow doors is a Kestrel figurehead that was fitted by Cammell Laird. The freight deck offers 265 lanemetres of capacity, ample for 12 full-size HGVs and a clear height of 5.60m. Unaccompanied trailers and smaller trucks can also be carried. A Deck is a mezzanine level for walkways and the mooring decks with a stairway on the starboard side leading from the freight deck up to B Deck where the accommodation can be found. Crew access stairs also link the main deck with the accommodation on the port side. The aft section of B Deck offers an office and day room/mess room and toilets for the crew of 6-7. Passenger toilets adjoin

The *Red Kestrel* is shown here departing Cowes for Southampton. *(Andrew Cooke)*

The 12 HGV capacity *Red Kestrel*'s functional form is shown here to good effect. *(Andrew Cooke)*

The uncluttered freight deck on the *Red Kestrel*. *(Andrew Cooke)*

The Driver accommodation featuring 9 reclining seats, food counter and at-table seating. *(Andrew Cooke)*

the crew facilities on the port side of B Deck and the forward area of B Deck provides a restaurant/lounge and the galley/food counter. Nine reclining seats (with footrests) are provided, which face to port with views ahead and to a wall-mounted TV. Bench and individual type seating is also provided at three tables. A small balcony for smokers is available facing forward on the port side. The stairway on the starboard side of B-Deck then continues to the full-width Bridge Deck. Identical navigation and control consoles are located centrally, facing fore and aft. The two seats are on runners, in the same manner as in a tug wheelhouse, so can be switched between the direction of travel. The Rolls Royce propeller units are controlled via joysticks and the controls are also repeated in each bridge wing.

Red Funnel has certainly had a variety of vehicle ferry tonnage since 1947 with the company now carrying 53% of all cross-Solent freight traffic per annum, in addition to 2.3m passengers and 857,000 vehicles on the conventional ferry service. Flexibility is the key to this new venture and the *Red Kestrel* brings a new 4-ship era to the route that welcomed its first purpose-built car ferry 60 years earlier. The new ship might be looked upon as "small" but she can make a big difference to the Cross-Solent freight business.

Andrew Cooke

Red Kestrel - Technical Specifications

Designer:	Cammell Laird
Order Date:	14 February 2018
Keel Laying:	31 May 2018
Launched:	19 February 2019
Delivered:	11 April 2019
Named:	25 April 2019
Service Debut:	24 May 2019
Shipyard:	Cammell Laird
Place of Build:	Birkenhead, Merseyside
Yard No.	V1393
IMO:	9847645
Flag:	UK
Port of Registry:	Southampton
Registered Owner:	Red Funnel Ferries Ltd
Operator:	Red Funnel Ferries Ltd
Route:	Southampton (Royal Pier Terminal 1) - East Cowes
Class Society:	Lloyds Register CL IX(A)
Classification: Ship	Passenger/Ro-Ro Cargo
Gross Tonnage:	1,102gt
Net Tonnage:	330nt
Deadweight:	541dwt
Length Overall:	74.25m
Beam:	17.00m
Hull Depth:	4.50m
Hull Draught:	2.82m
Machinery:	2x Cummins QSK38-M1 969kW 1800rpm
Power Output:	1,938kW
Auxiliary Engines:	2x Cummins KCD2 Circa 80kW 3 Phase 400V/230V 50Hz 1500rpm
Propulsion:	Rolls Royce US 155-P12 Azimuthing Fixed Pitch Shrouded Props 1.6m Diameter 1800RPM 1000kW Power input
Fuel:	MGO
Speed:	13 knots
Speed Ahead:	12.5 knots @ 85% MCR.
Speed Sideways:	3.5 knots
Bow/Stern Access:	Hinged Doors, opening outwards
Vehicle Lane Width:	3.5m approx. for HGVs
Vehicle Deck Area:	1,021sqm
Vehicle Deck Clear Height:	5.60m (UK motorway clearance is 5.1m)
Freight Capacity:	265 lanemetres
HGV Capacity:	12 artics
Passenger Capacity:	12 Drivers
Crew:	5-7

ROUND BRITAIN AND IRELAND REVIEW 2018/19

The following is a review of passenger and freight ferry activities during 2018 and the first half of 2019. Some events occurring in the first half of 2018 will have also been mentioned in 'Ferries 2018'.

EAST COAST & THAMES

In April 2018 DFDS closed down the Rosyth - Zeebrugge fright service following a fire aboard the vessel used, the *Finlandia Seaways*. The route continued to lose money and this was seen as the 'final straw' - a sad end to the hopes when a passenger and freight service was launched with two 'Superfast' vessel in 2002. Only a few weeks before Finnlines had announced a new facility for conveyance of trailers between Rosyth and Bilbao using this service and their own route from Zeebrugge to Bilbao. In addition, DFDS had announced that passengers (up to a maximum of 12) could also be conveyed. In January 2018 the *Stena Foreteller* was chartered by DFDS and is used mainly on the Immingham - Cuxhaven service.

The *Finlandia* Seaways returned to traffic in the autumn and was initially used on the Immingham - Cuxhaven service. In January 2019 she replaced a container vessel on the service from Immingham to Western Norway but this only lasted a few weeks until she was in turn replaced by a side-loading pallet carrier. However, in April a ro-ro service was re-instated using the chartered *Trader*.

Following DFDS's take over of Turkish operator UN RoRo in June 2018 it was decided that the first two large ro-ros under construction by Jinling Shipyard in China would be deployed on this operation rather than Göteborg - Gent as previously planned. Consequently the first ship, the *Gothia Seaways*, sailed from China to Turkey and was renamed the *Ephesus Seaways* and the second vessel, the *Belgia Seaways* became the *Troy Seaways*. During September 2018 an option was exercised for a further two vessels, bringing the total to six. Delivery is expected in 2020 but deployment is currently unknown.

In mid-June 2019, the contract to convey Stora Enso paper and card traffic from Göteborg to Zeebrugge passed to DFDS Seaways. For the last five years it had been carried by SOL Continent Line, using the *Schieborg* and *Slingeborg*, chartered from Wagenborg of The Netherlands. DFDS purchased the vessels, renaming them *Gothia Seaways* and *Belgia Seaways* respectively. The *Fionia Seaways* was added to the route, enabling six departures to be operated per week.

SOL Continent Line's parent company, Swedish Orient Line, set up Wallenius SOL, a joint venture with Wallenius Lines of Sweden to continue to operate their services from the Baltic to Antwerpen, Zeebrugge and Tilbury. Four new LNG powered 420 trailer ro-ros have been ordered from the Yantai CIMC Raffles Shipyard, Yantai, China for delivery in 2021.

CLdN started a direct twice weekly service between Zeebrugge and Santander in October 2018. Previously the Spanish port had been served by calls by ships operating between Rotterdam and Leixoes in Portugal. It was increased to three times a week in March 2019.

CLdN took delivery of the *Laureline*, the first of four 50,443 ton vessels was delivered from Hyundai Mipo at Ulsan, South Korea, in February 2019 and she entered service in March. Sister vessel *Ysaline* entered service in June. Similar in many ways to the larger *Celine* and *Delphine*, which were delivered in 2017 and early 2018, they are shorter and have one deck less. Numbers three and four, the *Sixtine* and *Hermine*, were due to enter service in the autumn. In July 2019 the option for a further two vessels of the type was exercised.

An order for two similar vessels from the Uljanik Shipyard in Pula, Croatia was cancelled because of the shipyard's failure to deliver.

In August 2018 the *Somerset* was chartered to Stena Line for three years and in March 2019 the *Wilhelmine* to P&O Ferries. In January 2019 the *Meleq* of Alternative Transport (Ekol) of Turkey was chartered in mainly for their Rotterdam – Leixoes services.

Stena Britannica *(John Bryant)*

Laureline *(Rob de Visser)*

Spirit of Britain *(George Holland)*

Dunkerque Seaways *(John Hendy)*

P&O Ferries chartered the *Stena Carrier* to boost capacity on their Teesport - Rotterdam service in June 2018. However this charter was not able to continue after August as owners, Stena RoRo, decided to sell the vessel. The smaller *Mistral*, which had been on charter to Stena Line, returned to the Zeebrugge route, allowing the *Estraden* to move to the single ship Rotterdam service. To compensate for the reduced capacity on this route, the company chartered the German registered *Wega*, a 749-TEU containership built in 1996. This arrangement continued until March 2019 when the *Wilhelmine* was chartered from CLdN. The *Mistral* was moved to the Irish Sea.

Mann Lines' new Visentini built freighter, the *ML Freyja*, was delivered in June 2017 but was then sub-chartered to SOL Continent Line, replacing the *Ark Forwarder* on the Zeebrugge - Gothenburg route. She was taken back by Mann Lines in January 2018.

During 2017 Finnlines embarked on a process to lengthen its six Jinling built ships, boosting capacity by 1,000 lane metres. A 35m long midships section was added to each vessel. The programme was completed in December 2018.

Stena Line made major changes to the services from Rotterdam to Killingholme and Harwich at the beginning of 2018. The charter of CLdN's *Capucine* and *Severine* on the Harwich route ended and they were replaced by the *Stena Scotia* and *Stena Forerunner*. On the Killingholme route the *Misana* and *Misida*, previously with Transfennica, took over to provide extra capacity. In September the *Stena Forerunner* and *Stena Scotia* and were transferred to the Irish Sea and were replaced by the *Somerset* and *Bore Bay*, chartered from CLdN and Bore Line respectively. In February 2019 the *Bore Bay* was replaced by the *Stena Forerunner*, which had returned from the Irish Sea and was placed on the Rotterdam - Killingholme service releasing the *Misana* to serve on the Harwich route.

New vessels for the historic Woolwich Free Ferry, operated by Briggs Marine, were delivered from Remontowa, Gdansk, Poland in November 2018 but did not enter service until February 2019. The *Ben Woollacott* and *Dame Vera Lynn* have 210 lane metres of vehicle deck space. The berths were reconstructed to accommodate the vessels. The previous vessels, which dated from the 1960s, were withdrawn in October 2018 and scrapped. During the interim period, the service was suspended.

In March 2018, MBNA Thames Clippers to delivery of a third Hunt Class catamaran, the *Venus Clipper* from the Wight Shipyard at Cowes.

EASTERN CHANNEL

Despite continuing to have no ferry services, the port of Ramsgate was very much in the headlines during early 2019 when Seaborne Freight, a company which had for some time been promising to resume ferry operations at the port, was awarded a contract to provide additional freight services to Oostende to relieve Dover in the event of a no-deal 'Brexit' (withdrawal of the UK from the EU) at the end of March. Controversy arose because the company had no vessels and no experience of running a service. In the event financial and technical backing from Arklow Shipping of Ireland was withdrawn, the company backed out and 'Brexit' was deferred. Some work was undertaken on dredging the port but subsequently the local council decided that it should no longer be kept 'ferry ready'. During 2018 and early 2019 some deliveries of new cars were made to the port by the vessels of UECC and LD Seaplane, but they were using the port as a backup to Sheerness.

Chaos at Dover at the end of March 2019 did not materialise due to the deferment of Brexit. Despite many strikes and protests in France during 2018 and 2019 in opposition to President Macron's reforms, the port of Calais remained open, although there were occasions when French immigration staff at Dover decided to impose more stringent passport checks without adequate staffing to do this. This resulted in major delays to passengers arriving at the port, although the operation of ferries was not affected.

In April 2018 DFDS Seaways signed an agreement with Stena RoRo to charter a 42,000t 'e-flexer' on delivery from her Chinese builders in 2021. This vessel, to be called *Côte d'Opale*, is likely to replace the *Calais Seaways* which will, by that time, be 30 years old. The original design will be modified during the build process to make her suitable for the 90 minute crossing - less cabins and more passenger and vehicle space. As the type name suggests, flexibility has been built into the basic layout.

Following a decision by the French courts in March 2016 that the agreement between DFDS Seaways and the local authorities to operate the Newhaven - Dieppe route was invalid and it should be put out to tender again, this duly took place. Not surprisingly, DFDS won and in November 2017 a new five year contact was awarded, starting in January 2018. The vessels remain in yellow 'Transmanche' livery.

WESTERN CHANNEL AND SOLENT

In 2016 Brittany Ferries ordered a new vessel from FSG in Flensburg for delivery in 2019. However, the *Honfleur* as she will be called, will be delivered later than expected and is not expected to enter service on the Portsmouth Caen (Ouistreham) service until Summer 2020. This is a knock on from the delays to the Irish Ferries vessel *W B Yeats*, caused by financial problems at the German yard, a shortage of experienced engineers and an unconventional building method - hull and engines built in the shed at Flensburg and the superstructure built in sections in Poland, delivered by barge and craned on top after launch. The *Honfleur* will later be joined by three further vessels, this time 'e-flexer' vessels chartered from Stena RoRo, one arriving in 2021, the second in 2022 and the third in 2023. The first of these vessels is to be named *Galicia*, the second *Salamanca* and the third *Santoña*.

Wightlink's new *Victoria of Wight* arrived from the Turkish shipyard, under tow, in August 2018. She had a 'soft' introduction, not entering daily traffic until the end of October. A new timetable was introduced - previously a basic half hourly service with a few gaps it became basically hourly with extra sailings at the peaks. The new vessel and the 2001 built *St. Clare* operate the basic service, with the 1989 built *St. Faith*, the last British Rail Sealink designed vessel (albeit built during Sea Containers ownership) still in UK waters, operating the peak sailings. In January 2019 the *St. Faith's* sister, the *St. Cecilia* was sold to an Italian operator.

In June 2019 a 50% share in the company was sold to Fiera Infrastructure Inc of Canada.

In February 2018 Red Funnel ordered a new vessel from Camell Laird, Birkenhead. Unlike the 'Raptor' class, the *Red Kestrel* is a freight only vessel with a passenger capacity of twelve. The order coincided with major terminal investments at Southampton and East Cowes. She was delivered in April 2019. A new catamaran, the *Red Jet 7*, an identical craft to the *Red Jet 6* and also built by Wight Shipyard at East Cowes, entered service in July 2018. The *Red Jet 3* was sold for operation in Croatia in March 2019.

Hovertravel's two new 2016 built hovercraft, built by an associated company, continued to cause problems and in October 2018, the timetable was cut from a basic half hourly service during the day and quarter-hourly during the peak to hourly during the day and half-hourly at the peak. In the summer a basic half hourly service operates all day. This was to allow additional time for maintenance and for the entire service to be operated by a single vessel if necessary. Both vessels were returned to their builders for major modifications.

IRISH SEA

In April 2018 Brittany Ferries chartered a second Visentini built vessel, the *Asterion*. She was renamed the *Connemara* and inaugurated a new twice weekly Cork - Santander service, with an additional weekly service from Cork to Roscoff. Unlike other Brittany Ferries vessels she flies the Cypriot flag and employs a mainly East European crew, although French unions were promised that if the new route is successful, the ship will be transferred to French registration. This will happen in November 2019 when a sister vessel, the *AF Michela*, renamed the *Kerry*, will be chartered and placed on the Cork - Santander route. The *Connemara* will then operate as a refit relief vessel on services from the UK to France, in particular that of the *Pont-Aven* which suffered a major engine failure in April 2019 and operated on reduced power throughout the summer period, her Portsmouth services being transferred to Plymouth to reduce mileage.

Honfleur *(Brittany Ferries)*

Etretat *(Miles Cowsill)*

Epsilon *(Miles Cowsill)*

Isle of Lewis *(John Hendy)*

Irish Ferries' new 54,975t ferry, the *W B Yeats*, was expected to be delivered by the start of the 2018 summer season to operate between Dublin and Cherbourg in the summer and Dublin and Holyhead in the winter. However, due to a number of problems during the construction, she was not delivered from the yard at Flensburg until December 2018 and entered service in January 2019. The late delivery of the *W B Yeats* and mechanical problems with the usually highly reliable *Ulysses* caused the company considerable problems during the peak summer period and serious damage to reputation. A second, even larger vessel, has been ordered from the same yard to replace the *Epsilon* on the Dublin - Holyhead route. The, as yet un-named, vessel is due to enter service in 2020, but is unlikely to be delivered before the peak summer season.

Early in 2019, Irish Ferries announced that the services from Rosslare to Roscoff and Cherbourg operated by the *Oscar Wilde* would not operate during 2019. The vessel was subsequently sold to Mediterranean Shipping Company SA of Italy.

In April 2018 Irish Ferries replaced the Austal fast ferry *Jonathan Swift* with the larger *Dublin Swift*, which came from the same Australian yard. Formerly named the *Westpac Express*, she had been purchased by Irish Ferries in May 2016 but continued to be chartered to the US Government for military transport until November 2017. She was given the same name as the marketing name of the Dublin - Holyhead service which had been operated by the *Jonathan Swift*. The *Jonathan Swift* was sold to sold to Baleària of Spain in January 2019. The fast ferry service will now operate summer only.

In March 2019 Stena Line sent the 38 year old *Stena Europe* to Turkey for a major life-extension refit, expected to take three months, she eventually returned to the Fishguard - Rosslare route in August. The *Stena Nordica* was moved from the Karlskrona - Gdynia route to cover while she was away.

In May 2018 the Isle of Man Steam Packet Company was purchased by the Manx Government for £124 million. The purchase included the *Ben-my-Chree*, *Manannan* and terminal facilities at Douglas (the *Arrow* being on long-term charter from Seatruck Ferries). Plans are being drawn up for a fast conventional vessel to replace both the *Ben-my-Chree* and *Manannan*.

In August 2018, *Stena Performer* and *Stena Precision* of Seatruck Ferries returned from their charter to Stena Line operating between Heysham and Belfast. They resumed their original names of *Seatruck Performance* and *Seatruck Precision* and replaced two of their older vessels on the Heysham - Warrenpoint service. The *Clipper Pennant* was, in November, chartered to Canary Bridge Seaways of Spain and the oldest vessel, the *Clipper Ranger*, was replaced on the Liverpool - Dublin service and was laid up until July 2019 when she was chartered to *CTMA* of Canada for one year, with an option to buy.

Stena Line responded to the ending of the charter by moving the *Stena Hibernia* from the Birkenhead - Belfast service to the Heysham - Belfast route and bringing up sister vessel *Stena Scotia* from Rotterdam. Both vessels were built by Norfolkine to operate between Scheveningen in the Netherlands to Felixstowe and, fortunately, 'Scheveningen max' length of about 142 metres was also 'Heysham max'. To maintain the Birkenhead - Belfast service the *Stena Forerunner* was also bought up from Harwich. In February 2019 she returned to the North Sea and was placed on the Rotterdam - Killingholme service, being replaced at Birkenhead by sister vessel *Stena Forecaster*.

The first of the new 'e-flexer' vessels, the *Stena Estrid*, was floated out of the construction dock at Weihai, China, in January 2019. She is expected to be delivered in the late autumn and replace the chartered *Stena Superfast X* on the Holyhead - Dublin route in early 2020. The second and fourth of these vessels, the *Stena Edda* and *Stena Embla* will take over the Birkenhead - Belfast service later in the year or early 2021.

In March P&O Ferries moved the freighter *Mistral* from the North Sea to the Liverpool - Dublin service, initially as refit cover but later as permanent replacement for the ro-pax *European Endeavour* which was sold to Eckerö Line of Finland and renamed the *Finbo Cargo*. The *Mistral* operated on the *European Endeavour's* schedules which had previously been available to car passengers but, with only twelve passengers allowed, this facility was withdrawn.

IRELAND

In June 2018 Arranmore Island Ferry Services resold the *Strangford Ferry*, which they had purchased in December 2017 and renamed the *Strangford 1*, to Frazer Ferries, having operated her on charter to them on the Lough Foyle service since May. She acts as a reserve vessel on their Lough Foyle, Carlingford Lough and Passage East routes.

The remaining CalMac island class ferries were purchased by Irish operators during 2018. The *Canna,* previously on charter to Rathlin Island Ferry and the *Raasay* were sold to Humphrey O'Leary of Clare Island and the *Eigg* to Clare Island Ferries. The *Raasay* was subsequently sold to Inishbofin Discovery to operate a twice weekly freight service to the Island and *Canna* to Arranmore Fast Ferries (Arranmore Blue Ferry) as a second vessel.

SCOTLAND

Caledonian MacBrayne had another difficult summer trying to cope with increasing traffic, an aging fleet and continuing delays in the two ships being built by Ferguson's at Port Glasgow. The introduction of Road Equivalent Tariff (RET) in 2017 and the increasing popularity of the Scottish Islands for tourists created a situation where island residents could not take their vehicles - cars and trucks - onto the mainland. The second factor caused a number of breakdowns which necessitated unwelcome shuffling of vessels and, with no reserve vessels, cancellations and disruption to people's travel plans. After her launch in late 2017 very little progress was made on the *Glen Sannox*, as the builders and the owners, Caledonian Maritime Assets argued about the impact of changes made to the design since the contract was awarded. The second hull remains un-launched and, whilst it is hoped that the *Glen Sannox* might be delivered in 2020, there is no certainty about this. Since the order of these two vessels, no further orders have been placed.

In 2018 the company said farewell to the last of the 'Island Class' vessels which had pioneered ro-ro services to many of the smaller Scottish islands. As mentioned above, they were all sold to Irish operators, all are still operating as ferries apart from the *Bruernish* which serves as a work boat for fish farms on Clare Island. All have retained their original names apart from the first to be sold, the *Kilbrannan*, which is now the *Clew Bay Queen*.

Clydelink, operators of the Gourock - Kilcreggan ferry service, were, in May 2018, relieved of their contract awarded by Strathclyde Partnership for Transport after several years of unreliable service with a small, superannuated vessel. The previous operator, Clyde Marine, resumed operating, using the *Chieftain*, which had been purpose built for the route as the *Seabus* in 2007. In autumn 2019 the vessel will chartered to Caledonian MacBrayne who will take over the operation of the service following Clyde Marine's withdrawal from the operation of passenger vessels.

In April 2018, the three passenger ferries serving the Northern Isles, the *Hamnavoe*, *Hrossey* and *Hjaltland* were purchased outright by Caledonian Maritime Assets Ltd (CMAL) with loan funding from the Scottish Government; they had previously been leased from Royal Bank of Scotland. An 18 month extension to the Northern Isles Ferry Services contract was also agreed, allowing Serco NorthLink Ferries to continue to operate the services until 31 October 2019.

In 2019, Orkney operator, Pentland Ferries, took delivery of the *Alfred*, an 85m catamaran. The new vessel, 25m longer than the existing craft, was built at the Strategic Marine Shipyard, Vũng Tàu, Vietnam.

Nick Widdows

Coruisk *(John Hendy)*

A **guide** to using this book

Sections Listing is in seven sections. ***Section 1*** - Services from Great Britain and Ireland to the Continent and between Great Britain and Ireland (including services to/from the Isle of Man and Channel Islands), ***Section 2*** - Domestic services within Great Britain and Ireland, ***Section 3*** - Freight-only services from Great Britain and Ireland and domestic routes, ***Section 4*** - Minor vehicle ferries in Great Britain and Ireland (chain and cable ferries etc), ***Section 5*** - Major passenger-only operators, ***Section 6*** - Major car ferry operators in Northern Europe, ***Section 7*** - Companies not operating regular services possessing vehicle ferries which may be chartered or sold to other operators.

Order The company order within each section is alphabetical. Note that the definite article and words meaning 'company' or 'shipping company' (eg. 'AG', 'Reederei') do not count. However, where this is part of a ship's name it does count. Sorting is by normal English convention eg. 'Å' is treated the same as 'A' and comes at the start, not as a separate character which comes at the end of the alphabet as is the Scandinavian convention. Where ships are numbered, order is by number whether the number is expressed in Arabic or Latin digits.

Listing of Ships When a ship owned by a company listed in this book is on charter to another company listed, then she is shown under the company which operates her. When a ship owned by a company listed in this book is on charter to another company not listed, then she is shown under the company which owns her.

IMO Number All ships of 100t or greater (except vessels solely engaged in fishing, ships without mechanical means of propulsion (eg. chain ferries), pleasure yachts, ships engaged on special service (eg. lightships), hopper barges, hydrofoils, air cushion vehicles, floating docks and structures classified in a similar manner, warships and troopships, wooden ships) are required to be registered by the International Maritime Organisation (IMO), an agency of the United Nations. The seven digit number (the final digit is a check digit) is retained by the ship throughout her life, however much the vessel is rebuilt. This number is now required to be displayed on the ship externally and on top so that it can be read from the air. The scheme is administered by Lloyd's Register-Fairplay, who maintain a database of all ships in excess of 100t (with some exceptions), not just those classified through them. Some vessels which do not qualify for an IMO number have a Lloyd's number in the same series.

Company Information This section gives general information regarding the status of the company. That is, nationality, whether it is public or private sector and whether it is part of a larger group.

Management The Managing Director and Marketing Director or Manager of each company are listed. Where these posts do not exist, other equivalent people are listed. Where only initials are given, that person is, as far as is known, male.

Address This is the address of the company's administrative headquarters. In the case of some international companies, British and overseas addresses are given.

Telephone and Fax Numbers are expressed as follows: + [*number*] (this is the international dialling code which is dialled in combination with the number dialled for international calls (00 in the UK, Ireland and most other European countries); it is not used for calling within the country), ([*number*]) (this is the number which precedes area codes when making long-distance domestic calls - it is not dialled when calling from another country or making local calls (not all countries have this)), [*number*] (this is the rest of the number including, where appropriate, the area dialling code). UK '08' numbers are sometimes not available from overseas and the full number must be dialled in all circumstances.

Internet Email addresses and **Website** URLs are given where these are available; the language(s) used is shown. The language listed first is that which appears on the home page when accessed from a UK based computer; the others follow in alphabetical order. In a few cases Email facility is only available through the Website. To avoid confusion, there is no other punctuation on the Internet line.

Routes operated After each route there are, in brackets, details of **1** normal journey time, **2** regular vessel(s) used on the route (number as in list of vessels) and **3** frequencies (where a number per day is given, this relates to return sailings). In the case of freight-only sailings which operate to a regular schedule, departure times are given where they have been supplied. Please note that times are subject to quite frequent change and cancellation.

Winter and Summer In this book, Winter generally means the period between October and Easter while Summer means Easter to October. The peak Summer period is generally June, July and August. In Scandinavia, the Summer peak ends in mid-August whilst in the UK it starts rather later and generally stretches into the first or second week of September. Dates vary according to operator.

Terms The following words mean ***'shipping company'*** in various languages: Redereja (Latvian), Rederi (Danish, Norwegian, Swedish), Rederij (Dutch), Reederei (German) and Zegluga (Polish). The following words mean ***'limited company':*** AB - Aktiebolaget (Swedish) (Finnish companies who use both the Finnish and Swedish terms sometimes express it as Ab), AG - Aktiengesellschaft (German), AS - Aksjeselskap (Norwegian), A/S - Aktie Selskabet (Danish), BV - Besloten Vennootschap (Dutch), GmbH - Gesellschaft mit beschränkter Haftung (German), NV - Naamloze Vennootschap (Dutch), Oy - (Finnish), Oyj - (Finnish (plc)) and SA - Société Anonyme (French).

Spelling The convention now used in respect of town and country names is that local names are used for towns and areas of countries (eg. Göteborg rather than Gothenburg) and English names for countries (eg. Germany rather than Deutschland). Many towns in Finland have both Finnish and Swedish names; we have used the Finnish name except in the case of Åland which is a Swedish-speaking area. In the case of Danish towns, the alternative use of 'å' or 'aa' follows local convention. The following towns, islands and territories, which have alternative English names, are expressed using their local names - the English name is shown following: Antwerpen/Anvers - Antwerp, Funen - Fyn, Génova - Genoa, Gent - Ghent, Gothenburg - Göteborg, Hoek van Holland - Hook of Holland, Jylland - Jutland, København -Copenhagen, Oostende - Ostend, Porto - Oporto, Sevilla - Seville, Sjælland - Sealand and Venezia - Venice.

Types of Ferry

These distinctions are necessarily general and many ships will have features of more than one category.

Car Ferry Until about 1970, most vehicle ferries were primarily designed for the conveyance of cars and their passengers and foot passengers. Little regard was paid to the conveyance of lorries and trailers, since this sort of traffic had not begun to develop. Few vessels of this type are still in service.

Multi-purpose Ferry From about 1970 onwards vehicle ferries began to make more provision for freight traffic, sharing the same ship with passengers and cars. Features usually include higher vehicle decks, often with retractable mezzanine decks, enabling two levels of cars or one level of freight and coaches, and separate facilities (including cabins on quite short crossings) for freight drivers.

Cruise Ferry In the 1980s the idea of travelling on a ferry, not just to get from A to B but for the pleasure of the travel experience, became more and more popular and ferries were built with increasingly luxurious and varied passenger accommodation. Such vessels also convey cars and freight but the emphasis is on passenger accommodation with a high level of berths (sometimes providing berths for all passengers).

Ro-pax Ferry A vessel designed primarily for the carriage of freight traffic but which also carries a limited number of ordinary passengers. Features generally include a moderate passenger capacity - up to about 500 passengers - and a partly open upper vehicle deck. Modern ro-pax vessels are becoming increasingly luxurious with facilities approaching those of a cruise ferry.

Ro-ro Ferry A vessel designed for the conveyance of road freight, unaccompanied trailers and containers on low trailers (known as 'Mafis' although often made by other manufacturers) and new cars. Some such vessels have no passenger accommodation but the majority can accommodate up to 12 passengers - the maximum allowed without a passenger certificate. On routes where there is a low level of driver-accompanied traffic (mainly the longer ones), ordinary passengers, with or without cars, can sometimes be conveyed. On routes with a high level of driver-accompanied traffic, passenger capacity will sometimes be higher but facilities tend to be geared to the needs of freight drivers eg. lounge with video, high level of cabins on routes of three hours or more. Technically such vessels are passenger ferries (having a passenger certificate).

Con-ro Many ro-ro vessels are capable of having ISO (International Standards Organisation) containers crane-loaded on the upper 'weather' deck. In this book the term con-ro applies only to vessels whose upper deck can only take containers and has no vehicle access.

Fast Ferry Streamlined vessel of catamaran or monohull construction, speed in excess of 30 knots, water jet propulsion, generally aluminium-built but some have steel hulls, little or no freight capacity and no cabins.

Propulsion systems

Unless otherwise stated, all vessels are diesel powered. However, there is a gradual move away from diesel propulsion towards the following types.

LNG Vessel uses Liquefied Natural Gas to drive reciprocating engines.

Hybrid Vessel has reciprocating engine, either diesel or LNG, which drives alternator to feed batteries which in turn feed electric motors or the electric motors are fed directly by the alternator.

Hybrid Vessel with shore-side power supply. Hybrid vessel with the facility to take on electric power when in port.

Pure Electric. Vessel runs off batteries which are fed when in port and has no other power supply.

Timescale Although the book goes to press in August 2019, I have sought to reflect the situation as it will exist in September 2019 with regard to the introduction of new ships or other known changes. Vessels due to enter service after September 2019 are shown as '**Under Construction**'. This term does not necessarily mean that physical work has started but an order has been placed with a shipyard. The book is updated at all stages of the production process where this is feasible, although major changes once the text has been paginated are not possible; there is also a 'Late News' section on page 218 for changes which cannot be incorporated into the text.

List of vessels

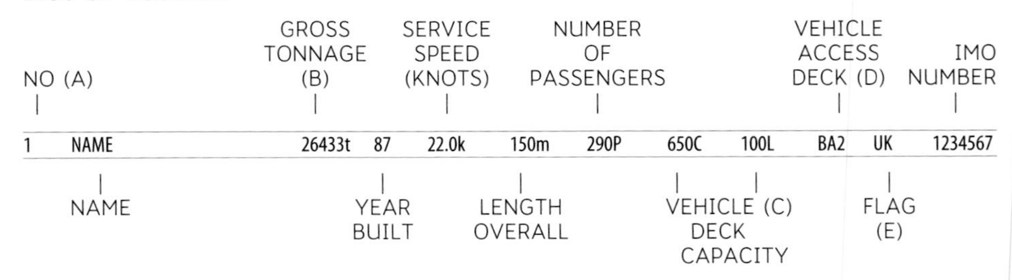

(A) >> = fast ferry, ● = vessel laid up, F = freight-only vessel (max 12 passengers), F+ = freight-only vessel (with passenger certificate), p = passenger-only vessel.

(B) C = Cars, L = Lorries (**15m**), T = Trailers (**13.5m**), r = can also take rail wagons, - = No figure quoted.

(C) B = Bow, A = Aft, S = Side, Q = Quarterdeck, R = Slewing ramp, 2 = Two decks can be loaded at the same time, C = Vehicles must be crane-loaded aboard, t = turntable ferry.

(D) The following abbreviations are used:

In the notes ships are in CAPITAL LETTERS, shipping lines and other institutions are in *italics*.

AG = Antigua and Barbuda
AL = Åland Islands
BB = Barbados
BE = Belgium
BM = Bermuda
BS = Bahamas
CY = Cyprus
DE = Germany
DK = Denmark
EE = Estonia
ES = Spain
FO = Faroes
FI = Finland
FR = France
GI = Gibraltar
IM = Isle of Man
IT = Italy
IR = Republic of Ireland
LU = Luxembourg
LT = Lithuania
LV = Latvia
MT = Malta
NL = Netherlands
NO = Norway
PA = Panama
PT = Portugal
PL = Poland
RU = Russia
SG = Singapore
SE = Sweden
TR = Turkey
UK = United Kingdom

Capacity In this book, capacities shown are the maxima. Sometimes vessels operate at less than their maximum passenger capacity due to reduced crewing or to operating on a route on which they are not permitted to operate above a certain level. Car and lorry/trailer capacities are the maximum for either type. The two figures are not directly comparable. Some parts of a vessel may allow cars on two levels to occupy the space that a trailer or lorry occupies on one level, some may not; some parts of a vessel with low headroom may only be accessible to cars. All figures have to be approximate.

Ownership The ownership of many vessels is very complicated. Some are actually owned by finance companies and banks, some by subsidiary companies of the shipping lines, some by subsidiary companies of a holding company of which the shipping company is also a subsidiary and some by companies which are jointly owned by the shipping company and other interests like a bank, set up specifically to own one ship or a group of ships. In all these cases the vessel is technically chartered to the shipping company. However, in this book, only those vessels chartered from one shipping company to another or from a ship-owning company unconnected with the shipping line are recorded as being on charter. Vessels are listed under the current operator rather than the owner. Charter is 'bareboat' (without crew) unless otherwise stated. If chartered with crew, vessels are 'time-chartered'.

Gross Tonnage This is a measure of enclosed capacity rather than weight, based on a formula of one gross ton = 100 cubic feet. Even small alterations can alter the gross tonnage. Under old measurement systems, the capacity of enclosed car decks was not included but, under the 1969 Convention, all vessels laid down after 1982 have been measured by a new system which includes enclosed vehicle decks as enclosed space, thereby considerably increasing the tonnage of vehicle ferries. Under this Convention, from 1st January 1995 all vessels were due to be re-measured under this system. Tonnages quoted here are, where possible, those given by the shipping companies themselves.

The following people are gratefully thanked for their assistance with this publication, many of them in ferry companies in the UK and abroad: John Bryant, Andrew Cooke, Matthew Davies, Ian Hall, Richard Kirkman, George Holland, Frank Lose, Darren Holdaway, Gordon Hislip, Brian Maxted, Peter Therkildsen, Ian Smith (Camrose Media) and Gomer Press.

Whilst every effort has been made to ensure that the facts contained here are correct, neither the publishers nor the writer can accept any responsibility for errors contained herein. We would, however, appreciate comments from readers, which we will endeavour to reflect in the next edition which we plan to publish in summer 2020.

***Cap Finistere* and *Normandie* at Portsmouth.** *(Darren Holdaway)*

SECTION 1 - GB AND IRELAND - MAJOR PASSENGER OPERATORS

BRITTANY FERRIES

THE COMPANY *Brittany Ferries* is the trading name of *BAI SA*, a French private sector company and the operating arm of the *Brittany Ferries Group*. The UK operations are run by *BAI (UK) Ltd*, a UK private sector company, wholly owned by the *Brittany Ferries Group*.

MANAGEMENT CEO Christophe Mathieu, **Commercial Directors, Passengers** Simon Johnson (interim), Joëlle Croc, Florence Gourdon, **Commercial Director, Freight** Simon Wagstaff.

ADDRESS Millbay Docks, Plymouth, Devon PL1 3EW.

TELEPHONE Reservations *All Services* +44 (0)330 159 7000, **Freight - Administration & Enquiries** +44 (0)330 159 5000, **Reservations** +44 (0)330 159 5000.

INTERNET Websites *Passenger* www.brittanyferries.com *(English, French, Spanish, German)*, ***Freight*** www.brittanyferriesfreight.co.uk *(English)*

ROUTES OPERATED Conventional Ferries *All year* Plymouth - Roscoff (6 hrs (day), 7 hrs - 9 hrs (night); ***ARMORIQUE, PONT-AVEN***; up to 2 per day (Summer), 1 per day (Winter)), Poole - Cherbourg (4 hrs 15 mins; ***BARFLEUR***; 1 per day), Portsmouth - St Malo (8 hrs 45 mins (day), 10 hrs 45 mins (night); ***BRETAGNE***; (1 per day), Portsmouth - Caen (Ouistreham) (6 hrs (day), 6 hrs - 8 hrs (night); ***NORMANDIE, MONT ST MICHEL***; 3 per day), Portsmouth - Le Havre (5 hrs 30 mins (day), 9 hrs (night); ***BAIE DE SEINE, ETRETAT***; 1 per day), Portsmouth - Santander (Spain) (24 hrs; ***BAIE DE SEINE, CAP FINISTERE, PONT-AVEN***; up to 3 per week, Portsmouth - Bilbao (Spain) (24/32 hrs; ***BAIE DE SEINE, CAP FINISTERE***; up to 3 per week, ***Summer only*** Plymouth - Santander (Spain) (19 hrs 30 mins; ***PONT-AVEN***; 1 per week (April - October)), Cork - Roscoff (14 hrs-16½ hrs; ***CONNEMARA, PONT-AVEN***; up to 2 per week), Cork - Santander (28 hrs-32 hrs; ***CONNEMARA***; 2 per week, **Fast Ferries *Summer only*** Portsmouth – Cherbourg (3 hrs; ***NORMANDIE EXPRESS***; up to 2 per day (April-September)). **Freight-only service** Poole - Bilbao (31 hrs; ***MN PELICAN***; 2 per week).

Note: Sailings to France and Spain operated by the CONNEMARA, BAIE DE SEINE and ETRETAT are branded 'économie'.

1	ARMORIQUE	29468t	09	23.0k	167.0m	1500P	470C	65L	BA2	FR	9364980
2	BAIE DE SEINE	22382t	03	22.0k	199.4m	596P	316C	154T	A	FR	9212163
3	BARFLEUR	20133t	92	19.0k	158.0m	1212P	590C	112T	BA2	FR	9007130
4	BRETAGNE	24534t	89	19.5k	151.0m	1926P	580C	84T	BA	FR	8707329
5	CAP FINISTERE	32728t	01	28.0k	203.9m	1608P	1000C	140T	BA	FR	9198927
6	CONNEMARA	26500t	07	24.0k	186.5m	800P	170C	140L	BA	CY	9349760
7	ETRETAT	26500t	08	23.5k	186.5m	800P	185C	120L	A	FR	9420423
8F	MN PELICAN	12076t	99	20.0k	154.5m	12P	-	115T	A2	FR	9170999
9	MONT ST MICHEL	35592t	02	21.2k	173.0m	2200P	880C	166T	BA2	FR	9238337
10	NORMANDIE	27541t	92	20.5k	161.0m	2120P	600C	126T	BA2	FR	9006253
11»	NORMANDIE EXPRESS	6581t	00	40.0k	97.2m	900P	260C	-	A	FR	8814134
12	PONT-AVEN	41748t	04	26.0k	184.3m	2400P	650C	85L	BA	FR	9268708

ARMORIQUE Built by STX Europe, Helsinki, Finland for *Brittany Ferries* to operate between Plymouth and Roscoff.

BAIE DE SEINE Built as the GOLFO DEI DELFINI by Stocznia Szczecinska, Szczecin, Poland for *Lloyd Sardegna* of Italy for service between Italy and Sardinia. However, due to late delivery the order was cancelled. In 2002 purchased by *DFDS Seaways*, and, during Winter 2002/03, passenger accommodation was enlarged and refitted, increasing passenger capacity from 308 to 596. In June 2003, renamed the DANA SIRENA, she replaced unmodified sister vessel, the DANA GLORIA on the Esbjerg – Harwich service. In February 2013 she was renamed the SIRENA SEAWAYS. At the end of September 2014 the route ceased and she moved to the

Armorique *(John Bryant)*

Baie de Seine *(Miles Cowsill)*

Normandie *(Brian Smith)*

Cap Finistere *(Darren Holdaway)*

Paldiski (Estonia) - Kapellskär route, replacing the PATRIA SEAWAYS. In December she was replaced by the LIVERPOOL SEAWAYS and laid up. During the early part of 2015 she performed relief work in the Baltic. In April 2015 she was chartered to *Brittany Ferries* for five years and renamed the BAIE DE SEINE. She entered service in May 2015.

BARFLEUR Built as the BARFLEUR by Kvaerner Masa-Yards, Helsinki for the *Truckline* (freight division of *Brittany Ferries*) Poole - Cherbourg service to replace two passenger vessels and to inaugurate a year-round passenger service. In 1999 the *Truckline* branding was dropped for passenger services and she was repainted into full *Brittany Ferries* livery. In 2005 operated partly Cherbourg - Poole and partly Cherbourg - Portsmouth but in 2006 returned to operating mainly to Poole. In February 2010, she was laid up. The conventional car ferry service ended the following month. In February 2011 she resumed service on the Poole - Cherbourg route. In September 2011 she was withdrawn again. In April 2012 chartered to *DFDS Seaways* to operate between Dover and Calais and renamed the DEAL SEAWAYS. In November 2012 returned to *Brittany Ferries* and renamed the BARFLEUR. Resumed the Poole - Cherbourg service in March 2013, replacing the COTENTIN but offering a service for both freight and passengers.

BRETAGNE Built by Chantiers de l'Atlantique, St Nazaire for the Plymouth - Santander and Cork - Roscoff services (with two sailings per week between Plymouth and Roscoff). In 1993 she was transferred to the Portsmouth - St Malo service. In 2004 also operated between Portsmouth and Cherbourg. In 2005 operated between Plymouth and Roscoff. In 2006 returned to the Portsmouth - St Malo route.

CAP FINISTERE Built as the SUPERFAST V by Howaldtswerke Deutsche Werft AG, Kiel, Germany for *Attica Enterprises* (now *Attica Group*) for use by *Superfast Ferries* of Greece. Initially operated between Patras and Ancona and in January 2007 switched to the Patras - Igoumenitsa - Bari route. In 2008 the route became Patras - Igoumenitsa - Ancona. In 2010 sold to *Brittany Ferries,* renamed the CAP FINISTERE and in March placed on the Portsmouth - Santander service, also operating some sailings between Portsmouth and Cherbourg. In 2011 began operating also between Portsmouth and Bilbao and only operated between Portsmouth and Cherbourg during the winter period. Now operates on Portsmouth – Santander and Portsmouth – Bilbao routes only.

CONNEMARA Built by CN Visentini, Porto Viro, Italy. Whilst under construction, sold to *Stena RoRo* of Sweden and provisionally named the STENA AUSONIA. However, before delivery a charter was arranged with *Balearia* of Spain and she was delivered as the BORJA. Operated between Barcelona and Palma (Majorca). In February 2010 the charter ended and she was laid up at Rotterdam. In April 2010 chartered to *Ave Line* and renamed the BALTIC AMBER. In October 2010 chartered to *DFDS Seaways* to replace the fire-damaged LISCO GLORIA. In March 2011 chartered to *LD Lines* to operate between Marseilles and Rades (Tunisia). In April she was moved to the Saint Nazaire (Nantes) - Gijon route. In June 2011 renamed the NORMAN ASTURIAS. In October 2011 the charter was ended but resumed the following month. Also operated between Poole, Santander and Gijon. In September 2014 chartered to *Intershipping,* Morocco and operated between Algeciras and Tangiers. In February 2016 chartered to *Anek Lines* of Greece, renamed the ASTERION and placed on the Patras - Igoumenitsa - Venezia route. In April 2018 chartered to *Brittany Ferries*, renamed the CONNEMARA and inaugurated a new twice weekly Cork - Santander service, with an additional service to Roscoff. During winter 2019/20 she is to be transferred to the French flag and operate on other routes.

ETRETAT Built as the NORMAN VOYAGER by CN Visentini, Porto Viro, Italy for *Epic Shipping* of the UK and chartered to *LD Lines*. Operated between Le Havre and Portsmouth and Le Havre and Rosslare. In September 2009 sub-chartered to *Celtic Link Ferries*. Initially operated between Cherbourg and Portsmouth and Cherbourg and Rosslare but the Portsmouth service was abandoned in November 2009. In October 2011 returned to *LD Lines* and placed on the St Nazaire - Gijon route. In November moved to the Portsmouth - Le Havre service and, following the establishment of the joint *LD Lines/DFDS* venture, the charter was transferred to *DFDS Seaways*. In April 2012 sold to *Stena RoRo*; she continued to be chartered to *DFDS*. In March 2014 chartered to *Brittany Ferries* and placed on the new 'économie' services between Portsmouth and Le Havre and Portsmouth and Santander. Renamed the ETRETAT.

MN PELICAN Built as the TRANS BOTNIA for *SeaTrans ANS* of Norway. Hull constructed by Santierul Naval, Galatz, Romania and vessel completed by Fosen Mekaniske Verksteder, Frengen, Norway. Chartered to *Transfennica* for service between Finland and Western Europe. In June 2006 sold to *Maritime Nantaise* of France. In January 2007 renamed the MN PELICAN. Placed on long term charter to the *French MOD*. In 2015 placed on the charter market. In January 2016 time chartered to *Brittany Ferries*.

MONT ST MICHEL Built by Van der Giessen-de Noord, Krimpen aan den IJssel, Rotterdam for *Brittany Ferries*. Used on the Portsmouth - Caen route.

NORMANDIE Built by Kvaerner Masa-Yards, Turku, Finland for *Brittany Ferries*. Used on the Portsmouth - Caen route.

NORMANDIE EXPRESS Incat Evolution 10 catamaran built as the INCAT TASMANIA. In November 2000 chartered to *TranzRail* of New Zealand and renamed THE LYNX. Placed on the Wellington – Picton service. In July 2003 replaced by 1997-built Incat 86m craft INCAT 046, given the marketing name 'The Lynx' and laid up. In Spring 2005 chartered to *Brittany Ferries* to operate on their Cherbourg – Portsmouth and Caen – Portsmouth services and renamed the NORMANDIE EXPRESS. In 2007 purchased by *Brittany Ferries*. In 2015 operated to Cherbourg and Le Havre but in 2016 and 2017 only operated to Cherbourg.

PONT-AVEN Built by Jos L Meyer Werft, Papenburg, Germany for *Brittany Ferries* to operate on the Plymouth - Roscoff, Plymouth - Santander and Cork - Roscoff routes.

To be chartered

13	KERRY	24418t	01	24.0k	186.5m	1000P	75C	120L	BA	CY	9243447

KERRY Built as the CARTOUR by CN Visentini, Porto Viro, Italy. In September 2001 sold to *Levantina Trasporti* of Italy and in October chartered to *Caronte & Tourist* of Italy and operated between Messina and Salerno. In October 2007, sold to *Vinashin Ocean Shipping Co* of Vietnam and renamed the VINASHIN PRINCE. In December, renamed the HOA SEN and operated between Ho Chi Min City and Hanang Bay. In May 2014 sold to a UK subsidiary of *Stena RoRo* and renamed the STENA EGERIA. Chartered to *Yantai Bohai International Ferry* of China and operated between Yantai and Pyeongtaek. In October 2017 chartered to *Adria Ferries* of Albania and operated between Durres (Albania) and Ancona (Italy). She was renamed the AF MICHELA. In November 2019 to be renamed the KERRY and chartered to *Brittany Ferries* to replaced the CONNEMARA on the Cork - Santander/Roscoff service.

Under Construction

14	HONFLEUR	42400t	20	22.0k	187.4m	1680P	550C	150L	BA	FR	9832119
15	GALICIA	42000t	20	22.0k	214.5m	1000P	300C	180L	BA2	FR	9856189
16	SALAMANCA	42000t	21	22.0k	214.5m	1000P	300C	180L	BA2	FR	9867592
17	SANTOÑA	42000t	23	22.0k	214.5m	1000P	300C	180L	BA2	FR	-

HONFLEUR Under construction by Flensburger Schiffbau-Gesellschaft, Flensburg, Germany. To operate on the Portsmouth - Caen route, replacing the NORMANDIE. To be LNG powered.

GALICIA Under construction by AVIC International Maritime Holdings, Weihai, China for *Stena Line*. Designed to run on either methanol or LPG but before delivery she will be fitted with scrubbers to run on fuel oil. Upon delivery to be chartered to *Brittany Ferries* for five years and replace the BAIE DE SEINE.

SALAMANCA Under construction by AVIC International Maritime Holdings, Weihai, China for *Stena Line*. Designed to run on LPG. Upon delivery to be chartered to *Brittany Ferries* for five years.

SANTOÑA Under construction by AVIC International Maritime Holdings, Weihai, China for *Stena Line* (9th in the series). Designed to run on LPG. Upon delivery to be chartered to *Brittany Ferries* for five years. Deployment not yet decided.

CALEDONIAN MACBRAYNE

THE COMPANY *Caledonian MacBrayne* is the trading name of *CalMac Ferries Ltd*, a subsidiary of *David MacBrayne Limited*, a Scottish registered company, wholly owned by the Scottish Ministers. The majority of *CalMac Ferries* vessels are owned by *Caledonian Maritime Assets Limited*, a separate company which is also owned by the Scottish Ministers.

MANAGEMENT Managing Director Robbie Drummond, **Business Development Director** Karen McGregor, **Head of Stakeholder Communications** David Cannon.

ADDRESS Ferry Terminal, Gourock PA19 1QP.

TELEPHONE Administration +44 (0)1475 650100, **Vehicle Reservations** +44 (0)800 066 5000.

FAX Administration +44 (0)1475 650336, **Vehicle Reservations** +44 (0)1475 635235.

INTERNET Email enquiries@calmac.co.uk **Website** www.calmac.co.uk *(English)*,

ROUTES OPERATED All-year vehicle ferries (frequencies are for Summer – services are listed alphabetically by mainland port or larger island port where service is between two islands). Ardmhor (Barra) - Eriskay (40 mins; ***LOCH ALAINN***; up to 5 per day), Ardrossan - Brodick (Arran) (55 mins; ***CALEDONIAN ISLES, ISLE OF ARRAN***; up to 6 per day), Colintraive - Rhubodach (Bute) (5 mins; ***LOCH DUNVEGAN***; frequent service), Kennacraig - Port Askaig (Islay) (2 hrs 5 mins; ***FINLAGGAN, HEBRIDEAN ISLES***; up to 4 per day), Kennacraig - Port Ellen (Islay) (2 hrs 20 mins; ***FINLAGGAN, HEBRIDEAN ISLES***; service currently suspended due to harbour works), Largs - Cumbrae Slip (Cumbrae) (10 mins; ***LOCH RIDDON, LOCH SHIRA***; every 30 or 15 mins), Leverburgh (Harris) - Berneray (1 hr 10 mins; ***LOCH PORTAIN***; 3-4 per day), Lochaline - Fishnish (Mull) (15 mins; ***LOCHINVAR***; up to 14 per day), Mallaig - Armadale (Skye) (23 mins; ***LOCHNEVIS*** (Winter) ***LOCH FYNE, LORD OF THE ISLES*** (Summer); up to 9 per day (2 in Winter)), Mallaig - Lochboisdale (South Uist) (3 hrs 30 mins; ***LORD OF THE ISLES***; 1 per day), Oban - Castlebay (Barra) (5 hrs); ***ISLE OF LEWIS***; 1 per day), Oban - Coll - Tiree (2 hrs 45 min to Coll 3 hrs 50 min to Tiree via Coll; ***CLANSMAN***; 1 per day), Oban - Colonsay (2 hrs 15 mins; ***CLANSMAN***; 5 per week), Oban - Craignure (Mull) (45 mins; ***CORUISK, ISLE OF MULL***; up to 7 per day), Oban - Lismore (50 mins; ***LOCH STRIVEN***; up to 5 per day), Sconser (Skye) - Raasay (15 mins; ***HALLAIG***; up to 11 per day), Tarbert (Loch Fyne) - Portavadie (25 mins; ***ISLE OF CUMBRAE***; up to 12 per day), Tayinloan - Gigha (20 mins; ***LOCH RANZA***; up to 10 per day), Tobermory (Mull) - Kilchoan (35 mins; ***LOCH TARBERT***; up to 7 per day), Uig (Skye) - Lochmaddy (North Uist) (1 hr 45 mins; ***HEBRIDES***; 1 or 2 per day), Uig (Skye) - Tarbert (Harris) (1 hr 40 mins; ***HEBRIDES***; 1 or 2 per day), Ullapool - Stornoway (Lewis) (2 hrs 45 mins; ***LOCH SEAFORTH***; up to 3 per day (one freight only)), Wemyss Bay - Rothesay (Bute) (35 mins; ***ARGYLE, BUTE***; hourly).

All-year passenger and restricted vehicle ferries (frequencies are for Summer) Gallanach (near Oban) - Kerrera (5 mins; ***CARVORIA***; up to 12 per day), Fionnphort (Mull) - Iona (5 mins; ***LOCH BUIE***; frequent), Mallaig - Eigg - Muck - Rum - Canna - Mallaig (round trip 7 hrs (all islands); ***LOCHNEVIS***; at least 1 sailing per day - most islands visited daily). **Note** Although these services are operated by vehicle ferries special permission is required to take a vehicle and tourist cars are not normally conveyed. **Summer-only vehicle ferries** Ardrossan - Campbeltown (2 hrs 30 mins; ***ISLE OF ARRAN***; 3 per week), Claonaig - Lochranza (Arran) (30 mins; ***CATRIONA***; up to 9 per day), Kennacraig - Port Askaig - Colonsay - Oban (3 hrs 35 mins; ***HEBRIDEAN ISLES***; 1 per week). **Winter-only vehicle ferry** Tarbert (Loch Fyne) - Lochranza (Arran) (1 hr; ***varies***; 1 per day). **All-year passenger-only ferries** Gourock - Dunoon (20 mins; ***ALI CAT, ARGYLL FLYER, CORUISK (winter only)***; 1 or 2 per hour, Gourock - Kilcreggan (13 mins; ***CHIEFTAIN***; approx hourly).

1p	ALI CAT	74t	99	-	19.8m	250P	0C	0L	-	UK	
2	ARGYLE	2643t	07	14.0k	69.0m	450P	60C	-	BAS	UK	9365178
3p	ARGYLL FLYER	300t	01	19.5k	29.9m	227P	0C	0L	-	UK	9231016
4	BUTE	2612t	05	14.0k	69.0m	450P	60C	-	AS	UK	9319741
5	CALEDONIAN ISLES	5221t	93	15.0k	94.3m	1000P	120C	10L	BA	UK	9051284

Loch Riddon *(Brian Maxted)*

Carvoria *(Brian Maxted)*

6	CARVORIA	9t	17	8.0k	-	12P	1C	-	B	UK	
7	CATRIONA	499t	16	9.0k	43.5m	150P	23C	2L	BA	UK	9759862
7p	CHIEFTAIN	60t	07	8.6k	19.5m	1-0P	0C	0L	-	UK	
8	CLANSMAN	5499t	98	16.5k	99.0m	638P	90C	6L	BA	UK	9158953
9	CORUISK	1599t	03	14.0k	65.0m	250P	40C	-	BA	UK	9274836
10	FINLAGGAN	5626t	11	16.5k	89.9m	550P	88C	-	BA	UK	9482902
11	HALLAIG	499t	13	9.0k	43.5m	150P	23C	2L	BA	UK	9652832
12	HEBRIDEAN ISLES	3040t	85	15.0k	85.1m	494P	68C	10L	BAS	UK	8404812
13	HEBRIDES	5506t	00	16.5k	99.0m	612P	110C	6L	BA	UK	9211975
14	ISLE OF ARRAN	3296t	84	15.0k	85.0m	446P	68C	8L	BA	UK	8219554
15	ISLE OF CUMBRAE	201t	77	8.5k	37.7m	139P	18C	-	BA	UK	7521625
16	ISLE OF LEWIS	6753t	95	18.0k	101.2m	680P	123C	10L	BA	UK	9085974
17	ISLE OF MULL	4719t	88	15.0k	90.1m	962P	80C	20L	BA	UK	8608339
18	LOCH ALAINN	396t	98	10.0k	43.0m	150P	24C	-	BA	UK	9147722
19	LOCH BHRUSDA	246t	96	8.0k	35.4m	150P	18C	-	BA	UK	9129483
20	LOCH BUIE	295t	92	9.0k	35.5m	250P	9C	-	BA	UK	9031375
21	LOCH DUNVEGAN	549t	91	9.0k	54.2m	200P	36C	-	BA	UK	9006409
22	LOCH FYNE	549t	91	9.0k	54.2m	200P	36C	-	BA	UK	9006411
23	LOCH LINNHE	206t	86	9.0k	35.5m	199P	12C	-	BA	UK	8512308
24	LOCH PORTAIN	950t	03	10.5k	50.0m	200P	32C	-	BA	UK	9274824
25	LOCH RANZA	206t	87	9.0k	35.7m	199P	12C	-	BA	UK	8519887
26	LOCH RIDDON	206t	86	9.0k	35.5m	199P	12C	-	BA	UK	8519875
27	LOCH SEAFORTH	8478t	14	19.2k	116.0m	700P	143C	20L	BA	UK	9665437
28	LOCH SHIRA	1024t	07	13.0k	43.0m	250P	24C	-	BA	UK	9376919
29	LOCH STRIVEN	206t	86	9.0k	35.7m	199P	12C	-	BA	UK	8512293
30	LOCH TARBERT	211t	92	9.0k	34.5m	149P	18C	-	BA	UK	9039389
31	LOCHINVAR	523t	14	9.0k	43.5m	150P	23C	2L	BA	UK	9652844
32	LOCHNEVIS	941t	00	13.0k	49.1m	190P	14C	-	A	UK	9209063
33	LORD OF THE ISLES	3504t	89	16.0k	84.6m	506P	56C	16L	BAS	UK	8710869

Note In the following list, Gaelic names are shown in parenthesis.

ALI CAT Catamaran built for *Solent & Wight Line Cruises* of Ryde, Isle of Wight. She operated a passenger service from Cowes to Hamble and Warsash and cruises from Cowes. At times chartered to *Wightlink* to cover for their fast catamarans. In 2002 chartered to *Red Funnel Ferries* who had contracted with *Caledonian MacBrayne* to operate passenger-only services between Gourock and Dunoon in the morning and evening peaks. In June 2011 purchased by and operated by *Argyll Ferries*. In January 2019, operation was transferred to *Caledonian MacBrayne*.

ARGYLE *(EARRA-GHÀIDHEAL)*, BUTE *(EILEAN BHÒID)* Built by Stocznia Remontowa, Gdansk, Poland to operate on the Wemyss Bay - Rothesay route.

ARGYLL FLYER Built as the QUEEN OF ARAN II by OCEA, Les Sables d'Olonne, France for *Inis Mór Ferries*. In 2007 sold to *Aran Island Ferries* and renamed the BANRION CHONAMARA. In June 2011 sold to *Argyll Ferries*, renamed the ARGYLL FLYER and replaced the car ferry SATURN on the Gourock - Dunoon service. In January 2019, operation was transferred to *Caledonian MacBrayne*.

CALEDONIAN ISLES *(EILEANAN CHALEDONIA)* Built by Richards Shipyard, Lowestoft, UK for the Ardrossan - Brodick (Arran) service.

CARVORIA Built by Malakoff Limited, Lerwick, Shetland for *Caledonian Maritime Assets* and chartered to *Caledonian MacBrayne* to replace the chartered GYLEN LADY on the Gallanach - Kerrera service.

CATRIONA Built by Ferguson Marine Engineering, Port Glasgow. Near sister vessel of the HALLAIG and LOCHINVAR. Operates on the Claonaig - Lochranza service during the summer and other routes during the winter.

CHIEFTAIN Built as the SEABUS by Voyager Boatyard, Millbrook, Plymouth for *Clyde Marine Services*, Scotland and operated on the ferry service between Gourock, Kilgreggan and Helensburgh. In 2013 the contract to operate this service was awarded to *Clydelink* (Gourock - Kilcreggan only) and she was transferred to private hire and excursion work. In January 2014 she was renamed the CHIEFTAIN. In May 2018 the contract returned to *Clyde Marine Services* and she returned to this route. In October 2019 the contract will be transferred to *Caledonian MacBrayne* and the CHIEFTAIN chartered to them.

CLANSMAN *(FEAR-CINNIDH)* Built by Appledore Shipbuilders Ltd, Appledore, UK to replace the LORD OF THE ISLES on the Oban - Coll and Tiree and Oban - Castlebay and Lochboisdale services in the summer. She also serves as winter relief vessel on the Stornoway, Tarbert, Lochmaddy, Mull/Colonsay and Brodick routes.

CORUISK *(COIR' UISG')* Built by Appledore Shipbuilders Ltd, Appledore, UK to operate on the Mallaig - Armadale route during the summer. During the winter she operates on the Gourock - Dunoon passenger service during peak periods and when the usual vessels cannot sail due to adverse weather. Since summer 2016 she has operated as second vessel on the Oban - Craignure service.

FINLAGGAN *(FIONN LAGAN)* Built by Stocznia Remontowa, Gdansk, Poland for the Kennacraig - Islay service.

HALLAIG *(HALLAIG)* Built by Ferguson Shipbuilders, Port Glasgow, UK to replace the LOCH STRIVEN on the Sconser - Raasay service. The vessel has both diesel and battery electric propulsion and can be 'plugged in' to a land supply on Raasay overnight.

HEBRIDEAN ISLES *(EILEANAN INNSE GALL)* Built by Cochrane Shipbuilders, Selby UK for the Uig - Tarbert/Lochmaddy service. She was used initially on the Ullapool - Stornoway and Oban - Craignure/Colonsay services pending installation of link-span facilities at Uig, Tarbert and Lochmaddy. She took up her regular role in May 1986. From May 1996 she no longer operated direct services in summer between Tarbert and Lochmaddy, this role being taken on by the new Harris - North Uist services of the LOCH BHRUSDA. In 2001 she was replaced by the HEBRIDES and transferred to the Islay service. In Autumn 2002 she operated between Scrabster and Stromness for *NorthLink Orkney and Shetland Ferries* before port modifications at Scrabster enabled the HAMNAVOE to enter service in Spring 2003. She then returned to the Islay service. She also relieved on the *NorthLink* Pentland Firth service between 2004 and 2007.

HEBRIDES *(INNSE GALL)* Built by Ferguson Shipbuilders Ltd, Port Glasgow, UK for the Uig - Tarbert and Uig - Lochmaddy services.

ISLE OF ARRAN *(EILEAN ARAINN)* Built by Ferguson Ailsa, Port Glasgow, UK for the Ardrossan - Brodick service. In 1993 transferred to the Kennacraig - Port Ellen/Port Askaig service, also undertaking the weekly Port Askaig - Colonsay - Oban summer service. From then until 1997/98 she also relieved on the Brodick, Coll/Tiree, Castlebay/Lochboisdale, Craignure and Tarbert/Lochmaddy routes in winter. In 2001 she was replaced by the HEBRIDEAN ISLES and became a reserve for the larger vessels. She has operated on the two-ship Islay service in summer since 2003; this service is now all-year-round. Following the delivery of the FINLAGGAN in May 2011 she became a spare vessel, and operates extra services between Ardrossan and Brodick and Ardrossan and Campbeltown during the peak summer period.

ISLE OF CUMBRAE *(EILEAN CHUMRAIGH)* Built by Ailsa Shipbuilding Ltd, Troon, UK for the Largs - Cumbrae Slip (Cumbrae) service. In 1986 she was replaced by the LOCH LINNHE and the LOCH STRIVEN and transferred to the Lochaline - Fishnish (Mull) service. She used to spend most of the winter as secondary vessel on the Kyle of Lochalsh - Kyleakin service; however, this ceased following the opening of the Skye Bridge in 1995. In 1997 she was transferred to the Colintraive - Rhubodach service. In Summer 1999 she was transferred to the Tarbert - Portavadie service. In May 2015 replaced by the new LOCHINVAR and laid up. In summer 2016 returned to the Tarbert - Portavadie service.

ISLE OF LEWIS *(EILEAN LEÒDHAIS)* Built by Ferguson Shipbuilders Ltd, Port Glasgow, UK for the Ullapool - Stornoway service. In February 2015 replaced by the new LOCH SEAFORTH. Now operates between Oban and Castlebay (Barra).

Isle of Mull *(George Holland)*

Hebridean Isles *(George Holland)*

ISLE OF MULL *(AN T-EILEAN MUILEACH)* Built by Appledore Ferguson, Port Glasgow, UK for the Oban - Craignure (Mull) service.

LOCH ALAINN *(LOCH ÀLAINN)* Built by Buckie Shipbuilders Ltd, Buckie, UK for the Lochaline - Fishnish service. Launched as the LOCH ALINE but renamed the LOCH ALAINN before entering service. After a brief period on the service for which she was built, she was transferred to the Colintraive - Rhubodach route. In 1998 she was transferred to the Largs - Cumbrae Slip service. In 2007 moved to the Ardmhor (Barra) - Eriskay service. She relieves the larger 'Loch' class vessels in the winter, with her own service covered by the LOCH BHRUSDA.

LOCH BHRUSDA *(LOCH BHRÙSTA)* Built by McTay Marine, Bromborough, Wirral, UK to inaugurate a new Otternish (North Uist) - Leverburgh (Harris) service. In 2001 the service became Berneray - Leverburgh. In 2003 she moved to the Eriskay - Barra service, previously operated by *Comhairle Nan Eilean Siar* vessels. In 2007 she became a spare vessel on the Clyde. In summer 2016 operated between Mallaig and Armadale. Note 'Bhrusda' is pronounced "Vroosta".

LOCH BUIE *(LOCH BUIDHE)* Built by J W Miller & Sons Ltd, St Monans, Fife, UK for the Fionnphort (Mull) - Iona service to replace the MORVERN (see *Arranmore Island Ferry Services*) and obviate the need for a relief vessel in the summer. Due to height restrictions, loading arrangements for vehicles taller than private cars are stern-only. Only islanders' cars and service vehicles (eg mail vans, police) are carried; no tourist vehicles are conveyed.

LOCH DUNVEGAN *(LOCH DÙNBHEAGAN)* Built by Ferguson Shipbuilders Ltd, Port Glasgow, UK for the Kyle of Lochalsh - Kyleakin service. On the opening of the Skye Bridge in October 1995 she was withdrawn from service and offered for sale. In Autumn 1997, she returned to service on the Lochaline - Fishnish route. In 1998 she was due to be transferred to the Colintraive - Rhubodach route but this was delayed because of problems in providing terminal facilities. She operated on the Clyde and between Mallaig and Armadale during the early summer and spent the rest of that summer laid up. In 1999 she was transferred to the Colintraive - Rhubodach route.

LOCH FYNE *(LOCH FINE)* Built by Ferguson Shipbuilders Ltd, Port Glasgow, UK for the Kyle of Lochalsh - Kyleakin service (see the LOCH DUNVEGAN). In Autumn 1997, she also served on the Lochaline - Fishnish route and was transferred to this route as regular vessel in 1998. In summer 2017 transferred to the Mallaig - Armadale route.

LOCH LINNHE *(AN LINNE DHUBH)* Built by Richard Dunston (Hessle) Ltd, Hessle, UK. Until 1997 she was used mainly on the Largs - Cumbrae Slip (Cumbrae) service and until Winter 1994/95 she was usually used on the Lochaline - Fishnish service during the winter. Since then she has relieved on various routes in winter. In Summer 1998 she operated mainly on the Tarbert - Portavadie route. In 1999 she was transferred to the Tobermory - Kilchoan service in summer.

LOCH PORTAIN *(LOCH PORTAIN)* Built by McTay Marine, Bromborough, Wirral, UK (hull constructed in Poland) to replace the LOCH BHRUSDA on the Berneray - Leverburgh service.

LOCH RANZA *(LOCH RAONASA)* Built by Richard Dunston (Hessle) Ltd, Hessle, UK for the Claonaig - Lochranza (Arran) seasonal service and used a relief vessel in the winter. In 1992 she was replaced by the LOCH TARBERT and transferred to the Tayinloan - Gigha service.

LOCH RIDDON *(LOCH RAODAIN)* Built by Richard Dunston (Hessle) Ltd, Hessle, UK. Until 1997 she was used almost exclusively on the Colintraive - Rhubodach service. In 1997, she was transferred to the Largs - Cumbrae Slip service. In January 2014 she became regular vessel on the Oban - Lismore service. However, after problems with using the slipways, she became the second vessel on the Largs - Cumbrae Slip service.

LOCH SEAFORTH *(LOCH SHIPHOIRT)* Built by Flensburger Schiffbau-Gesellschaft, Flensburg, Germany for the Stornoway - Ullapool service, replacing the ISLE OF LEWIS and freight vessel CLIPPER RANGER.

LOCH SHIRA *(LOCH SIORA)* Built by Ferguson Shipbuilders, Port Glasgow, UK for the Largs – Cumbrae Slip route.

LOCH STRIVEN *(LOCH SROIGHEANN)* Built by Richard Dunston (Hessle) Ltd, Hessle, UK. Used mainly on the Largs - Cumbrae Slip service until 1997. In Winter 1995/96 and 1996/97 she was used on the Tarbert - Portavadie and Claonaig - Lochranza routes. In 1997 she took over the Sconser - Raasay service. In winter 2014 replaced by the HALLAIG. In summer 2014 transferred to the Oban - Lismore route.

LOCH TARBERT *(LOCH AN TAIRBEIRT)* Built by J W Miller & Sons Ltd, St Monans, Fife, UK for the Claonaig - Lochranza service. Now a relief vessel.

LOCHINVAR *(LOCH AN BARR)* As the HALLAIG. Initially operated on the Tarbert - Portavadie route. In summer 2016 transferred to Mallaig - Armadale and in summer 2017 to the Lochaline - Fishnish route.

LOCHNEVIS *(LOCH NIBHEIS)* Built by Ailsa Shipbuilding, Troon, UK to replace the LOCHMOR on the Mallaig - Small Isles service and the winter Mallaig - Armadale service. Although a vehicle ferry, cars are not normally carried to the Small Isles; the ro-ro facility is used for the carriage of agricultural machinery and livestock and it is possible to convey a vehicle on the ferry from which goods can be unloaded directly onto local transport rather than transhipping at Mallaig.

LORD OF THE ISLES *(RIGH NAN EILEAN)* Built by Appledore Ferguson, Port Glasgow, UK to replace the CLAYMORE on the Oban - Castlebay and Lochboisdale services and also the COLUMBA (1420t, 1964) on the Oban - Coll and Tiree service. Now in the winter she operates as a relief vessel. In summer she operates between Mallaig and Lochboisdale and also between Mallaig and Armadale.

Under Construction

34	GLEN SANNOX	5000t	20	16.5k	102.4m	1000P	127C	16L	BA	UK	9794513
35	NEWBUILDING	5000t	20	16.5k	102.4m	1000P	127C	16L	BA	UK	-

GLEN SANNOX *(GLEANN SHANNAIG)*, NEWBUILDING Under construction by Ferguson Marine Engineering, Port Glasgow for *Caledonian Maritime Assets* and to be chartered to *Caledonian MacBrayne*. The GLEN SANNOX will operate on the Ardrossan - Brodick service and the second vessel is likely to operate between Uig and Harris and North Uist. Construction has been heavily delayed and delivery in 2020 is uncertain.

CONDOR FERRIES

THE COMPANY *Condor Ferries Ltd* is a Channel Islands' private sector company owned by the *Condor Group*, Guernsey which is owned by *Macquarie European Infrastructure*.

MANAGEMENT Chief Executive Officer Paul Luxon, **Executive Director – Commercial** Greg Yeoman, **Executive Director – Operations** Elwyn Dop, **Executive Director – Freight** Steve Champion-Smith, **Head of Sales and Marketing** Justin Amey, **Trade Sales Manager** Jonathan Godson.

ADDRESS Head Office New Jetty Offices, White Rock, St Peter Port, Guernsey GY1 2LL, **Sales and Marketing** Condor House, New Harbour Road South, Hamworthy, Poole BH15 4AJ.

TELEPHONE Administration *Guernsey* +44 (0)1481 728620, ***Poole*** +44 (0)1202 207207, **Passenger Reservations** +44 (0)345 609 1024, **Freight Reservations** +44 (0)1481 728620.

INTERNET Email *Passenger* contactcentre@condorferries.co.uk **Freight** freight@condorferries.co.uk **Website** www.condorferries.com *(English, French)*,

ROUTES OPERATED *COMMODORE CLIPPER (Conventional Passenger and Freight Ferry)* Portsmouth to Guernsey (from 7 hrs) and Jersey (from 9 hrs) daily except Sun. ***Fast Ferries CONDOR LIBERATION***; Poole - Guernsey (3 hrs) and Jersey (4 hrs 30 min); 1 per day (operates on a seasonal basis; less frequent during off-peak seasons), ***CONDOR RAPIDE***; Guernsey (1 hr 55 min) and Jersey (1 hr 25 mins) to St Malo (1 per day). ***Freight Ferry COMMODORE GOODWILL***; Portsmouth - Guernsey - Jersey (10 hrs 30 min; 1 per day), Guernsey - Jersey - St Malo (13 hrs; 1 per week).

1	COMMODORE CLIPPER	14000t	99	18.0k	129.1m	500P	100C	92T	A	BS	9201750
2F	COMMODORE GOODWILL	11166t	96	17.3k	126.4m	12P	-	92T	A	BS	9117985
3»	CONDOR LIBERATION	6307t	10	39.0k	102.0m	873P	245C	12L	A	BS	9551363
4»	CONDOR RAPIDE	5007t	97	40.5k	86.6m	870P	200C	-	A	BS	9161560

COMMODORE CLIPPER Ro-pax vessel built by Van der Giessen-de Noord, Krimpen aan den IJssel, Rotterdam for *Commodore Ferries* to operate between Portsmouth and the Channel Islands. She replaced the ISLAND COMMODORE, a freight-only vessel. Her passenger capacity is normally restricted to 300 between the Channel Islands and the UK but is increased to 500 between Jersey and Guernsey.

COMMODORE GOODWILL Built by Koninklijke Scheldegroep BV, Vlissingen, The Netherlands for *Commodore Ferries*.

CONDOR LIBERATION Austal 102-metre Trimaran built speculatively by Austal Ships Pty, Fremantle, Australia as AUSTAL HULL 270. Laid up. In August 2014 sold to *Condor Ferries*. During autumn and early winter 2014/15 she was modified by Austal Ships in their shipyard at Balamban, Cebu, Philippines and in March 2015 renamed the CONDOR LIBERATION and placed on the Poole - Channel Islands service.

CONDOR RAPIDE Incat 86m catamaran built at Hobart, Tasmania, Australia as the INCAT 045. Chartered to *Transport Tasmania* of Australia and operated between Melbourne (Victoria) and Devonport (Tasmania). In 1999 she was chartered to the *Royal Australian Navy*, renamed the HMAS JERVIS BAY and took part in moving Australian troops from Darwin to Dili (East Timor) as part of the United Nations operation. She operated over 75 trips between the two points carrying personnel and equipment for the United Nations Transitional Administration in East Timor (UNTAET). The charter ended in May 2001 and she was renamed the INCAT 045 and laid up. In Spring 2003 she was chartered to *Traghetti Isole Sarde (TRIS)* of Italy, renamed the WINNER and operated between Genoa and Palau (Sardinia). In Autumn 2003 the charter ended, she resumed the name INCAT 045 and was laid up at Portland, Dorset. In 2004 chartered to *SpeedFerries* and renamed the SPEED ONE. In May 2008 purchased by *SpeedFerries*. In November 2008 the services ceased and the company went into administration. She was laid up at Tilbury. In May she was sold at auction to *Epic Shipping* of the UK and renamed the SEA LEOPARD. In April 2010 sold to *Condor Ferries* and renamed the CONDOR RAPIDE. Entered service in May 2010.

DFDS SEAWAYS

THE COMPANY *DFDS Seaways* is a business unit within *DFDS A/S*, a Danish private sector company. Services from Dover, Newhaven and Marseilles are operated by *DFDS Seaways France* which was inaugurated in March 2013 following the establishment of a *DFDS Seaways/LD Lines* joint venture in November 2012. It is 82% owned by *DFDS* and 18% by *Louis Dreyfus Armateurs*. The Newhaven - Dieppe route is branded as *Transmanche Ferries*, operating under a franchise awarded by *Syndicat Mixte de L'Activité Transmanche* in Dieppe. In June 2018 *DFDS* acquired *UN RoRo* of Turkey. The Mediterranean fleet is outside the scope of this book.

MANAGEMENT President and CEO DFDS A/S Niels Smedegaard, **Executive Vice President Shipping Division** Peder Gellert Pedersen, **Managing Director, DFDS Seaways PLC** Sean Potter, **Senior Vice President South** Kell Robdrup, **Head of English Channel Business Area** Kasper Moos, **Head of Passenger Business Area** Brian Thorsted Hansen.

ADDRESS (UK) DFDS A/S, Whitfield Court, White Cliffs Business Park Whitfield, Dover CT16 3PX.

TELEPHONE Administration +44 (0)1304 874001. **Passenger Reservations *Dover-Calais*** 0871 574 7223, +44 (0)208 127 8303, ***Newcastle - Ijmuiden*** 0871 522 9955, +44 330 333 0245, ***Newhaven - Dieppe*** 0844 576 8836, +33 232 144 729 **Freight Reservations** see website.

INTERNET Websites *Passenger* www.dfdsseaways.co.uk *(various)* ***Freight*** freight.dfdsseaways.com *(English)* ***Corporate*** www.dfds.com *(English)*

Commodore Clipper *(Kevin Mitchell)*

Commodore Goodwill *(Brian Maxted)*

ROUTES OPERATED ***Passenger ferries*** Newcastle (North Shields) - IJmuiden (near Amsterdam, The Netherlands) (15 hrs; ***KING SEAWAYS, PRINCESS SEAWAYS***; daily). **ROUTES OPERATED** Dover - Dunkerque (2 hrs; ***DELFT SEAWAYS, DOVER SEAWAYS, DUNKERQUE SEAWAYS***; 12 per day), Dover - Calais (1 hr 30 mins; ***CALAIS SEAWAYS, CÔTE DES FLANDRES, CÔTE DES DUNES***; 15 per day), Newhaven - Dieppe (4 hrs; ***CÔTE D'ALBÂTRE, SEVEN SISTERS***; up to 3 per day, ***Freight ferries*** Esbjerg - Immingham (18 hrs; ***ARK DANIA, ARK GERMANIA***; 6 per week), Cuxhaven - Immingham (19 hrs; ***JUTLANDIA SEAWAYS, STENA FORETELLER***; 5 per week), Göteborg - Immingham (26 hrs (direct), *45 hrs (via Brevik (Fri)); ***FICARIA SEAWAYS, FREESIA SEAWAYS, MAGNOLIA SEAWAYS***; 7 per week), Brevik - Immingham (25 hrs (direct), 42 hrs (via Göteborg); ***FICARIA SEAWAYS, FREESIA SEAWAYS, MAGNOLIA SEAWAYS***; 2 per week), Göteborg - Brevik (Norway) - Gent (Belgium) (Göteborg 32 hrs, Brevik 32 hrs; ***BEGONIA SEAWAYS, PETUNIA SEAWAYS, PRIMULA SEAWAYS***; 6 per week (1 per week via Brevik), Göteborg - Zeebrugge (34 hrs; ***BELGIA SEAWAYS, FIONIA SEAWAYS, GOTHIA SEAWAYS***; 6 per week), Vlaardingen - Immingham (14 hrs; ***GARDENIA SEAWAYS, TULIPA SEAWAYS***; 8 per week), Vlaardingen - Felixstowe (7 hrs; ***BRITANNIA SEAWAYS, SELANDIA SEAWAYS, SUECIA SEAWAYS***; 3 per day), Zeebrugge - Immingham - Halden (Norway) - Fredrikstad - Zeebrugge (***TRANSPORTER***; weekly circuit). *DFDS Seaways* also operates services in the Baltic (see section 7) and Mediterranean (which are outside the scope of this book). Note: vessels are often switched between routes.

1F	ARK DANIA	33313t	14	20.0k	195.2m	12P	-	206T	A	DK	9609964
2F	ARK GERMANIA	33313t	14	20.0k	195.2m	12P	-	206T	A	DK	9609952
3F	BEGONIA SEAWAYS	37722t	04	22.5k	230.0m	12P	-	340T	AS	DK	9262089
4F	BELGIA SEAWAYS	21005t	00	18.0k	183.4m	12P	-	180T	A	LT	9188245
5F	BRITANNIA SEAWAYS	24196t	00	21.1k	197.5m	12P	-	200T	AS	DK	9153032
6	CALAIS SEAWAYS	28833t	91	21.0k	163.6m	1850P	600C	100L	BA2	FR	8908466
7	CÔTE D'ALBÂTRE	18425t	06	22.0k	112.0m	600P	300C	62L	BA	FR	9320128
8	CÔTE DES DUNES	33796t	01	25.0k	186.0m	1500P	700C	120L	BA2	FR	9232527
9	CÔTE DES FLANDRES	33940t	05	25.0k	186.0m	1500P	700C	120L	BA2	FR	9305843
10	DELFT SEAWAYS	35923t	06	25.5k	187.0m	780P	200C	120L	BA2	UK	9293088
11	DOVER SEAWAYS	35923t	06	25.8k	187.0m	780P	200C	120L	BA2	UK	9318345
12	DUNKERQUE SEAWAYS	35923t	05	25.8k	187.0m	780P	200C	120L	BA2	UK	9293076
13F	FICARIA SEAWAYS	37939t	04	22.5k	230.0m	12P	-	340T	AS	DK	9320568
14F	FINLANDIA SEAWAYS	11530t	00	20.0k	162.2m	12P	-	140T	A	LT	9198721
15F	FIONIA SEAWAYS	25609t	09	20.0k	184.8m	12P	-	250T	AS	UK	9395343
16F	FREESIA SEAWAYS	37722t	04	22.5k	230.0m	12P	-	340T	AS	DK	9274848
17F	GARDENIA SEAWAYS	32000t	17	21.0k	209.6m	12P	-	262T	A2	LT	9809095
18F	GOTHIA SEAWAYS	21005t	00	18.0k	183.4m	12P	-	180T	A	LT	9188233
19F	JUTLANDIA SEAWAYS	25609t	10	20.0k	184.8m	12P	-	250T	AS	UK	9395355
20	KING SEAWAYS	31788t	87	20.0k	161.6m	1400P	600C	104T	BA	DK	8502406
21F	MAGNOLIA SEAWAYS	32289t	03	22.5k	199.8m	12P	-	280T	AS	DK	9259496
22F	PETUNIA SEAWAYS	32289t	04	22.5k	199.8m	12P	-	280T	AS	DK	9259501
23F	PRIMULA SEAWAYS	37985t	04	22.5k	229.8m	12P	-	340T	AS	DK	9259513
24	PRINCESS SEAWAYS	31356t	86	18.5k	161.0m	1600P	600C	100T	BA	DK	8502391
25F	SELANDIA SEAWAYS	24196t	98	21.0k	197.5m	12P	-	206T	A	DK	9157284
26	SEVEN SISTERS	18425t	06	22.0k	112.0m	600P	300C	62L	BA	FR	9320130
27F	STENA FORETELLER	24688t	02	22.0k	195.3m	12P	-	210T	A2	DK	9214666
28F	SUECIA SEAWAYS	24196t	99	21.0k	197.5m	12P	-	206T	AS	DK	9153020
30F	TRANSPORTER	6620t	91	16.5k	122.0m	0P	-	90T	A	FI	8820858
31F	TULIPA SEAWAYS	32000t	17	21.0k	209.6m	12P	-	262T	A2	LT	9809100

ARK DANIA, ARK GERMANIA Built by P+S Werften GmbH, Stralsund, Germany. They are used for the German/Danish joint ARK Project providing NATO transport but are also available for *DFDS* use and charter when not required. They have a crane for loading containers on the weather deck. In December 2012 the order for these vessels was cancelled due to late delivery. Following negotiations with the shipyard it was agreed that they would be completed under a new contract which was signed in February 2013. Both vessels were delivered to *DFDS* in April

King Seaways *(George Holland)*

Suecia Seaways *(Frank Lose)*

2014, the ARK GERMANIA almost complete, the ARK DANIA still incomplete. The latter vessel was towed to the Fayard shipyard, Odense, to be completed. The ARK GERMANIA entered service a few days after delivery, the ARK DANIA in November 2014.

BEGONIA SEAWAYS Built as the TOR BEGONIA by Flensburger Schiffbau-Gesellschaft, Flensburg, Germany for *DFDS Tor Line*. Operates on the Göteborg - Immingham/Brevik route. In Summer 2009 lengthened by 30m by MWB Motorenwerke Bremerhaven AG, Germany. In July 2012 renamed the BEGONIA SEAWAYS.

BELGIA SEAWAYS, GOTHIA SEAWAYS Built as the SLINGEBORG and SCHIEBORG by Flender Werft AG, Lübeck, Germany for *Wagenborg* of The Netherlands and time-chartered to *Cobelfret Ferries* to operate on the *Stora Enso* (a paper and card manufacturer)/*Cobelfret Ferries* service between Zeebrugge and Göteborg. In November 2014 the arrangement between *Stora Enso* and *Cobelfret Ferries* ended and they were chartered to *SOL Continent Line* who took over the operation of the service. In June 2019 the service was taken over by *DFDS Seaways* and both vessels were purchased by that company. They were renamed the BELGIA SEAWAYS and GOTHIA SEAWAYS respectively.

BRITANNIA SEAWAYS Built as the TOR BRITANNIA by Fincantieri-Cantieri Navali Italiani SpA, Ancona, Italy for *DFDS Tor Line*. Operated on the Göteborg - Immingham route until 2004 when she was transferred to the Esbjerg - Immingham route. In January 2010 chartered to *Norfolkline* to operate between Vlaardingen and Felixstowe. In May 2011 renamed the BRITANNIA SEAWAYS.

CALAIS SEAWAYS Built as the PRINS FILIP by NV Boelwerf SA, Temse, Belgium for *Regie voor Maritiem Transport (RMT)* of Belgium for the Oostende - Dover service. Although completed in 1991, she did not enter service until May 1992. In 1994 the British port became Ramsgate. Withdrawn in 1997 and laid up for sale. In 1998 she was sold to *Stena RoRo* and renamed the STENA ROYAL. In November 1998 she was chartered to *P&O Ferries* to operate as a freight-only vessel on the Dover - Zeebrugge route. In Spring 1999 it was decided to charter the vessel on a long-term basis and she was repainted into *P&O Stena Line* (later *P&O Ferries*) colours and renamed the P&OSL AQUITAINE. In Autumn 1999 she was modified to make her suitable to operate between Dover and Calais and was transferred to that route, becoming a passenger vessel again. In 2002 renamed the PO AQUITAINE and in 2003 the PRIDE OF AQUITAINE. In September 2005 sold to *LD Lines* and renamed the NORMAN SPIRIT. In October, inaugurated a Le Havre - Portsmouth service, replacing that previously operated by *P&O Ferries*. In November 2009 moved to the Dover - Boulogne route. In March 2010 chartered to *TransEuropa Ferries*, placed on the Oostende - Ramsgate service (as part of a joint venture) and renamed the OOSTENDE SPIRIT. In May 2011 returned to the Portsmouth - Le Havre route and renamed the NORMAN SPIRIT. In November 2011 chartered to *DFDS Seaways* to add extra capacity to their Dover - Dunkerque route. In February 2012 transferred to the new Dover - Calais route, joint with *DFDS Seaways*. Ownership transferred to *DFDS Seaways* in late 2012. In March 2013 refurbished, repainted into *DFDS Seaways* colours and renamed the CALAIS SEAWAYS.

CÔTE D'ALBÂTRE Built by Astilleros Barreras SA, Vigo, Spain for *Transmanche Ferries* to operate between Newhaven and Dieppe. In February 2009 she was moved to the Boulogne - Dover and Dieppe - Dover routes for *LD Lines*. In September 2009 moved to the Le Havre - Portsmouth route. The vessel has had periods laid up when not required on the Newhaven – Dieppe route.

CÔTE DES DUNES Built as the SEAFRANCE RODIN by Aker Finnyards, Rauma, Finland for *SeaFrance*. Launched in November 2001. In November 2011 laid up. In June 2012 sold to *Eurotransmanche*. In July 2012 renamed the RODIN. In August 2012 chartered to *MyFerryLink* and resumed operation between Calais and Dover. In July 2015 chartered to *DFDS Seaways* and *MyFerryLink* operations ceased. After a prolonged occupation by former *MyFerryLink* workers. *DFDS Seaways* took possession in early September and in November 2015 she was renamed the CÔTE DES DUNES. She re-entered service on the Dover - Calais route in February 2016. In June 2017 purchased by *DFDS Seaways*.

CÔTE DES FLANDRES Built as the SEAFRANCE BERLIOZ by Chantiers de l'Atlantique, St Nazaire for *SeaFrance*. Launched in March 2005. In November 2011 laid up. In June 2012 sold to *Eurotransmanche*, a *Groupe Eurotunnel* company. In July 2012 renamed the BERLIOZ. In August 2012 chartered to *MyFerryLink* and resumed operation between Calais and Dover. In July 2015 chartered to *DFDS Seaways* and *MyFerryLink* operations ceased. After a prolonged occupation by former *MyFerryLink* workers, *DFDS Seaways* took possession in early September and, in November 2015, she was renamed the CÔTE DES FLANDRES. She re-entered service on the Dover - Calais route in February 2016. In June 2017 purchased by *DFDS Seaways*.

DELFT SEAWAYS, DOVER SEAWAYS, DUNKERQUE SEAWAYS Built as the MAERSK DELFT, DOVER SEAWAYS and MAERSK DUNKERQUE by Samsung Heavy Industries, Koje (Geoje) Island, South Korea for *Norfolkline* to operate between Dover and Dunkerque. In July and August 2010 renamed the DELFT SEAWAYS, DOVER SEAWAYS and DUNKERQUE SEAWAYS.

FICARIA SEAWAYS Built as the TOR FICARIA by Flensburger Schiffbau-Gesellschaft, Flensburg, Germany for *DFDS Tor Line*. Operated on the Göteborg - Immingham/Brevik service. In Summer 2009 lengthened by 30m by MWB Motorenwerke Bremerhaven AG, Germany. In July 2011 renamed the FICARIA SEAWAYS. In March 2015 placed on the Vlaardingen - Immingham service.

FINLANDIA SEAWAYS Launched as the FINNMAID but renamed the FINNREEL before delivery. Built by Jinling Shipyard, Nanjing, China for the *Macoma Shipping Group* and chartered to *Finnlines*. In 2008 sold to *DFDS Lisco* and in January 2009 delivered, chartered to *DFDS Tor Line* and renamed the TOR FINLANDIA. Operated on the Immingham - Rotterdam route until January 2011 when she was transferred to the Rosyth - Zeebrugge route. In May 2012 moved to the Cuxhaven - Immingham service but returned in July. In December 2012 renamed the FINLANDIA SEAWAYS. In October 2013 moved to the Kiel - St Petersburg service. In April 2014 returned to the Rosyth - Zeebrugge route. In April 2018 she had a serious engine room fire and the route closed. She returned to service in November 2018 on the Immingham - Cuxhaven service.

FIONIA SEAWAYS Built as the TOR FIONIA by Jinling Shipyard, Nanjing, China for *Macoma Shipping Ltd* of the UK. Launched as the JINGLING 3. She was time-chartered to *DFDS Tor Line* for ten years (with an option on a further three). Delivered in May 2009 and initially replaced the TOR BEGONIA, TOR FICARIA and TOR FREESIA while they were being lengthened. In October 2011 renamed the FIONIA SEAWAYS. In March 2015 placed on the Göteborg - Immingham service.

FREESIA SEAWAYS Built as the TOR FREESIA by Flensburger Schiffbau-Gesellschaft, Flensburg, Germany for *DFDS Tor Line*. Operates on the Göteborg - Immingham/Brevik service. In Summer 2009 lengthened by 30m by MWB Motorenwerke Bremerhaven AG, Germany. In August 2012 renamed the FREESIA SEAWAYS.

GARDENIA SEAWAYS, TULIPA SEAWAYS Built by Flensburger Schiffbau-Gesellschaft, Flensburg, Germany for the Siem Industries Inc (owners of FSG). They are bareboat chartered to *DFDS Seaways* for five years with an option to purchase at the end of the charter period. Operate between Vlaardingen and Immingham.

JUTLANDIA SEAWAYS Built as the TOR JUTLANDIA by Jinling Shipyard, Nanjing, China for *Macoma Shipping Ltd* of the UK and time-chartered to *DFDS Tor Line* for ten years. In July 2011 renamed the JUTLANDIA SEAWAYS.

KING SEAWAYS Built as the NILS HOLGERSSON by Schichau Seebeckwerft AG, Bremerhaven, Germany for *Rederi AB Swedcarrier* of Sweden for their service between Trelleborg and Travemünde, joint with *TT-Line* of Germany (trading as *TT-Line*). In 1992 purchased by *Brittany Ferries* for entry into service in Spring 1993. After a major rebuild, she was renamed the VAL DE LOIRE and introduced onto the Plymouth - Roscoff, Plymouth - Santander and Cork - Roscoff routes. In 2004 transferred to the Portsmouth - St Malo and Portsmouth – Cherbourg services. In 2005 operated mainly Portsmouth - St Malo. In 2006 sold to *DFDS*, renamed the KING OF SCANDINAVIA and placed on the Newcastle – IJmuiden route. In January 2011 renamed the KING SEAWAYS.

Côte D'Albâtre *(Brian Maxted)*

Côte des Dunes *(George Holland)*

MAGNOLIA SEAWAYS Built as the TOR MAGNOLIA by Flensburger Schiffbau-Gesellschaft, Flensburg, Germany for *DFDS Tor Line*. In July 2011 renamed the MAGNOLIA SEAWAYS.

PETUNIA SEAWAYS Built as the TOR PETUNIA by Flensburger Schiffbau-Gesellschaft, Flensburg, Germany for *DFDS Tor Line*. In July 2011 renamed the PETUNIA SEAWAYS.

PRIMULA SEAWAYS Built as the TOR PRIMULA by Flensburger Schiffbau-Gesellschaft, Flensburg, Germany for *DFDS Tor Line*. In July 2010 renamed the PRIMULA SEAWAYS. In July 2016 lengthened by 30m by MWB Motorenwerke Bremerhaven AG, Germany.

PRINCESS SEAWAYS Built by Schichau Seebeckwerft AG, Bremerhaven, Germany as the PETER PAN for *TT-Line* for the service between Travemünde and Trelleborg. In 1992 sold to *TT Line* of Australia (no connection) for use on their service between Port Melbourne (Victoria) and Devonport (Tasmania) and renamed the SPIRIT OF TASMANIA. In 2002 sold to *Nordsjøferger K/S* of Norway and renamed the SPIR. After modification work she was, in 2003, renamed the FJORD NORWAY and chartered to *Fjord Line*. Placed on the Bergen - Egersund - Hanstholm route. In 2005 placed on the Bergen - Stavanger - Newcastle route, but operated once a week to Hanstholm. In October 2006 sold to *DFDS* and renamed the PRINCESS OF NORWAY, remaining on the Newcastle - Norway service but no longer serving Hanstholm. In May 2007 moved to the Newcastle - IJmuiden route. In February 2011 renamed the PRINCESS SEAWAYS.

SELANDIA SEAWAYS Built as the TOR SELANDIA by Fincantieri-Cantieri Navali Italiani SpA, Ancona, Italy for *DFDS Tor Line*. Operated on the Göteborg - Immingham route until 2004 when she was moved to the Göteborg – Gent route. In 2005 she moved to the Göteborg – Harwich route. In July the UK terminal moved to Tilbury. In August 2010 renamed the SELANDIA SEAWAYS. Currently operates on the Rotterdam - Felixstowe route.

SEVEN SISTERS Built by Astilleros Barreras SA, Vigo, Spain for *Transmanche Ferries* to operate between Newhaven and Dieppe. In recent years generally held as a reserve vessel. In March 2014 transferred to the *DFDS Seaways* Portsmouth - Le Havre service. She continues to carry *Transmanche Ferries* branding. In 2015 returned to the Newhaven - Dieppe service as second vessel, continuing to operate for *DFDS Seaways*. The vessel has had periods laid up when not required on the Newhaven – Dieppe route.

STENA FORETELLER Built as the STENA FORETELLER by Dalian Shipyard Co Ltd, Dalian, China for *Stena RoRo*. Initially chartered to *Cetam* of France to operate between Marseilles and Tunis and renamed the CETAM MASSILIA. In November 2003 the charter ended and she resumed her original name. A number of short-term commercial and military charters followed until June 2006 when she was chartered to *StoraEnso* paper group to operate between Göteborg and Finnish ports. In September 2009 she was chartered to *Rederi AB Transatlantic* who took over responsibility to operate all *StoraEnso's* Baltic services. In February 2012 she was chartered to *Transfennica*. In January 2015 chartered to *Mann Lines*. In December 2017 chartered to *DFDS Seaways*.

SUECIA SEAWAYS Built as the TOR SUECIA by Fincantieri-Cantieri Navali Italiani SpA, Ancona, Italy for *DFDS Tor Line*. Operated on the Göteborg - Immingham route until 2004 when she was transferred to the Esbjerg - Immingham route. Later transferred to the Danish flag. In March 2010 chartered to *Norfolkline* to operate between Vlaardingen and Felixstowe and continued on the route when it was taken over by *DFDS*. In June 2011 renamed the SUECIA SEAWAYS.

TRANSPORTER Built as the HAMNÖ by Brodogradiliste "Sava", Macvanska Mitrovica, Yugoslavia (fitted out by Fosen Mekaniske Verksteder of Rissa, Norway) for *Rederi AB Gustav Erikson* of Finland and chartered to *Transfennica* for service between Finland and Germany. In 1995 the owning company became *United Shipping* and in 2002 *Birka Cargo AB*. In 2000 she was chartered to the *Korsnäs Paper Group* to carry their traffic from Gävle (Sweden) to Chatham and Terneuzen (The Netherlands). In 2002 she was renamed the BIRKA TRANSPORTER. In April 2004 chartered to *Grimaldi Lines* of Italy to operate between Marseille and Tunis and in 2010 to *Holmen Paper Ab* of Sweden. In April 2013 ownership was transferred to *Eckerö Shipping Ab* of Finland and in June she was renamed the TRANSPORTER. In January 2016 she was sold to *Naviera Benzu Sl* of Spain. In March 2019 she was sold back to *Eckerö Shipping* and in April she was chartered to *DFDS Seaways* to operate on the Zeebrugge - Immingham - Halden - Fredrikstad service.

Under Construction

32F	HOLLANDIA SEAWAYS	60465t	19	21.0k	237.4m	12P	-	480T	A2	DK	9832585
33F	NEWBUILDING 2	60465t	20	21.0k	237.4m	12P	-	480T	A2	DK	9832597
34F	NEWBUILDING 3	60465t	20	21.0k	237.4m	12P	-	480T	A2	DK	9860142
35F	NEWBUILDING 4	60465t	20	21.0k	237.4m	12P	-	480T	A2	DK	9864681
36	CÔTE D'OPALE	42000t	21	22.0k	214.5m	1000P	300C	180L	BA2	FR	-

HOLLANDIA SEAWAYS, NEWBUILDING 2, NEWBUILDING 3, NEWBUILDING 4 Under construction by Jinling Shipyard, Nanjing, China. May be deployed in either the North Sea or Mediterranean.

CÔTE D'OPALE Under construction by AVIC International Maritime Holdings, Weihai, China for *Stena RoRo*. Designed to run on either methanol or LPG but before delivery she will be fitted with scrubbers to run on fuel oil. Upon delivery to be chartered to *DFDS Seaways* for ten years to operate between Dover and Calais. Passenger capacity may be changed.

IRISH FERRIES

THE COMPANY *Irish Ferries* is a Republic of Ireland private sector company, part of the *Irish Continental Group*. It was originally mainly owned by the state-owned *Irish Shipping* and partly by *Lion Ferry AB* of Sweden. *Lion Ferry* participation ceased in 1977 and the company was sold into the private sector in 1987. Formerly state-owned *B&I Line* was taken over in 1991 and from 1995 all operations were marketed as *Irish Ferries*.

MANAGEMENT Irish Continental Group Chief Executive Office Eamonn Rothwell, **Irish Ferries Limited Managing Director** Andrew Sheen.

ADDRESS PO Box 19, Ferryport, Alexandra Road, Dublin 1, D01 W2F5, Republic of Ireland.

TELEPHONE Administration +353 (0)1 607 5700, **Reservations *Ireland*** +353 (0)818300 400, ***Rosslare Harbour*** +353 (0)53 913 3158, ***Holyhead*** +44 (0)8717 300200, ***Pembroke Dock*** +44 (0)8717 300500, ***National*** 44 (0)8717 300400, ***24 hour information*** +353 (0)818300 400 (Ireland) or 44 (0)8717 300400 (UK).

FAX Administration & Reservations *Dublin* +353 (0)1 607 5660, ***Rosslare*** +353 (0)53 913 3544.

INTERNET Email info@irishferries.com **Website** www.irishferries.com *(English, French, German, Italian)*

ROUTES OPERATED Conventional Ferries Dublin - Holyhead (3 hrs 15 mins; ***EPSILON, ULYSSES, W. B. YEATS***; 2-4 per day), Rosslare - Pembroke Dock (4 hrs; ***ISLE OF INISHMORE***; 4 per day), Dublin - Cherbourg (17-19 hrs; ***W. B. YEATS***; up to 4 per week). **Fast Ferry** Dublin - Holyhead (1 hr 49 min; ***DUBLIN SWIFT***; 2 per day).

1»	DUBLIN SWIFT	8403t	01	35.0k	101.0m	900P	200C	16T	BA	CY	9243227
2	EPSILON	26375t	11	24.0k	177.5m	500P	500C	190T	A	IT	9539054
3	ISLE OF INISHMORE	34031t	97	21.3k	182.5m	2200P	802C	152T	BA2	CY	9142605
4	ULYSSES	50938t	01	22.0k	209.0m	1875P	1342C	241L	BA2	CY	9214991
5	W. B. YEATS	54975t	18	22.5k	194.8m	1850P	1216C	165L	BA2	CY	9809679

DUBLIN SWIFT Austal Auto-Express 101 catamaran built by Austal Ships Pty, Fremantle, Australia as the WESTPAC EXPRESS. Chartered through a number of third party companies to the *US Marine Corps* as a support vessel. In 2015 returned to *Austal Ships*. In May 2016 sold to the *Irish Continental Group*. Chartered to *Sealift Inc* of the USA and continued to be operated for the *US Marine Corps*. In November 2017 charter ended; laid up in Belfast. In March 2018 renamed the DUBLIN SWIFT and in April replaced the JONATHAN SWIFT on the Holyhead - Dublin route.

EPSILON Built as the CARTOUR EPSILON by CN Visentini, Porto Viro, Italy. Chartered to *Caronte & Tourist SPA* of Italy. In November 2013 chartered to *Irish Ferries*. In February 2014 renamed the EPSILON. In March 2019 purchased by *Caronte & Tourist SPA* of Italy. Charter to *Irish Ferries* continued.

ISLE OF INISHMORE Built by Van der Giessen-de Noord, Krimpen aan den IJssel, Rotterdam for *Irish Ferries* to operate on the Holyhead - Dublin service. In 2001 replaced by the ULYSSES and moved to the Rosslare - Pembroke Dock route. She also relieves on the Dublin – Holyhead route when the ULYSSES receives her annual overhaul.

ULYSSES Built by Aker Finnyards, Rauma, Finland for *Irish Ferries* for the Dublin - Holyhead service.

W. B. YEATS Built by Flensburger Schiffbau-Gesellschaft, Flensburg, Germany. Operates between Dublin and Cherbourg in the summer and Dublin and Holyhead in the winter. Entered Service on the Dublin to Holyhead Service on 22 January 2019 and then transfer to Dublin to Cherbourg Service on 14 March.

Under Construction

7	NEWBUILDING	67300t	20	22.8k	226.0m	1800P	1526C	330L	BA2	CY	9847530

NEWBUILDING Under construction by Flensburger Schiffbau-Gesellschaft, Flensburg, Germany. This vessel is to effectively to replace the EPSILON service on the Dublin - Holyhead route.

ISLE OF MAN STEAM PACKET COMPANY

THE COMPANY The *Isle of Man Steam Packet Company Limited* is an Isle of Man-registered company owned by the Isle of Man Government.

MANAGEMENT Chief Executive Officer Mark Woodward.

ADDRESS Imperial Buildings, Douglas, Isle of Man IM1 2BY.

TELEPHONE Administration +44 (0)1624 645645, **Reservations** +44 (0)1624 661661

FAX Administration +44 (0)1624 645627.

INTERNET Email iom.reservations@steam-packet.com **Website** www.steam-packet.com *(English)*,

ROUTES OPERATED Conventional Ferries *All year* Douglas (Isle of Man) - Heysham (3 hrs 30 mins; ***BEN-MY-CHREE***; up to 2 per day), November-March Douglas - Liverpool (Birkenhead) (4 hrs 15 mins; ***BEN-MY-CHREE***; 2 per week). Fast Ferries March-October Douglas - Liverpool (2 hrs 40 mins; ***MANANNAN***; up to 2 per day), Douglas - Belfast (2 hrs 55 mins; ***MANANNAN***; up to 2 per week), Douglas - Dublin (2 hrs 55 mins; ***MANANNAN***; up to 2 per week), Douglas - Heysham (2 hrs; ***MANANNAN***; occasional), Freight Ferry Douglas - Heysham (3 hrs 30 mins; ARROW; as required).

1F	ARROW	7606t	98	15.0k	122.3m	12P	-	84T	A	IM	9119414
2	BEN-MY-CHREE	12747t	98	18.0k	124.9m	630P	275C	90T	A	IM	9170705
3»	MANANNAN	5743t	98	43.0k	96.0m	865P	200C	-	A	IM	9176072

ARROW Built as the VARBOLA by Astilleros de Huelva SA, Huelva, Spain for the *Estonian Shipping Company*. On completion, chartered to *Dart Line* and placed on the Dartford - Vlissingen route. In 1999 she was renamed the DART 6. At the end of August 1999, the charter was terminated and she was renamed the VARBOLA. She undertook a number of short-term charters, including *Merchant Ferries*. In 2000 long-term chartered to *Merchant Ferries* to operate between Heysham and Dublin. In 2003 the charter ended and she was chartered to *Dart Line* to replace the DART 9; she was placed initially on the Dartford - Vlissingen route but later transferred to the Dartford - Dunkerque route. Later sub-chartered to *NorseMerchant Ferries* and placed on the Heysham – Dublin route. In 2004 the charter transferred to *NorseMerchant Ferries*. In 2005 sold to *Elmira Shipping* of Greece and renamed the RR ARROW. In October 2007 sold to *Seatruck Ferries* but the charter to *Norfolkline* continued. Renamed

the ARROW. In June 2009 returned to *Seatruck Ferries*. In April 2014 long term chartered to *IOMSP*. When not required she is sub-chartered to other operators.

BEN-MY-CHREE Built by Van der Giessen-de Noord, Krimpen aan den IJssel, Rotterdam for the *IOMSP Co* and operates between Douglas and Heysham. Additional passenger accommodation was added at her spring 2004 refit. In 2005 her passenger certificate was increased from 500 to 630. She operates some sailings between Douglas and Liverpool (Birkenhead) in the winter.

MANANNAN Incat 96m catamaran built at Hobart, Tasmania. Initially chartered to *Transport Tasmania* of Australia and operated between Port Melbourne (Victoria) and Georgetown (Tasmania). In 1999 chartered to *Fast Cat Ferries* of New Zealand and operated between Wellington (North Island) and Picton (South Island) under the marketing name 'Top Cat'. In 2000 she was laid up. In 2001 she was chartered to the *US Navy* and renamed the USS JOINT VENTURE (HSV-X1). In 2008 the charter was terminated and she was renamed the INCAT 050. Later purchased by *IOMSP*. Following conversion back to civilian use she was renamed the MANANNAN and entered service in May 2009.

NORTHLINK FERRIES

THE COMPANY *NorthLink Ferries* is a UK based company, wholly owned by *Serco Group plc*. The service is operated on behalf of Scottish Ministers.

MANAGEMENT Managing Director Stuart Garrett, **Customer Service Director** Peter Hutchinson.

ADDRESS Ferry Terminal, Ferry Road, Stromness, Orkney KW16 3BH.

TELEPHONE Customer Services 0845 6000 449, (International +44 (0)1856 885500), **Freight Reservations** 0845 6060 449.

FAX +44 (0)1856 851795.

INTERNET Email info@northlinkferries.co.uk **Website** www.northlinkferries.co.uk *(English)*,

ROUTES OPERATED ***Passenger Ferries*** Scrabster - Stromness (Orkney) (1 hr 30 min; ***HAMNAVOE***; up to 3 per day), Aberdeen - Lerwick (Shetland) (direct) (12 hrs; ***HJALTLAND, HROSSEY***; 3 northbound/4 southbound per week), Aberdeen - Kirkwall, Hatston New Pier (Orkney) (5 hrs 45 mins) - Lerwick (14 hrs; ***HJALTLAND, HROSSEY***; 4 northbound/3 southbound per week). ***Freight Ferries*** Aberdeen - Kirkwall (Orkney) (12 hrs; ***HELLIAR, HILDASAY***; 4 per week), Aberdeen - Lerwick (Shetland) (***HELLIAR, HILDASAY***; 4 per week).

1	HAMNAVOE	8780t	02	19.3k	112.0m	600P	95C	20L	BA	UK	9246061
2F	HELLIAR	7800t	98	17.0k	122.3m	12P	-	86T	A	IM	9119397
3F	HILDASAY	7606t	99	17.0k	122.3m	12P	-	84T	A	IM	9119426
4	HJALTLAND	11720t	02	24.0k	125.0m	600P	150C	30L	BA	UK	9244958
5	HROSSEY	11720t	02	24.0k	125.0m	600P	150C	30L	BA	UK	9244960

HAMNAVOE Built by Aker Finnyards, Rauma, Finland for *NorthLink Orkney and Shetland Ferries Ltd* to operate on the Scrabster - Stromness route. Did not enter service until Spring 2003 due to late completion of work at Scrabster to accommodate the ship. *Caledonian MacBrayne's* HEBRIDEAN ISLES covered between October 2002 and Spring 2003. Initially owned by the *Royal Bank of Scotland*, she was acquired by *Caledonian Maritime Assets Ltd* (owned by *Transport Scotland*) in May 2018.

HELLIAR Built as the LEHOLA by Astilleros de Huelva SA, Huelva, Spain for the *Estonian Shipping Company*. Initially used on *ESCO* Baltic services. In 1998 chartered to *Czar Peter Line* to operate between Moerdijk (The Netherlands) and Kronstadt (Russia). In 1999 chartered to *Delom* of France to operate between Marseilles and Sete and Tunis. In 2000 she returned to *ESCO*, operating between Kiel and Tallinn. In 2003 chartered to *Scandlines AG* and transferred to subsidiary *Scandlines Estonia AS*. Operated Rostock - Helsinki – Muuga initially and later Rostock – Helsinki. Service finished at the end of 2004 and in 2005 she was chartered to *P&O Ferries* to operate between Hull and Rotterdam and Hull and Zeebrugge. In 2005 sold to *Elmira Shipping* of Greece. Later renamed the RR TRIUMPH. In 2006 transferred to *P&O Irish Sea* to

Isle of Inishmore *(George Holland*

Arrow *(Miles Cowsill)*

operate between Liverpool and Dublin. In 2007 chartered to *Balearia* of Spain and operated from Barcelona. In December 2007 purchased by *Seatruck Ferries* and renamed the TRIUMPH. In Spring 2008 she was sub-chartered to *Condor Ferries* to cover for the refit period of the COMMODORE GOODWILL. In June 2008 placed on the Liverpool - Dublin route and in July renamed the CLIPPER RACER. In February 2009 replaced by the new CLIPPER PACE. In April 2009 again chartered to *Balearia*. In January 2011 chartered to *NorthLink Ferries* and renamed the HELLIAR. In June 2017 sold to *CF Clip Helliar LLC*; the charter continued. In March 2019 purchased by *Caledonian Maritime Assets Ltd* (owned by *Transport Scotland*).

HILDASAY Built as the LEILI by Astilleros de Huelva SA, Huelva, Spain for the *Estonian Shipping Company*. Used on Baltic services. In 2002 chartered to *Crowley Maritime* of the USA and renamed the PORT EVERGLADES EXPRESS. In 2004 resumed the name LEILI and chartered to *NorseMerchant Ferries* to operate between Birkenhead and Dublin. In July 2005 moved to the Heysham - Belfast route and at the same time sold to *Elmira Shipping* of Greece and renamed the RR SHIELD. In 2007 sold to *Attica Group* of Greece and renamed the SHIELD. In January 2008 sold to *Seatruck Ferries* but continued to be chartered to *Norfolkline*. In June 2009 returned to *Seatruck Ferries*. In January 2009 chartered to *NorthLink Orkney and Shetland Ferries* and renamed the HILDASAY. In June 2017 sold to *CF Clip Hildasay LLC*; the charter continued. In March 2019 purchased by *Caledonian Maritime Assets Ltd* (owned by *Transport Scotland*).

HJALTLAND, HROSSEY Built by Aker Finnyards, Rauma, Finland for *NorthLink Orkney and Shetland Ferries* to operate on the Aberdeen - Kirkwall - Lerwick route when services started in 2002. Initially owned by the *Royal Bank of Scotland*, they were acquired by *Caledonian Maritime Assets Ltd* (owned by *Transport Scotland*) in May 2018.

ORKNEY FERRIES

THE COMPANY *Orkney Ferries Ltd* (previously the *Orkney Islands Shipping Company*) is a British company, owned by *Orkney Islands Council*.

MANAGEMENT Ferry Services Manager Andrew Blake.

ADDRESS Shore Street, Kirkwall, Orkney KW15 1LG.

TELEPHONE Administration +44 (0)1856 872044, **Reservations** +44 (0)1856 872044.

FAX Administration & Reservations +44 (0)1856 872921.

INTERNET Email info@orkneyferries.co.uk **Website** www.orkneyferries.co.uk *(English)*,

ROUTES OPERATED Kirkwall (Mainland) to Eday (1 hr 15 mins), Rapness (Westray) (1 hr 25 mins), Sanday (1 hr 25 mins), Stronsay (1 hr 35 mins), Papa Westray (1 hr 50 mins), North Ronaldsay (2 hrs 30 mins) ('North Isles service') (timings are direct from Kirkwall - sailings via other islands take longer; ***EARL SIGURD, EARL THORFINN, VARAGEN***; 1/2 per day except Papa Westray which is twice weekly and North Ronaldsay which is weekly), Pierowall (Westray) - Papa Westray (25 mins; ***GOLDEN MARIANA***; up to six per day (Summer service - passenger-only)), Kirkwall - Shapinsay (25 mins; ***SHAPINSAY***; 6 per day), Houton (Mainland) to Lyness (Hoy) (35 mins; ***HOY HEAD***; 5 per day), and Flotta (35 mins; ***HOY HEAD***; 4 per day) ('South Isles service') (timings are direct from Houton - sailings via other islands take longer), Tingwall (Mainland) to Rousay (20 mins; ***EYNHALLOW***; 6 per day), Egilsay (30 mins; ***EYNHALLOW***; 5 per day) and Wyre (20 mins; ***EYNHALLOW***; 5 per day) (timings are direct from Tingwall - sailings via other islands take longer), Stromness (Mainland) to Moaness (Hoy) (25 mins; ***GRAEMSAY***; 2/3 per day) and Graemsay (25 mins; ***GRAEMSAY***; 2/3 per day) (passenger/cargo service - cars not normally conveyed).

1	EARL SIGURD	771t	90	12.5k	45.0m	190P	26C	-	BA	UK	8902711
2	EARL THORFINN	771t	90	12.5k	45.0m	190P	26C	-	BA	UK	8902723
3	EYNHALLOW	104t	87	10.5k	28.8m	95P	11C	-	BA	UK	8960880
4p	GOLDEN MARIANA	33t	73	9.5k	15.2m	40P	0C	-	-	UK	
5	GRAEMSAY	90t	96	10.0k	20.6m	73P	2C	-	C	UK	
6	HOY HEAD	358t	94	11.0k	53.5m	125P	24C	3L	BA	UK	9081722

Hamnavoe *(Miles Cowsill)*

Earl Thorfinn *(Miles Cowsill)*

7	SHAPINSAY	199t	89	10.0k	32.6m	91P	16C	-	B	UK	8814184
8	THORSVOE	385t	91	10.6k	35.0m	122P	16C	-	BA	UK	9014743
9	VARAGEN	928t	88	14.5k	49.9m	144P	33C	5L	BA	UK	8818154

EARL SIGURD, EARL THORFINN Built by McTay Marine, Bromborough, Wirral, UK to inaugurate ro-ro working on the 'North Isles service'.

EYNHALLOW Built by David Abels Boat Builders, Bristol, UK to inaugurate ro-ro services from Tingwall (Mainland) to Rousay, Egilsay and Wyre. In 1991 she was lengthened by 5 metres, to increase car capacity.

GOLDEN MARIANA Built by Bideford Shipyard Ltd, Bideford, UK for *A J G England* of Padstow as a dual-purpose passenger and fishing vessel. In 1975 sold to *M MacKenzie* of Ullapool, then to *Pentland Ferries*, *Wide Firth Ferry* in 1982, and *Orkney Islands Council* in 1986. Passenger-only vessel. Generally operates summer-only feeder service between Pierowall (Westray) and Papa Westray.

GRAEMSAY Built by Ailsa Shipbuilding, Troon UK to operate between Stromness (Mainland), Moaness (Hoy) and Graemsay. Designed to offer an all-year-round service to these islands, primarily for passengers and cargo. Between October 2009 and January 2010 lengthened by 4.4 metres.

HOY HEAD Built by Appledore Shipbuilders Ltd, Appledore, UK to replace the THORSVOE on the 'South Isles service'. During winter 2012/13 extended by 14 metres at Cammell Laird Shiprepairers & Shipbuilders, Birkenhead, England.

SHAPINSAY Built by Yorkshire Drydock Ltd, Hull, UK for the service from Kirkwall (Mainland) to Shapinsay. In April 2011 lengthened by 6 metres at the Macduff Shipyards, Macduff, Scotland to increase car capacity from 12 to 16 and re-engined.

THORSVOE Built by Campbeltown Shipyard, Campbeltown, UK for the 'South Isles service'. In 1994 replaced by the new HOY HEAD and became the main reserve vessel for the fleet.

VARAGEN Built by Cochrane Shipbuilders, Selby, UK for *Orkney Ferries*, a private company established to start a new route between Gills Bay (Caithness, Scotland) and Burwick (South Ronaldsay, Orkney). However, due to problems with the terminals it was not possible to maintain regular services. In 1991, the company was taken over by *Orkney Islands Shipping Company* and the VARAGEN became part of their fleet, sharing the 'North Isles service' with the EARL SIGURD and the EARL THORFINN and replacing the freight vessel ISLANDER (494t, 1969).

P&O FERRIES

THE COMPANY *P&O Ferries Holdings Ltd* is a private sector company, a subsidiary of *Dubai World*, owned by the Government of Dubai. In Autumn 2002 *P&O North Sea Ferries*, P&O Irish Sea, *P&O Portsmouth* and *P&O Stena Line* (*Stena Line* involvement having ceased) were merged into a single operation.

MANAGEMENT Chief Executive Janette Bell, **Chief Financial Officer** Karl Howarth, **Managing Director Short Routes** David Stretch, **Business Unit Director of Freight Services** Stijn Gheyl, **Business Unit Director Overnight Routes**, Peter Hebblethwaite.

ADDRESSES ***Head Office and Dover Services*** Channel House, Channel View Road, Dover, Kent CT17 9TJ, ***Hull*** King George Dock, Hedon Road, Hull HU9 5QA, ***Larne*** P&O Irish Sea, Larne Harbour, Larne, Co Antrim BT40 1AW ***Rotterdam*** Beneluxhaven, Rotterdam (Europoort), Postbus 1123, 3180 Rozenburg, Netherlands, ***Zeebrugge*** Leopold II Dam 13, Havendam, 8380 Zeebrugge, Belgium.

TELEPHONE Administration *UK* +44 (0)1304 863000, **Passenger Reservations *UK*** 08716 64 64 64, ***France*** +33 (0)825 12 01 56, ***Belgium*** +32 (0)70 70 77 71, ***The Netherlands*** +31 (0)20 20 08333, ***Spain*** +34 (0)902 02 04 61, ***Luxembourg*** +34 (0)20 80 82 94. **Freight Reservations *UK*** 0870 6000 868, ***Republic of Ireland*** +353 (0)1 855 0522.

FAX Passenger Reservations ***UK East and South Coast*** +44 (0)1304 863464, ***West Coast*** 44 (0)02828 872195, ***The Netherlands*** +31 (0)118 1225 5215, ***Belgium*** +32 (0)50 54 71 12, **Freight Reservations** ***Cairnryan*** +44 (0)1581 200282, ***Larne*** +44 (0)28 2827 2477..

INTERNET Email customer.services@poferries.com **Website** www.poferries.com *(English, French, Dutch, German)* www.poirishsea.com *(English)* www.poferriesfreight.com *(English, French, German)*

ROUTES OPERATED Passenger Dover - Calais (1 hr 30 mins; ***PRIDE OF BURGUNDY, PRIDE OF CANTERBURY, PRIDE OF KENT, SPIRIT OF BRITAIN, SPIRIT OF FRANCE***; up to 25 per day), Hull - Zeebrugge (Belgium) (from 12 hrs 30 mins; ***PRIDE OF BRUGES, PRIDE OF YORK;*** 1 per day), Hull - Rotterdam (Beneluxhaven, Europoort) (The Netherlands) (from 10 hrs; ***PRIDE OF HULL, PRIDE OF ROTTERDAM***; 1 per day), Cairnryan - Larne (1 hr 45 min; ***EUROPEAN CAUSEWAY, EUROPEAN HIGHLANDER***; 7 per day), Liverpool - Dublin (8 hrs; ***NORBANK, NORBAY***; up to 2 per day. **Freight-only** Dover - Calais (1 hr 30 mins; ***EUROPEAN SEAWAY***; 2/3 per day (plus services on passenger ferries)), Tilbury - Zeebrugge (8 hrs; ***NORSKY, NORSTREAM***; 10 per week), Middlesbrough (Teesport) - Rotterdam (Beneluxhaven, Europoort) (16 hrs; ***WILHELMINE***; 3 per week), Middlesbrough (Teesport) - Zeebrugge (15 hrs 30 mins; ***BORE SONG, ESTRADEN***; 6 per week), Liverpool - Dublin (8 hrs; ***MISTRAL***; 1 per day (plus services on passenger ferries)). **Container service** Hull - Zeebrugge (Belgium) (from 12 hrs 30 mins; ***ELISABETH***; 3 per week).

1F	BORE SONG	25586t	11	18.5k	195.0m	12P	-	210T	A2	NL	9443566
2F	ELISABETH	5067t	00	-	118.3m	0P		648teu	C	NL	9219862
3F	ESTRADEN	18205t	99	19.0k	162.7m	12P	130C	170T	A	FI	9181077
4	EUROPEAN CAUSEWAY	20646t	00	22.7k	159.5m	410P	315C	84T	BA2	BS	9208394
6	EUROPEAN HIGHLANDER	21128t	02	22.6k	162.7m	410P	315C	84T	BA2	BS	9244116
7F+	EUROPEAN SEAWAY	22986t	91	21.0k	179.7m	200P	-	120L	BA2	CY	9007283
8F	MISTRAL	10471t	98	22.0k	153.5m	12P	-	112T	A	FI	9183788
9	NORBANK	17464t	93	22.5k	166.7m	114P	-	125T	A	NL	9056583
10	NORBAY	17464t	92	21.5k	166.7m	114P	-	125T	A	BM	9056595
11F	NORSKY	19992t	99	20.0k	180.0m	12P	-	194T	A	FI	9186182
12F	NORSTREAM	19992t	99	20.0k	180.0m	12P	-	194T	A	FI	9186194
13	PRIDE OF BRUGES	31598t	87	18.5k	179.0m	1050P	310C	185T	A	NL	8503797
14	PRIDE OF BURGUNDY	28138t	92	21.0k	179.7m	1420P	465C	120L	BA2	CY	9015254
15	PRIDE OF CANTERBURY	30635t	91	21.0k	179.7m	2000P	537C	120L	BA2	CY	9007295
16	PRIDE OF HULL	59925t	01	22.0k	215.4m	1360P	205C	263T	AS	BS	9208629
17	PRIDE OF KENT	30635t	92	21.0k	179.7m	2000P	537C	120L	BA2	CY	9015266
18	PRIDE OF ROTTERDAM	59925t	00	22.0k	215.4m	1360P	205C	263T	AS	NL	9208617
19	PRIDE OF YORK	31785t	87	18.5k	179.0m	1050P	310C	185T	A	BS	8501957
20	SPIRIT OF BRITAIN	47592t	11	22.0k-	212.0m	2000P	194C	180L	BA2	CY	9524231
21	SPIRIT OF FRANCE	47592t	12	22.0k-	212.0m	2000P	194C	180L	BA2	CY	9533816
22	WILHELMINE	21020t	12	15.8k	150.0m	12P	-	170T	A	MT	9539080

BORE SONG Built by Flensburger Schiffbau-Gesellschaft, Flensburg, Germany for *Bore Shipowners (Rettig Group Bore)* of Finland. In July 2011 chartered to *Mann Lines* to cover for the ESTRADEN'S refit. In September 2011 chartered to *P&O Ferries* and placed on the Middlesbrough - Zeebrugge route.

ELISABETH Container ship built by J.J. Sietas KG Schiffswerft GmbH & Co for *Holwerda Shipmanagement BV* of The Netherlands. In May 2017 introduced onto the Hull - Zeebrugge route to relieve pressure on the two passenger ships.

ESTRADEN Built as the ESTRADEN by Aker Finnyards, Rauma, Finland for *Rederi Ab Engship* (later *Bore Shipowners*) of Finland and chartered to *ArgoMann*. Later in 1999 renamed the AMAZON. In 2001 the charter was taken over by *Mann Lines* and in August she resumed the name ESTRADEN. In 2006 *Rederi AB Engship* was taken over by *Rettig Group Bore* and she remained on charter to *Mann Lines*. In January 2015 chartered to *P&O Ferries* to replace the WILHELMINE of *Cobelfret Ferries* on the Rotterdam - Middlesbrough (Teesport) service. In June 2018 transferred to the Zeebrugge - Teesport service.

European Causeway *(George Holland)*

Mistral *(Miles Cowsill)*

EUROPEAN CAUSEWAY Built by Mitsubishi Heavy Industries, Shimonoseki, Japan for *P&O Irish Sea* for the Cairnryan - Larne service.

EUROPEAN HIGHLANDER Built by Mitsubishi Heavy Industries, Shimonoseki, Japan for *P&O Irish Sea* for the Cairnryan - Larne service.

EUROPEAN SEAWAY Built by Schichau Seebeckwerft AG, Bremerhaven, Germany for *P&O European Ferries* for the Dover - Zeebrugge freight service. In 2000 a regular twice-daily freight-only Dover-Calais service was established, using this vessel which continued to operate to Zeebrugge at night. In 2001 car passengers (not foot or coach passengers) began to be conveyed on the Dover - Zeebrugge service. In 2003 the Zeebrugge service ended and she operated only between Dover and Calais in a freight-only mode. In 2004 withdrawn and laid up. In January 2005 returned to the Dover – Calais route. In July 2012 chartered to GLID, a joint venture between Centrica Renewable Energy Limited and EIG, for use by technicians working on the North Sea Lynn and Inner Dowsing wind farm array four miles off Skegness. In October 2012 returned to the Dover - Calais service. In April 2013 laid up at Tilbury. In August 2014 chartered as a wind farm accommodation and support vessel near the North German coast. In April 2015 returned to layup at Tilbury. In August 2015 returned to service on the Dover - Calais route.

MISTRAL Built by J J Sietas KG, Hamburg, Germany for *Godby Shipping AB* of Finland. Chartered to *Transfennica*. In 2003 chartered to *UPM-Kymmene Oy* of Finland and operated between Rauma and Santander. In 2005 chartered to *Finnlines*. Until the end of 2007 used on a Helsinki - Hamina - Zeebrugge service only available northbound for general traffic. From January 2008 operated on *UPM-Kymmene Seaways'* service from Hamina to Lübeck, Amsterdam and Tilbury. In June 2013 charter ended. During the ensuing period she undertook several short charters. In October 2014 chartered to *P&O Ferries* as second ship on the Zeebrugge - Middlesbrough (Teesport) service; she has also operated between Tilbury and Zeebrugge. In early June 2018 replaced by the *Estraden* and at the end of the month sub-chartered to *Stena Line* to operate between Rotterdam and Harwich. In August 2018 returned to *P&O Ferries* and operated between Teesport and Rotterdam. In March 2019 moved to the Liverpool - Dublin route, initially as a relief vessel and then as a permanent replacement for the EUROPEAN ENDEAVOUR.

NORBANK Built by Van der Giessen-de Noord, Krimpen aan den IJssel, Rotterdam, The Netherlands for *North Sea Ferries* for the Hull - Rotterdam service. She was originally built for and chartered to *Nedlloyd* but the charter was taken over by *P&O* in 1996 and she was bought by *P&O* in 2003. She retains Dutch crew and registry. In May 2001 moved to the Felixstowe - Europoort route. In January 2002 transferred to *P&O Irish Sea* and operated on the Liverpool – Dublin route.

NORBAY Built by Van der Giessen-de Noord, Krimpen aan den IJssel, Rotterdam, The Netherlands for *North Sea Ferries* for the Hull - Rotterdam service. Owned by *P&O*. In January 2002 transferred to *P&O Irish Sea* and operated on the Liverpool – Dublin route.

NORSKY, NORSTREAM Built by Aker Finnyards, Rauma, Finland for *Bore Line* of Finland and chartered to *P&O North Sea Ferries*. They generally operated on the Teesport - Zeebrugge service. In September 2011, the NORSTREAM was moved to the Tilbury - Zeebrugge route. In January 2013, the NORSKY was also moved to the Tilbury - Zeebrugge route.

PRIDE OF BRUGES Built as the NORSUN by NKK, Tsurumi, Japan for the Hull - Rotterdam service of *North Sea Ferries*. She was owned by *Nedlloyd* and was sold to *P&O* in 1996 but retains Dutch crew and registry. In May 2001 replaced by the PRIDE OF ROTTERDAM and in July 2001, after a major refurbishment, she was transferred to the Hull - Zeebrugge service, replacing the NORSTAR (26919t, 1974). In 2003 renamed the PRIDE OF BRUGES.

PRIDE OF BURGUNDY Built by Schichau Seebeckwerft AG, Bremerhaven, Germany for *P&O European Ferries* for the Dover - Calais service. When construction started she was due to be a sister vessel to the EUROPEAN SEAWAY (see Section 3) called the EUROPEAN CAUSEWAY and operate on the Zeebrugge freight route. However, it was decided that she should be completed as a passenger/freight vessel (the design allowed for conversion) and she was launched as the PRIDE OF BURGUNDY. In 1998, transferred to *P&O Stena Line* and renamed the P&OSL BURGUNDY. In 2002 renamed the PO BURGUNDY and in 2003 renamed the PRIDE OF BURGUNDY. In 2004 she operated mainly in freight-only mode. In 2005 returned to full passenger service.

PRIDE OF CANTERBURY Built as the EUROPEAN PATHWAY by Schichau Seebeckwerft AG, Bremerhaven, Germany for *P&O European Ferries* for the Dover - Zeebrugge freight service. In 1998 transferred to *P&O Stena Line*. In 2001 car/foot passengers were again conveyed on the route. In 2002/03 rebuilt as a full passenger vessel and renamed the PRIDE OF CANTERBURY; now operates between Dover and Calais.

PRIDE OF HULL Built by Fincantieri-Cantieri Navali Italiani SpA, Venezia, Italy for *P&O North Sea Ferries* to replace (with the PRIDE OF ROTTERDAM) the NORSEA and NORSUN plus the freight vessels NORBAY and NORBANK on the Hull - Rotterdam service.

PRIDE OF KENT Built as the EUROPEAN HIGHWAY by Schichau Seebeckwerft AG, Bremerhaven, Germany for *P&O European Ferries* for the Dover - Zeebrugge freight service. In 1998 transferred to *P&O Stena Line*. In Summer 1999 she operated full-time between Dover and Calais. She returned to the Dover - Zeebrugge route in the autumn when the P&OSL AQUITAINE was transferred to the Dover - Calais service. In 2001 car/foot passengers were again conveyed on the route. In 2002/03 rebuilt as a full passenger vessel and renamed the PRIDE OF KENT; now operates between Dover and Calais.

PRIDE OF ROTTERDAM Built by Fincantieri-Cantieri Navali Italiani SpA, Venezia, Italy. Keel laid as the PRIDE OF HULL but launched as the PRIDE OF ROTTERDAM. Owned by Dutch interests until 2006 when she was sold to *P&O Ferries*. Further details as the PRIDE OF HULL.

PRIDE OF YORK Built as the NORSEA by Govan Shipbuilders Ltd, Glasgow, UK for the Hull - Rotterdam service of *North Sea Ferries* (jointly owned by *P&O* and *The Royal Nedlloyd Group* of The Netherlands until 1996). In December 2001 she was replaced by the new PRIDE OF HULL and, after a two-month refurbishment, in 2002 transferred to the Hull - Zeebrugge service, replacing the NORLAND (26290t, 1974). In 2003 renamed the PRIDE OF YORK.

SPIRIT OF BRITAIN, SPIRIT OF FRANCE Built by STX Europe, Rauma, Finland for the Dover - Calais service. Car capacity relates to dedicated car deck only; additional cars can be accommodated on the freight decks as necessary.

WILHELMINE Built by the Kyokuyo Shipyard, Shimonoseki, Japan for *CLdN*. After completion, a additional deck and sponsons were retro-fitted at the Chengxi Shipyard, Jiangyin, China. Initially used on the Zeebrugge - Purfleet service. In January 2013 chartered to *P&O Ferries* to operate between Tilbury and Zeebrugge. After three weeks moved to the Middlesbrough - Rotterdam service. In November 2014 the charter ended and she was placed on the Zeebrugge - Purfleet service. She returned to *P&O Ferries* for five weeks during the refit period in January and February 2015 and again operated Middlesbrough - Rotterdam. In March 2019 chartered to *P&O Ferries* and placed on the Middlesbrough - Rotterdam route on a long-term basis.

PENTLAND FERRIES

THE COMPANY *Pentland Ferries* is a UK private sector company.

MANAGEMENT Managing Director Andrew Banks, **Designated Person Ashore** Kathryn Scollie.

ADDRESS Pier Road, St Margaret's Hope, South Ronaldsay, Orkney KW17 2SW.

TELEPHONE Administration & Reservations +44 (0)1856 831226.

FAX Administration & Reservations +44 (0)1856 831697.

INTERNET Email sales@pentlandferries.co.uk **Website** www.pentlandferries.co.uk *(English)*

ROUTE OPERATED Gills Bay (Caithness) - St Margaret's Hope (South Ronaldsay, Orkney) (1 hour; ***ALFRED***; up to 4 per day).

1	ALFRED	2963t	19	16.0k	84.5m	430P	98C	12L	A	UK	9823467

Pride of Canterbury *(George Holland)*

Pentalina *Brian Maxted)*

Red Osprey *(Andrew Cooke)*

Red Falcon *(Andrew Cooke)*

2	ORCADIA	899t	78	13.0k	69.5m	-	40C	-	AS	UK	7615490
3	PENTALINA	2382t	08	17.1k	59.0m	345P	70C	9L	A	UK	9437969

ALFRED Built by Strategic Marine Shipyard, Vũng Tàu, Vietnam.

ORCADIA Built as the SATURN by Ailsa Shipbuilding, Troon for *Caledonian MacBrayne* and initially used on the Wemyss Bay - Rothesay services. Between 1986 and 2005 she usually rotated on this service and services from Gourock; until 2000 this, in summer, included Clyde cruising but this was not repeated in 2001. In the summers 2005 - 2010, she operated additional peak summer sailings between Ardrossan and Brodick with a maximum capacity of 250 passengers. In October 2010 she took over the Gourock - Dunoon service. In June 2011 replaced by *Argyll Ferries* passenger ferries. During Summer 2011 she operated additional sailings between Ardrossan and Brodick. In September returned to the Gourock - Dunoon route to provide additional capacity for the Cowal Games. She was then laid up. In February 2015 sold to *Pentland Ferries* and renamed the ORCADIA.

PENTALINA Catamaran built by FBMA Marine, Cebu, Philippines for *Pentland Ferries.*

RED FUNNEL FERRIES

THE COMPANY *Red Funnel Ferries* is the trading name of the *Southampton, Isle of Wight and South of England Royal Mail Steam Packet Company Limited*, a British private sector company owned by a consortium of British and Canadian pension funds led by the West Midland Pensions Fund of the UK and the Workplace Safety and Insurance Board of the Province of Ontario, Canada.

MANAGEMENT CEO Fran Collins, **Commercial Director** Colin Hetherington.

ADDRESS 12 Bugle Street, Southampton SO14 2JY.

TELEPHONE Administration +44 (0)23 8024 8500, **Reservations *UK*** 0844 844 9988, ***Elsewhere*** +44 (0)23 8001 9192.

FAX Administration & Reservations *UK* +44 (0)23 8024 8501.

INTERNET Email post@redfunnel.co.uk **Website** www.redfunnel.co.uk *(English),*

ROUTES OPERATED Conventional Ferries Southampton - East Cowes (55 mins; ***RED EAGLE, RED FALCON, RED OSPREY***; hourly). **Fast Passenger Ferries** Southampton - Cowes (22 mins; ***RED JET 4, RED JET 6, RED JET 7***; every hour or half hour). **Freight Ferry** (1 hour, 10 mins; ***RED KESTREL***; every 3 hours).

1	RED EAGLE	3953t	96	13.0k	93.2m	895P	200C	18L	BA	UK	9117337
2	RED FALCON	3953t	94	13.0k	93.2m	895P	200C	18L	BA	UK	9064047
3»p	RED JET 4	342t	03	35.0k	39.8m	277P	0C	0L	-	UK	9295854
4»p	RED JET 6	363t	16	35.0k	41.1m	275P	0C	0L	-	UK	9788083
5»p	RED JET 7	363t	18	35.0k	41.1m	275P	0C	0L	-	UK	9847645
6F	RED KESTREL	1070t	19	12.5k	74.3m	12P	-	12L	BA	UK	9847645
7	RED OSPREY	3953t	94	13.0k	93.2m	895P	200C	18L	BA	UK	9064059

RED EAGLE Built by Ferguson Shipbuilders, Port Glasgow, UK for the Southampton - East Cowes service. During Winter 2004/05 stretched by 10 metres and height raised by 3 metres at Gdansk, Poland. In spring 2018 she received an upgrade (as RED FALCON in 2014).

RED FALCON Built by Ferguson Shipbuilders, Port Glasgow, UK for the Southampton - East Cowes service. In 2004 stretched by 10 metres and height raised by 3 metres at Gdansk, Poland. In spring 2014 she received a £2m upgrade.

RED JET 4 Catamaran built North West Bay Ships Pty Ltd Hobart, Tasmania, Australia.

RED JET 6, RED JET 7 Catamaran built by Wight Shipyard, Cowes, Isle of Wight, UK.

RED KESTREL Built by Cammell Laird, Birkenhead. She is designed to provide additional year-round freight capacity for the Southampton - East Cowes route.

RED OSPREY Built by Ferguson Shipbuilders, Port Glasgow, UK for the Southampton - East Cowes service. In 2003 stretched by 10 metres and height raised by 3 metres at Gdansk, Poland. In spring 2015 she received an upgrade (as RED FALCON in 2014).

SHETLAND ISLANDS COUNCIL

THE COMPANY *Shetland Islands Council* is a British local government authority.

MANAGEMENT Ferry Services Manager Craig Robertson, **Marine Superintendent** Ian Pearson.

ADDRESS Port Administration Building, Sella Ness, Mossbank, Shetland ZE2 9QR.

TELEPHONE Administration +44 (0)1806 244234, 244266, **Reservations *Yell Sound & Bluemull*** +44 (0)1595 745804, ***Fair Isle*** +44 (0)1595 760363, ***Whalsay*** +44(0)1595 745804, ***Skerries*** +44 (0)1595 745804, ***Papa Stour*** +44 (0)1595 745804.

FAX +44 (0)1806 244232.

INTERNET Email ferries@shetland.gov.uk **Website:** www.shetland.gov.uk/ferries *(English)*

ROUTES OPERATED Yell Sound Service Toft (Mainland) - Ulsta (Yell) (20 mins; ***DAGALIEN, DAGGRI***; up to 26 per day), **Bluemull Sound Service** *(*Gutcher (Yell) - Belmont (Unst) (10 mins; ***BIGGA, FIVLA, GEIRA***; up to 28 per day), Gutcher – Hamars Ness (Fetlar) (25 mins; ***BIGGA, FIVLA, GEIRA***; up to 8 per day), **Bressay** Lerwick (Mainland) - Maryfield (Bressay) (5 mins; ***LEIRNA***; up to 23 per day), **Whalsay** Laxo/Vidlin (Mainland) - Symbister (Whalsay) (30-45 mins; ***HENDRA, LINGA***; up to 18 per day), **Skerries** Vidlin (Mainland) – Out Skerries (1 hr 30 mins; ***FILLA***; up to 10 per week), Out Skerries – Lerwick (3 hours; ***FILLA***; 2 per week), **Fair Isle** *(*Grutness (Mainland) - Fair Isle (3 hrs; ***GOOD SHEPHERD IV***; 2 per week), **Papa Stour** West Burrafirth (Mainland) – Papa Stour (40 mins; ***SNOLDA***; up to 7 per week).

1	BIGGA	274t	91	11.0k	33.5m	96P	21C	2L	BA	UK	9000821
2	DAGALIEN	1861t	04	12.0k	65.4m	144P	30C	4L	BA	UK	9291626
3	DAGGRI	1861t	04	12.0k	65.4m	144P	30C	4L	BA	UK	9291614
4	FILLA	356t	03	12.0k	35.5m	30P	10C	2L	BA	UK	9269192
5	FIVLA	230t	85	11.0k	29.9m	95P	15C	2L	A	UK	8410237
6	GEIRA	226t	88	10.8k	29.9m	95P	15C	2L	BA	UK	8712489
7	GOOD SHEPHERD IV	76t	86	10.0k	18.3m	12P	2C	0L	C	UK	
8	HENDRA	248	82	11.0k	30.2m	95P	18C	2L	BA	UK	8200254
9	LEIRNA	420t	92	9.0k	35.1m	124P	20C	2L	BA	UK	9050199
10	LINGA	658t	01	11.0k	36.2m	100P	16C	2L	BA	UK	9242170
11	SNOLDA	130t	83	9.0k	24.4m	12P	6C	1L	A	UK	8302090

BIGGA Built by JW Miller & Sons Ltd, St Monans, Fife, UK. Used on the Toft - Ulsta service. In 2005 moved to the Bluemull Sound service.

DAGALIEN, DAGGRI Built by Stocznia Polnócna, Gdansk, Poland to replace the BIGGA and HENDRA on Toft - Ulsta service.

FILLA Built by Stocznia Polnócna, Gdansk, Poland for the Lerwick /Vidlin - Out Skerries service. She looks like an oil rig supply vessel and is capable of transporting fresh water for replenishing the tanks on the Skerries in case of drought.

FIVLA Built by Ailsa Shipbuilding, Troon, UK. Now a spare vessel, though often used on the Bluemull service.

GEIRA Built by Richard Dunston (Hessle), Hessle, UK. Formerly used on the Laxo - Symbister route. Replaced by the HENDRA in 2005 and moved to the Bluemull Sound service.

GOOD SHEPHERD IV Built by JW Miller & Sons Ltd, St Monans, Fife, UK. Used on the service between Grutness (Mainland) and Fair Isle. This vessel is not roll-on roll-off; vehicles are conveyed by special arrangement and generally consist of agricultural vehicles. She is pulled up on the marine slip on Fair Isle at the conclusion of each voyage.

Good Shepherd IV *(Miles Cowsill)*

Hendra *(Miles Cowsill)*

HENDRA Built by McTay Marine, Bromborough, Wirral, UK for the Laxo - Symbister service. In 2002 transferred to the Toft - Ulsta service. In 2004 replaced by new vessels DAGGRI and DAGALIEN and moved to the Bluemull Sound service. In May 2005 returned to the Laxo - Symbister service as second vessel.

LEIRNA Built by Ferguson Shipbuilders, Port Glasgow, UK. Used on the Lerwick - Maryfield (Bressay) service.

LINGA Built by Stocznia Polnócna, Gdansk, Poland. Used on the Laxo - Symbister service.

SNOLDA Built as the FILLA by Sigbjorn Iversen, Flekkefjord, Norway. Used on the Lerwick (Mainland) - Out Skerries and Vidlin (Mainland) - Out Skerries services. At other times she operated freight and charter services around the Shetland Archipelago. She resembles a miniature oil rig supply vessel. Passenger capacity was originally 20 from 1st April to 31st October inclusive but is now 12 all year. In 2003 renamed the SNOLDA; replaced by the new FILLA and, in 2004, transferred to the West Burrafirth - Papa Stour route.

STENA LINE

MANAGEMENT Chief Executive Niclas Mårtensson, **Trade Director North Sea** Annika Hult, **Trade Director Irish Sea North** Stephen Bryden, **Trade Director Irish Sea South** Ian Davies.

ADDRESS *UK* Stena House, Station Approach, Holyhead, Anglesey LL65 1DQ, ***The Netherlands*** PO Box 2, 3150 AA, Hoek van Holland, The Netherlands.

TELEPHONE Administration *UK* +44 (0)1407) 606631, ***The Netherlands*** +31 (0)174 389333, **Reservations *UK*** 0844 7707070 (from UK only), ***The Netherlands*** +31 (0)174 315811.

FAX Administration & Reservations *UK* +44 (0)1407 606811, ***The Netherlands*** +31 (0)174 387045, **Telex** 31272.

INTERNET Email info@stenaline.com **Website** www.stenaline.co.uk *(English),*

ROUTES OPERATED Conventional Ferries Cairnryan - Belfast (2 hrs 15 mins; ***STENA SUPERFAST VII, STENA SUPERFAST VII***; up to 6 per day, Port of Liverpool (Twelve Quays River Terminal, Birkenhead) - Belfast (8 hrs; ***STENA LAGAN, STENA MERSEY***; up to 2 per day), Holyhead - Dublin (3 hrs 15 mins; ***STENA ADVENTURER, STENA SUPERFAST X***; 4 per day), Fishguard - Rosslare (3 hrs 15 mins on day sailings ***STENA EUROPE***; 2 per day), Rosslare - Cherbourg (17 - 20 hrs; ***STENA HORIZON***; 3 per week), Harwich - Hoek van Holland (The Netherlands) (7 hrs 30 mins; ***STENA BRITANNICA, STENA HOLLANDICA***; 2 per day). **Freight Ferries** Port of Liverpool (Twelve Quays River Terminal, Birkenhead) - Belfast (8 hrs; ***STENA FORECASTER***; 1 per day), Heysham - Belfast (7 hrs; ***STENA HIBERNIA, STENA SCOTIA***; 2 per day), Harwich - Rotterdam (8 hrs; ***MISANA, SOMERSET***; 11 per week), Killingholme - Hoek van Holland (11 hrs; ***STENA TRANSIT, STENA TRANSPORTER***; 1 per day), Killingholme - Rotterdam (13 hrs; ***MISIDA***; ***STENA FORERUNNER***; 6 per week).

1F	MISANA	14100t	07	20.0k	163.9m	12P	-	150T	A	FI	9348936
2F	MISIDA	14100t	07	20.0k	163.9m	12P	-	150T	A	FI	9348948
3F	SOMERSET	21005t	00	18.0k	183.4m	12P	-	180T	A	NL	9188221
4	STENA ADVENTURER	43532t	03	22.0k	210.8m	1500P	-	210L	BA2	UK	9235529
5	STENA BRITANNICA	63600t	10	22.0k	240.0m	1200P	-	300T	BA2	UK	9419175
6	STENA EUROPE	24828t	81	20.5k	149.0m	2076P	456C	60T	BA	UK	7901760
7	STENA FORECASTER	24688t	03	22.0k	195.3m	12P	-	210T	A2	UK	9214666
8F	STENA FORERUNNER	24688t	02	22.0k	195.3m	12P	-	210T	A2	NL	9227259
9F	STENA HIBERNIA	13017t	96	18.6k	142.5m	12P	-	114T	A	UK	9121637
10	STENA HOLLANDICA	63600t	10	22.5k	240.0m	1200P	-	300T	BA2	NL	9419163
11	STENA HORIZON	26500t	06	23.5k	186.5m	720P	160C	135L	A	IT	9332559
12	STENA LAGAN	27510t	05	23.5k	186.5m	720P	160C	135T	A	UK	9329849
13	STENA MERSEY	27510t	05	23.5k	186.5m	720P	160C	135T	A	UK	9329851
14F	STENA SCOTIA	13017t	96	18.6k	142.5m	12P	-	114T	A	UK	9121625

15	STENA SUPERFAST VII	30285t	01	22.0k	203.3m	1200P	660C	110L	BA2	UK	9198941
16	STENA SUPERFAST VIII	30285t	01	22.0k	203.3m	1200P	660C	110L	BA2	UK	9198953
17	STENA SUPERFAST X	30285t	02	22.0k	203.3m	1200P	660C	110L	BA2	UK	9211511
18F+	STENA TRANSIT	34700t	11	22.2k	212.0m	300P	-	290T	A2	NL	9469388
19F+	STENA TRANSPORTER	34700t	11	22.2k	212.0m	300P	-	290T	A2	NL	9469376

MISANA, MISIDA Built by J J Sietas, Hamburg, Germany for *Godby Shipping AB* of Finland and time-chartered to *UPM-Kymmene* of Finland to operate between Finland, Spain and Portugal. In July 2013 charter taken over by *Finnlines*. In January 2016 long-term chartered to *Stena RoRo*, who then sub-chartered them to *Transfennica*. In January 2018 sub-chartered to *Stena Line* and placed on the Harwich - Rotterdam service.

SOMERSET Built as the SPAARNEBORG by Flender Werft AG, Lübeck, Germany for *Wagenborg* of The Netherlands and time-chartered to *Stora-Enso* to operate between Zeebrugge and Göteborg in conjunction with *Cobelfret Ferries*. She also operated between Tilbury and Göteborg during 2010. In August 2011 chartered to the *Canadian MoD* to operate between Montreal and Cyprus in connection with the Libyan 'no fly zone'. On return in November she was laid up in Zeebrugge and in January 2012 moved to Göteborg. In August 2012 chartered to *LD Lines* to operate between Marseilles and Tunis. In March 2013 returned to the *Stora Enso/Cobelfret Ferries* Zeebrugge - Göteborg service. In November 2014 the arrangement between *Stora Enso* and *Cobelfret Ferries* ended and she was chartered to *SOL Continent Line* who took over the operation of the service, operating between Finland, Germany, Belgium and the UK. In January 2015 sold to *CNdL* and renamed the SOMERSET. Generally operated between Zeebrugge and Göteborg. In August 2018 chartered to *Stena Line* to operate between Rotterdam and Harwich.

STENA ADVENTURER Ro-pax vessel built by Hyundai Heavy Industries, Ulsan, South Korea, for *Stena RoRo* and chartered to *Stena Line* to operate between Holyhead and Dublin.

STENA BRITANNICA Built by Waden Yards in Wismar and Warnemünde, Germany, for *Stena Rederi* (bow sections constructed at Warnemünde and stern and final assembly at Wismar). Replaced the 2003 built STENA BRITANNICA on the Harwich - Hoek van Holland service.

STENA EUROPE Built as the KRONPRINSESSAN VICTORIA by Götaverken Arendal AB, Göteborg, Sweden for *Göteborg-Frederikshavn Linjen* of Sweden (trading as *Sessan Linjen*) for their Göteborg - Frederikshavn service. Shortly after delivery, the company was taken over by *Stena Line* and services were marketed as *Stena-Sessan Line* for a period. In 1982 she was converted to an overnight ferry by changing one vehicle deck into two additional decks of cabins and she was switched to the Göteborg - Kiel route (with, during the summer, daytime runs from Göteborg to Frederikshavn and Kiel to Korsør (Denmark)). In 1989 she was transferred to the Oslo - Frederikshavn route and renamed the STENA SAGA. In 1994, transferred to *Stena Line BV*, renamed the STENA EUROPE and operated between Hoek van Holland and Harwich. She was withdrawn in June 1997, transferred to the *Lion Ferry* (a *Stena Line* subsidiary) Karlskrona - Gdynia service and renamed the LION EUROPE. In 1998 she was transferred back to *Stena Line* (remaining on the same route) and renamed the STENA EUROPE. In early 2002 the cabins installed in 1982 were removed and other modifications made and she was transferred to the Fishguard - Rosslare route.

STENA FORERUNNER Built by Dalian Shipyard Co Ltd, Dalian, China for *Stena RoRo* and chartered to *Transfennica*. In January 2018 chartered to *Stena Line* and placed on the Rotterdam - Harwich service. In August 2018 transferred to the Birkenhead - Belfast service. In February 2019 transferred to the Rotterdam - Killingholme service.

STENA FORECASTER Built by Dalian Shipyard Co Ltd, Dalian, China for *Stena RoRo* and chartered to *Transfennica*. In 2015 chartered *CoTuNav* of Tunisia for Mediterranean service. In February 2019 chartered to *Stena Line* and placed on the Birkenhead - Belfast service.

STENA HIBERNIA Built as the MAERSK IMPORTER by Miho Shipyard, Shimizu, Japan for *Norfolkline*. Used on the Scheveningen (from 2007 Vlaardingen) - Felixstowe service. In October 2009 moved to the Heysham-Belfast service. In July 2010 renamed the HIBERNIA SEAWAYS. In July 2011 renamed the STENA HIBERNIA. In September 2012 transferred to

Stena Superfast VIII *(George Holland)*

Stena Horizon *(Nick Widdows)*

Stena Adventurer *(George Holland)*

Stena Hibernia *(George Holland)*

Stena RoRo. In November chartered to *Stena Line* and placed on the Birkenhead - Belfast service. In September 2015 moved to the Heysham - Belfast route.

STENA HOLLANDICA Built by Nordic Yards in Wismar and Warnemünde, Germany, for *Stena Rederi* (bow sections constructed at Warnemünde and stern and final assembly at Wismar) to replace the previous STENA HOLLANDICA on the Harwich - Hoek van Holland service. Entered service May 2010.

STENA HORIZON Built as the CARTOUR BETA by CN Visentini, Porto Viro, Italy for Levantina Trasporti of Italy. Chartered to *Caronte & Tourist* of Italy and operated between Messina and Salerno (Sicily). In October 2011 chartered to *Celtic Link Ferries*, renamed the CELTIC HORIZON and placed on the Rosslare - Cherbourg route. In March 2014 service and charter taken over by *Stena Line*. Renamed the STENA HORIZON.

STENA LAGAN, STENA MERSEY Built as the LAGAN VIKING and MERSEY VIKING by CN Visentini, Donada, Italy for *Levantina Trasporti* of Italy. Chartered to *NorseMerchant Ferries* and placed on the Birkenhead - Belfast route. In 2008 sold to *Norfolkline*, then resold to *Epic Shipping* and chartered back. In August 2010, following *Norfolkline's* purchase by *DFDS Seaways*, they were renamed the LAGAN SEAWAYS and MERSEY SEAWAYS respectively. Between January and July 2011 they were operated by *Stena Line Irish Sea Ferries*, a 'stand-alone' company pending consideration of a take-over by *Stena Line* by the UK and Irish competition authorities. In July 2011 the take-over was confirmed and in August 2011 they were renamed the STENA LAGAN and STENA MERSEY. In April 2012 they were sold to *Stena RoRo* and chartered back by *Stena Line*.

STENA SCOTIA Built as the MAERSK EXPORTER by Miho Shipyard, Shimizu, Japan for *Norfolkline*. Used on the Scheveningen (from 2007 Vlaardingen) - Felixstowe service until March 2009 when she was moved to the Heysham - Belfast route. In July 2010 renamed the SCOTIA SEAWAYS. In July 2011 renamed the STENA SCOTIA. In September 2013 transferred to *Stena RoRo* and placed on the charter market. In September 2014 chartered to *Stena Line* and inaugurated a new service between Rotterdam and Killingholme. In January 2018 transferred to Rotterdam - Harwich service. In August 2018 transferred to the Heysham - Belfast service.

STENA SUPERFAST VII, STENA SUPERFAST VIII Built as the SUPERFAST VII and SUPERFAST VIII by Howaldtswerke Deutsche Werft AG, Kiel, Germany for *Attica Enterprises* (now *Attica Group*) for use by *Superfast Ferries* between Rostock and Hanko. In 2006 sold to *Tallink*. The Finnish terminal was transferred to Helsinki and daily return trips between Helsinki and Tallinn were introduced. These ceased in September 2008. The operation was ceased for the winter season in December 2009 and 2010. Service resumed at the end of April 2010 and 2011. In August 2011 chartered to *Stena Line* and renamed the STENA SUPERFAST VII, STENA SUPERFAST VIII. In November 2011, after a major refit, they were placed on a service between Cairnryan and Belfast (replacing the Stranraer - Belfast service). In December 2017 purchased by *Stena Ropax*.

STENA SUPERFAST X Built as the SUPERFAST X by Howaldtswerke Deutsche Werft AG, Kiel, Germany for *Attica Enterprises* (now *Attica Group*) for use by *Superfast Ferries*. In May 2002 she and the SUPERFAST IX (see ATLANTIC VISION, *Tallink*, Section 6) began operating between Rosyth (Scotland) and Zeebrugge. In 2004 fitted with additional cabins and conference/seating areas. In 2007 sold to *Veolia Transportation* and renamed the JEAN NICOLI. Chartered to *CoTuNav* of Tunisia and operated between France/Italy and Tunisia. Later chartered to *ANEK Lines* of Greece and operated on the Patras - Corfu - Igoumenitsa - Venezia route. In July 2008 chartered to *SeaFrance* and renamed the SEAFRANCE MOLIERE. After modifications she was placed on the Dover - Calais route. In November 2011 laid up. In January 2012 offered for sale or charter. In July 2012 sold to *Scapino Shipping Ltd* of Monaco and renamed the MOLIERE. In October 2012 chartered to the *DFDS/LD Lines* joint venture and, in November, renamed the DIEPPE SEAWAYS and placed on the Dover - Calais service. In May 2014 sold to *Stena Line North Sea Ltd*. In December 2014 charter ended. Refurbished and, in March 2015, chartered to *Stena Line*, renamed the STENA SUPERFAST X and placed on the Holyhead - Dublin route.

STENA TRANSIT, STENA TRANSPORTER Built by Samsung Heavy Industries, Koje, South Korea. Used on the Hoek van Holland - Killingholme service.

Somerset *(John Bryant)*

Stena Hollandica *(John Bryant)*

Under Construction

20	STENA ESTRID	40500t	19	22k	214.5m	927P	300C	180L	BA2	UK	9807293
21	STENA EDDA	40500t	20	22k	214.5m	927P	300C	180L	BA2	UK	9807308
22	STENA EMBLA	40500t	20	22k	214.5m	927P	300C	180L	BA2	UK	9807322
23	NEWBUILDING 7	-	22	22k	239.7m	1200P	300C	220L	BA2	-	-
24	NEWBUILDING 8	-	22	22k	239.7m	1200P	300C	220L	BA2	-	-

STENA ESTRID, STENA EDDA, STENA EMBLA Under construction for *Stena Line* by AVIC International Maritime Holdings, Weihai, China. They are known as 'E-Flexers' being of flexible construction so that their internal layout can be tailored to the needs of the routes they will operate on. They are designed to run traditional fuel but are under the class notation "gas ready" and can be converted to run on natural gas. STENA ESTRID, due to be delivered autumn 2019, is planned to operated on Holyhead-Dublin. STENA EDDA, due to be delivered spring 2020, and STENA EMBLA is planned to operate on the Liverpool - Belfast route. There are also a NEWBUILDING 3, a NEWBUILDING 6 and a NEWBUILDING 9 which are to be chartered to *Brittany Ferries* on delivery and are listed under that heading (under their chosen names where known) and a NEWBUILDING 5 which is to be chartered to *DFDS Seaways* on delivery and is listed under that heading.

NEWBUILDING 7, NEWBUILDING 8 Lengthened version of NEWBUILDING 1-6. It has been announced they will operate for *Stena Line* but whether this is in UK waters or in the Baltic is not known. There is also a NEWBUILDING 9 which is to be chartered to *Brittany Ferries*. *Stena Line* have an option for four more similar vessels.

WESTERN FERRIES

THE COMPANY *Western Ferries (Clyde) Ltd* is a British private sector company.

MANAGEMENT Managing Director Gordon Ross.

ADDRESS Hunter's Quay, Dunoon, Argyll PA23 8HJ.

TELEPHONE Administration +44 (0)1369 704452, **Reservations** Not applicable.

INTERNET Email enquiries@western-ferries.co.uk **Website** www.western-ferries.co.uk *(English)*,

ROUTE OPERATED McInroy's Point (Gourock) - Hunter's Quay (Dunoon) (20 mins; ***SOUND OF SCARBA, SOUND OF SEIL, SOUND OF SHUNA, SOUND OF SOAY***; every 20 mins (15 mins in peaks)).

1	SOUND OF SCARBA	489t	01	11.0k	49.95m	220P	40C	4/5L	BA	UK	9237424
2	SOUND OF SEIL	497t	13	11.0k	49.95m	220P	40C	4/5L	BA	UK	9665217
3	SOUND OF SHUNA	489t	03	11.0k	49.95m	220P	40C	4/5L	BA	UK	9289441
4	SOUND OF SOAY	497t	13	11.0k	49.95m	220P	40C	4/5L	BA	UK	9665229

SOUND OF SCARBA, SOUND OF SHUNA Built by Ferguson Shipbuilders, Port Glasgow, UK for *Western Ferries*.

SOUND OF SEIL, SOUND OF SOAY Built by Cammell Laird Shiprepairers & Shipbuilders, Birkenhead, UK for *Western Ferries*.

WIGHTLINK

THE COMPANY *Wightlink* is a British private sector company, 50% owned by *Basalt Infrastructure Partners LLP of the UK* (formerly known as *Balfour Beatty Infrastructure Partners (BBIP)*) and 50% by *Fiera Infrastructure Inc* of Canada.

MANAGEMENT Chief Executive Keith Greenfield, **Finance Director** Jonathan Pascoe **Operations Director** Daryl Palmer, **Marketing and Innovation Director** Stuart James, **Fleet and Property Director** John Burrows, **Business Development Director** Clive Tilley, **Human Resources Director** Karen Wellman.

ADDRESS Gunwharf Road, Portsmouth PO1 2LA.

Sound of Scarba *(Miles Cowsill)*

Sound of Shuna *(John Hendy)*

Wight Ryder II *(Miles Cowsill)*

Wight Sky *(Andrew Cooke)*

TELEPHONE Administration and Reservations +44 (0)333 999 7333.

INTERNET Email bookings@wightlink.co.uk **Website** www.wightlink.co.uk *(English, Dutch, French, German)*

ROUTES OPERATED Conventional Ferries Lymington - Yarmouth (Isle of Wight) (approx 40 mins; ***WIGHT LIGHT, WIGHT SKY***; ***WIGHT SUN***; hourly), Portsmouth - Fishbourne (Isle of Wight) (approx 45 mins; ***ST. CLARE, ST. FAITH, VICTORIA OF WIGHT***; mainly hourly depending on time of day). **Fast Cats** Portsmouth - Ryde (Isle of Wight) (passenger-only) (under 22 mins; ***WIGHT RYDER I, WIGHT RYDER II***; 2 per hour).

1	ST. CLARE	5359t	01	13.0k	86.0m	878P	186C	-	BA2	UK	9236949
2	ST. FAITH	3009t	89	12.5k	77.0m	771P	142C	12L	BA	UK	8907228
3	VICTORIA OF WIGHT	8200t	18	13.0k	89.7m	1208P	178C	-	BA2	UK	9791028
4	WIGHT LIGHT	2546t	08	11.0k	62.4m	360P	65C	-	BA	UK	9446972
5»p	WIGHT RYDER I	520t	09	20.0k	40.9m	260P	0C	-	-	UK	9512537
6»p	WIGHT RYDER II	520t	09	20.0k	40.9m	260P	0C	-	-	UK	9512549
7	WIGHT SKY	2456t	08	11.0k	62.4m	360P	65C	-	BA	UK	9446984
8	WIGHT SUN	2546t	09	11.0k	62.4m	360P	65C	-	BA	UK	9490416

ST. CLARE Built by Stocznia Remontowa, Gdansk, Poland for the Portsmouth - Fishbourne service. She is a double-ended ferry with a central bridge. During winter 2015/16 modified for double deck loading.

ST. FAITH Built by Cochrane Shipbuilders, Selby, UK for *Sealink British Ferries* for the Portsmouth - Fishbourne service.

VICTORIA OF WIGHT Built by the Cemre Shipyard, Yalova, Turkey for the Portsmouth - Fishbourne service. She is a hybrid diesel/battery electric vessel.

WIGHT LIGHT, WIGHT SKY, WIGHT SUN Built by Brodogradilište Kraljevica, Croatia for the Lymington - Yarmouth route.

WIGHT RYDER I, WIGHT RYDER II Catamarans built by FBMA Marine, Balamban, Cebu, Philippines. Operate on the Portsmouth - Ryde service.

Victoria of Wight *(Miles Cowsill)*

***Shannon Breeze* arriving at Killimer.** *(Miles Cowsill)*

SECTION 2 - MINOR FERRY OPERATORS

ARGYLL AND BUTE COUNCIL

THE COMPANY *Argyll and Bute Council* is a British local government authority.

MANAGEMENT Head of Roads and Amenity Services Jim Smith.

Marine Operations Manager Stewart Clark.

ADDRESS 1A Manse Brae, Lochgilphead, Argyll PA31 8RD.

TELEPHONE Administration +44 (0)1546 604673.

FAX Administration +44 (0)1546 604738.

INTERNET Email stewart.clark@argyll-bute.gov.uk **Website** www.argyll-bute.gov.uk/transport-and-streets/ferry-travel

ROUTES OPERATED Vehicle ferries Seil - Luing (5 mins; ***BELNAHUA***; approx half-hourly), Port Askaig (Islay) - Feolin (Jura) (5 mins; ***EILEAN DHIURA***; approx half-hourly). **Passenger-only ferries** Port Appin – Lismore (10 mins; ***THE LISMORE***; approx hourly), Ellenabeich – Easdale (5 mins; ***EASDALE***; approx quarter-hourly).

1	BELNAHUA	35t	72	8.0k	17.1m	40P	5C	1L	BA	UK
2p	EASDALE	-	93	6.5k	6.4m	11P	0C	0L	-	UK
3	EILEAN DHIURA	86t	98	9.0k	25.6m	50P	13C	1L	BA	UK
4p	THE LISMORE	12t	88	8.0k	9.7m	20P	0C	0L	-	UK

BELNAHUA Built by Campbeltown Shipyard, Campbeltown, UK for *Argyll County Council* for the Seil - Luing service. In 1975, following local government reorganisation, transferred to *Strathclyde Regional Council*. In 1996, transferred to *Argyll and Bute Council*.

EASDALE Built for *Strathclyde Regional Council* for the Ellenabeich - Easdale passenger-only service. In 1996, following local government reorganisation, transferred to *Argyll and Bute Council*.

EILEAN DHIURA Built by McTay Marine, Bromborough, Wirral, UK for *Argyll and Bute Council* to replace the *Western Ferries (Argyll)* SOUND OF GIGHA on the Islay - Jura route. *ASP Ship Management* manage and operate this vessel on behalf of *Argyll and Bute Council*.

THE LISMORE Built for *Strathclyde Regional Council* for the Port Appin – Lismore passenger-only service. In 1996, following local government reorganisation, transferred to *Argyll and Bute Council*.

ARRANMORE FAST FERRIES

THE COMPANY *Arranmore Fast Ferries*, trading as *Arranmore Blue Ferry* and *Tory Ferry*, is a Republic of Ireland private sector company.

MANAGEMENT Managing Director Seamus Boyle.

ADDRESS Blue Ferry Office, Burtonport, Letterkenny, Co. Donegal, Republic of Ireland.

TELEPHONE Administration & Reservations +353 (0)87 3171810**.**

INTERNET Email: info.fastferry@gmail.com **Website** www.arranmorefastferry.com *(English)*.

ROUTES OPERATED Arranmore Blue Ferry Burtonport (County Donegal) - Leabgarrow (Arranmore Island) (20 mins; ***CANNA, MORVERN***; up to 8 per day), **Tory Ferry** Magheroarty (County Donegal) - Tory Island (45 mins; ***QUEEN OF ARAN***; up to 4 per day).

1	CANNA	69t	76	8.0k	24.3m	140P	6C	1L	B	IR	7340423
2	MISNEACH	30t	78	7.0k	18.9m	80P	4C	-	B	IR	
3	MORVERN	83t	73	8.0k	26.6m	96P	10C	1L	B	IR	7235501
4p	OCEAN WARRIOR	18t	89	18.0k	14.3m	12P	0C	-	-	IR	
5p	QUEEN OF ARAN	113t	76	-	20.1m	96P	0C	-	-	IR	7527928

Eilean Dhiura *(Brian Maxted)*

Morvern *(Brian Maxted)*

CANNA Built by James Lamont & Co Ltd, Port Glasgow, UK for *Caledonian MacBrayne*. She was the regular vessel on the Lochaline - Fishnish (Mull) service. In 1986 she was replaced by the ISLE OF CUMBRAE and until 1990 she served in a relief capacity in the north, often assisting on the Iona service. In 1990 she was placed on the Kyles Scalpay (Harris) - Scalpay service (replaced by a bridge in Autumn 1997). In Spring 1997 *Caledonian MacBrayne* was contracted to operate the Ballycastle - Rathlin Island route and she was transferred to this service. In June 2008 she was chartered by *Caledonian Maritime Assets Limited* to *Rathlin Island Ferry Ltd* who took over the operation of the service. In June 2017 replaced by the SPIRIT OF RATHLIN and withdrawn. In autumn 2017 sold to *Humphrey O'Leary, Clare Island* and chartered to *Arranmore Fast Ferries*.

MISNEACH Built at New Ross, Irish Republic for *Arranmore Island Ferry Services* of the Irish Republic and used on the Burtonport - Arranmore service. In 1992 sold to *Bere Island Ferries*. In 1993 inaugurated a car ferry service between Castletownbere and Bere Island. In 2004 disposed of and since then has been used as a work boat until purchased by *Arranmore Fast Ferries*, refurbished and became a reserve vessel.

MORVERN Built by James Lamont & Co Ltd, Port Glasgow, UK for *Caledonian MacBrayne*. After service on a number of routes she was, after 1979, the main vessel on the Fionnphort (Mull) - Iona service. In 1992 she was replaced by the LOCH BUIE and became a spare vessel. In 1995 sold to *Arranmore Island Ferry Services*. In 2001 sold to *Bere Island Ferries*. In February 2010 refurbished by Bere Island Boatyard and sold to *Arranmore Charters* (now *Arranmore Fast Ferries*). Extended in June 2012.

OCEAN WARRIOR Built by FBM Marine, Cowes, Isle of Wight as an RNLI Tyne class lifeboat ALEXANDER COUTANACHE (No1157) and operated at St Helier, Channel Islands until June 2009 when she became a relief vessel. Bought by *Arranmore Fast Ferries* in December 2014 and renamed the OCEAN WARRIOR.

QUEEN OF ARAN built in 1976 as the SHONAG OF KISHORN to work at the oil rig construction site in Loch Kishorn in Scotland. Moved to Ireland in1985 and eventually became the QUEEN OF ARAN. In 2017 sold to *Arranmore Fast Ferries* and, after a major refit, placed on the Tory Island service.

ARRANMORE ISLAND FERRY SERVICES

THE COMPANY *Arranmore Island Ferry Services (Bád Farrantoireacht Arainn Mhór)*, trading as *Arranmore Red Ferry*, is a Republic of Ireland company, supported by *Roinn na Gaeltachta (The Gaeltacht Authority)*, a semi-state-owned body responsible for tourism and development in the Irish-speaking areas of The Republic of Ireland. They also operate the summer only Lough Swilly service.

MANAGEMENT Managing Director Dominic Sweeney.

ADDRESS Cara na nOilean, Burtonport Pier, Letterkenny, Co. Donegal, Republic of Ireland.

TELEPHONE Administration & Reservations *Arranmore Island Service* +353 (0)7495 42233, ***Lough Swilly Service*** +353 (0)87 211 2331.

INTERNET Email info@arranmoreferry.com loughswillyferry@gmail.com **Websites** www.arranmoreferry.com swillyferry.com *(English)*

ROUTES OPERATED *Arranmore Island Service* Burtonport (County Donegal) - Leabgarrow (Arranmore Island) (15 mins; ***RHUM***; up to 8 per day (Summer), 6 per day (Winter)), ***Lough Swilly Service (summer only)*** Buncrana (County Donegal) - Rathmullan (County Donegal) (20 mins; ***SPIRIT OF LOUGH SWILLY***; up to 8 per day).

1	COLL	69t	74	8.0k	25.3m	96P	6C	-	B	IR	7327990
2	RHUM	69t	73	8.0k	25.3m	96P	6C	-	B	IR	7319589
3	SPIRIT OF LOUGH SWILLY	110t	59	-	32.0m	130P	80C	-	BA	IR	

COLL Built by James Lamont & Co Ltd, Port Glasgow, UK for *Caledonian MacBrayne*. For several years she was employed mainly in a relief capacity. In 1986 she took over the Tobermory (Mull)

- Kilchoan service from a passenger-only vessel; the conveyance of vehicles was not inaugurated until 1991. In 1996 she was transferred to the Oban - Lismore route. In 1998 she was sold to *Arranmore Island Ferry Services*. Operates as spare vessel and also conveys cargo to Tory Island and is available for charter.

RHUM Built by James Lamont & Co Ltd, Port Glasgow, UK for *Caledonian MacBrayne*. Until 1987, she was used primarily on the Claonaig - Lochranza (Arran) service. After that time she served on various routes. In 1994 she inaugurated a new service between Tarbert (Loch Fyne) and Portavadie. In 1997 she operated between Kyles Scalpay and Scalpay until the opening of the new bridge on 16th December 1997. In 1998 she was sold to *Arranmore Island Ferry Services*.

SPIRIT OF LOUGH SWILLY Built as the LORELEY V by Ruthof, Mainz, Germany to operate between St Goarshausen and St Goar on the River Rhine. In 2004 replaced by a new vessel (the LORELEY VI) and became a reserve vessel. In 2007, sold to the *Waterford Castle Hotel* and renamed the LORELEY and, in 2008, replaced the previous ferry. She was modified for cable guidance. In August 2014 replaced by the MARY FITZGERALD and laid up. In July 2017 sold to sold to *Arranmore Island Ferry Services*, changed back to self steering and renamed the SPIRIT OF LOUGH SWILLY. Placed on the Lough Swilly service.

BERE ISLAND FERRIES

THE COMPANY *Bere Island Ferries Ltd* is a Republic of Ireland private sector company.

MANAGEMENT Operator Colum Harrington.

ADDRESS Ferry Lodge, West End, Bere Island, Beara, County Cork, Republic of Ireland.

TELEPHONE Administration +353 (0)27 75009, **Reservations** Not applicable, **Mobile** +353 (0)86 2423140.

FAX Administration +353 (0)27 75000, **Reservations** Not applicable.

INTERNET Email biferry@eircom.net **Website** www.bereislandferries.com (English)

1	HOUTON LASS	58t	60	9.0k	22.9m	12P	10C	1L	B	IR
2	OILEAN NA H-OIGE	69t	80	7.0k	18.6m	75P	4C	-	B	IR
3	SANCTA MARIA	67t	83	7.0k	18.6m	75P	4C	-	B	IR

HOUTON LASS Built by Magnaport Marine Ltd, Poole, UK for Flotta Oil Terminals, Stromness, Orkney Islands. Later sold for use as an antipollution vessel on the Black Isle, near Inverness. In November 2013 delivered to *Bere Island Ferries Ltd*. During 2014-2016 refurbished and lengthened in Galway. Mainly in use for transporting lorries but is also used for taking (up to) 10 cars during busy times.

OILEAN NA H-OIGE Built as the EILEAN NA H-OIGE by Lewis Offshore Ltd, Stornoway, UK for *Western Isles Islands Council* (from 1st April 1996 the *Western Isles Council* and from 1st January 1998 *Comhairle Nan Eilean Siar*) for their Ludaig (South Uist) - Eriskay service. From 2000 operated from a temporary slipway at the Eriskay causeway. This route ceased in July 2001 following the full opening of the causeway and she was laid up. In 2002 she was moved to the Eriskay - Barra service. In 2003 replaced by the LOCH BHRUSDA of *Caledonian MacBrayne* and laid up. Later sold to *Bere Island Ferries* and renamed the OILEAN NA H-OIGE (same name - "The Island of Youth" - in Irish rather than Scots Gaelic).

SANCTA MARIA Built as the EILEAN BHEARNARAIGH by George Brown & Company, Greenock, UK for *Western Isles Islands Council* for their Otternish (North Uist) - Berneray service. From 1996 until 1999 she was operated by *Caledonian MacBrayne* in conjunction with the LOCH BHRUSDA on the service between Otternish and Berneray and during the winter she was laid up. Following the opening of a causeway between North Uist and Berneray in early 1999, the ferry service ceased and she became reserve vessel for the Eriskay route. This route ceased in July 2001 following the opening of a causeway and she was laid up. In 2002 operated between Eriskay and Barra as reserve vessel. In 2003 sold to *Transalpine Redemptorists Inc*, a community of monks who live on Papa Stronsay, Orkney. Used for conveying supplies to the island - not a public service. In 2008 sold to *Bere Island Ferries*. Entered service in May 2009.

Spirit of Lough Swilly *(Nick Widdows)*

Frazer Tintern *(Nick Widdows)*

BK MARINE

THE COMPANY *BK Marine* is a UK company.

MANAGEMENT Managing Director Donald Gordon Fraser Ross.

ADDRESS Herrislea House Hotel, Veensgarth, Tingwall, Shetland ZE2 9SB.

TELEPHONE Administration & Reservations +44 (0)1595 840208.

INTERNET Email boats@bkmarine.co.uk **Website** www.bkmarine.co.uk *(English)*

ROUTE OPERATED ***All year*** Foula - Walls (Mainland) (2 hours; ***NEW ADVANCE***; 2 per week (Winter), 3 per week (Summer)), ***Summer only*** Foula - Scalloway (3 hrs 30 mins; ***NEW ADVANCE***; alternate Thursdays).

1	NEW ADVANCE	25t	96	8.7k	9.8m	12P	1C	0L	C	UK	

NEW ADVANCE Built by Richardson's, Stromness, Orkney, UK for *Shetland Islands Council* for the Foula service. Although built at Penryn, Cornwall, she was completed at Stromness. She has a Cygnus Marine GM38 hull and is based on the island where she can be lifted out of the water. Vehicle capacity is to take residents' vehicles to the island - not for tourist vehicles. In 2004 it was announced that the vessel and service would be transferred to the *Foula Community*. However, it was then found that under EU rules the route needed to be offered for competitive tender. In July 2006 the contract was awarded to *Atlantic Ferries Ltd* which began operations in October 2006. In August 2011 replaced by *BK Marine*.

CLARE ISLAND FERRY COMPANY

THE COMPANY *Clare Island Ferry Company* is owned and operated by the O'Grady family, natives of Clare Island, Republic of Ireland, who have been operating the Clare Island Mail Boat Ferry service since 1880.

MANAGEMENT Managing Director Chris O'Grady.

ADDRESS Clare Island Ferry Co Ltd, Clare Island, Co Mayo, F28 AT04, Republic Of Ireland.

TELEPHONE +353 (0)98 23737, +353 (0)98 25212, +353 (0)87 9004115.

INTERNET Email bookings@clareislandferry.com **Website** www.clareislandferry.com *(English)*

ROUTE OPERATED Roonagh (Co Mayo) - Clare Island (15 mins; ***CLEW BAY QUEEN, EIGG, PIRATE QUEEN, SEA SPRINTER***; ***Winter*** 1 to 2 trips per day, ***Summer*** up to 5 per day, Roonagh - Inishturk (50 mins; ***CLEW BAY QUEEN, EIGG, PIRATE QUEEN, SEA SPRINTER***; ***Winter*** 1 per day ***Summer*** up to 2 per day. Tourist vehicles are not normally carried.

1	CLEW BAY QUEEN	64t	72	10.0k	21.9m	96P	6C	-	B	IR	7217872
2	EIGG	91t	75	8.0k	24.2m	75P	6C	-	B	IR	7340411
3p●	PIRATE QUEEN	73t	96	10.5k	19.8m	96P	0C	-	-	IR	
4p	SEA SPRINTER	16t	93	22.0k	11.6m	35P	0C		-	IR	

CLEW BAY QUEEN Built as the KILBRANNAN by James Lamont & Co Ltd, Port Glasgow, UK for *Caledonian MacBrayne*. Used on a variety of routes until 1977, she was then transferred to the Scalpay (Harris) - Kyles Scalpay service. In 1990 she was replaced by the CANNA and, in turn, replaced the CANNA in her reserve/relief role. In 1992 sold to *Arranmore Island Ferry Services* and renamed the ÁRAINN MHÓR. She was subsequently sold to *Údarás na Gaeltachta* and leased back to *Arranmore Island Ferry Services*. In 2008 she was sold to *Clare Island Ferry Company* and renamed the CLEW BAY QUEEN. She operates a passenger and heavy freight service to both Clare Island and Inishturk all year round. In winter passenger capacity is reduced to 47 with 3 crew. Fitted with crane for loading and unloading cargo. Number is Lloyd's Number, not IMO.

EIGG Built by James Lamont & Co, Port Glasgow, UK. Since 1976 she was employed mainly on the Oban - Lismore service. In 1996 she was transferred to the Tobermory (Mull) - Kilchoan route, very occasionally making sailings to the Small Isles (Canna, Eigg, Muck and Rum) for special cargoes. In 1999 her wheelhouse was raised to make it easier to see over taller lorries and she returned to the Oban - Lismore route. In June 2018 sold to *Clare Island Ferry Company*. She is a reserve ferry and also available for charter as a workboat. Number is Lloyd's Number, not IMO.

PIRATE QUEEN Built by Arklow Marine Services in 1996 for *Clare Island Ferry Company*. She operated a daily passenger and light cargo service to Clare Island and Inishturk all year round. In winter passenger capacity was reduced to 47 with 3 crew. Fitted with crane for loading and unloading cargo. Currently laid up for sale or charter.

SEA SPRINTER Built by Lochin Marine, East Sussex, UK for *Island Ferries* (now *Aran Island Ferries*) of the Irish Republic. In June 2015 sold to *Clare Island Ferries*.

CROSS RIVER FERRIES

THE COMPANY *Cross River Ferries Ltd* is a Republic of Ireland company, part of the *Doyle Shipping Group*.

MANAGEMENT Operations Manager Eoin O'Sullivan.

ADDRESS Westlands House, Rushbrooke, Cobh, County Cork, P24 H940, Republic of Ireland.

TELEPHONE Administration +353 (0)21 481 1485 **Reservations** Not applicable.

INTERNET Email cork@dsg.ie **Website** crossriverferries.ie *(English)*

ROUTE OPERATED Carrigaloe (near Cobh, on Great Island) - Glenbrook (Co Cork) (4 mins; ***CARRIGALOE, GLENBROOK***; frequent service 07.00 - 00.15 (one or two vessels used according to demand)).

1	CARRIGALOE	225t	70	8.0k	49.1m	200P	27C	-	BA	IR	7028386
2	GLENBROOK	225t	71	8.0k	49.1m	200P	27C	-	BA	IR	7101607

CARRIGALOE Built as the KYLEAKIN by Newport Shipbuilding and Engineering Company, Newport (Gwent), UK for the *Caledonian Steam Packet Company* (later *Caledonian MacBrayne*) for the Kyle of Lochalsh - Kyleakin service. In 1991 sold to *Marine Transport Services Ltd* and renamed the CARRIGALOE. She entered service in March 1993. In Summer 2002 chartered to the *Lough Foyle Ferry Company*, returning in Spring 2003.

GLENBROOK Built as the LOCHALSH by Newport Shipbuilding and Engineering Company, Newport (Gwent), UK for the *Caledonian Steam Packet Company* (later *Caledonian MacBrayne*) for the Kyle of Lochalsh - Kyleakin service. In 1991 sold to *Marine Transport Services Ltd* and renamed the GLENBROOK. She entered service in March 1993.

FRAZER FERRIES

THE COMPANY *Frazer Ferries Ltd*, is a Republic of Ireland company. In June 2016 it took over *Passage East Ferries* and *Lough Foyle Ferry Service*. The *Carlingford Ferry* started in June 2017.

MANAGEMENT Director John Driscol, **Chief Executive** Pamela Houston **Manager, Passage East Ferry** Gary O Hanlon.

ADDRESSES Registered Office Riverfront, Howley's Quay, Limerick, V94 WTK7, Republic of Ireland, **Lough Foyle Ferry** The Pier, Greencastle, Co Donegal, Republic of Ireland, **Carlingford Ferry** Greenore Port, The Harbour, Greenore, Co. Louth, A91 A0V1, Republic of Ireland. **Passage East Ferry** Barrack Street, Passage East, Co Waterford, X91 C52E, Republic of Ireland.

TELEPHONE Passage East Ferry +353 (0)51 382480.

INTERNET Carlingford Ferry Website carlingfordferry.com *(English)* **Lough Foyle Ferry** www.loughfoyleferry.com *(English)* **Passage East Ferry Email** passageferry@eircom.net **Website** www.passageferry.ie *(English)*

ROUTES OPERATED *All Year Service* Carlingford Ferry Greenore, Co Louth, Republic of Ireland - Greencastle, Co Down, Northern Ireland (15 minutes; ***AISLING GABRIELLE***; hourly), **Passage East Ferry** Passage East (County Waterford) - Ballyhack (County Wexford) (7 mins; ***FBD TINTERN***; frequent service), ***Summer Service* Lough Foyle Ferry *July - September*** Greencastle (Inishowen, Co Donegal, Republic of Ireland) - Magilligan (Co Londonderry, Northern Ireland) (15 mins; ***FRAZER MARINER***; frequent service).

1	AISLING GABRIELLE	324t	78	10.0k	47.9m	300P	44C	-	BA	IR	7800033
2	FRAZER MARINER	-	83	7.2k	43.0m	100P	20C	-	BA	IR	
3	FRAZER STRANGFORD	186t	69	10.0k	32.9m	263P	20C	-	BA	UK	6926311
4	FRAZER TINTERN	236t	71	9.0k	54.8m	130P	30C	-	BA	IR	

AISLING GABRIELLE Built as the SHANNON WILLOW by Scott & Sons (Bowling) Ltd, Bowling, Glasgow, UK for *Shannon Ferry Ltd*. In 2000 replaced by the SHANNON BREEZE and laid up for sale. In 2003 sold to the *Lough Foyle Ferry Company Ltd* and renamed the FOYLE VENTURE. In November 2015 sold to *Frazer Ferries*. In July 2016 re-opened the *Lough Foyle Ferry;* this ceased in October. In February 2017 renamed the AISLING GABRIELLE. In July 2017 inaugurated a new Carlingford Lough service.

FRAZER MARINER Built as the BERNE-FARGE for *Schnellastfähre Berne-Farge GmbH* (from 1993 *Fähren Bremen-Stedingen GmbH*) to operate across the River Weser (Vegesack - Lemwerder and Berne - Farge). In January 2017 sold to *Frazer Ferries*. In July 2017 renamed the FRAZER MARINER and began operating between Greencastle and Magilligan.

FRAZER TINTERN Built as the STADT LINZ by Schiffswerft Oberwinter, Oberwinter, Rhein, Germany for *Rheinfähre Linz - Remagen GmbH* of Germany and operated on the Rhine between Linz and Remagen. In 1990 renamed the ST JOHANNES. In 1997 sold to *Fähren Bremen-Stedingen GmbH*, renamed the VEGESACK and operated across the Weser between Lemwerder and Vegesack. In 2003 she became a reserve vessel and in 2004 was renamed the STEDINGEN. Later sold to *Schraven BV* of The Netherlands and refurbished. In Autumn 2005 sold to *Passage East Ferry* and renamed the FBD TINTERN. During 2017 renamed the FRAZER TINTERN

FRAZER STRANGFORD Built as the STRANGFORD FERRY by Verolme Dockyard Ltd, Cork, Republic of Ireland for *Down County Council*. Subsequently transferred to the *DOE (Northern Ireland)* and then the *DRD (Northern Ireland)*. Following entry into service of the STRANGFORD II in February 2016, she was withdrawn. In December 2017 sold to *Arranmore Island Ferry Services* (Red Boats) and renamed the STRANGFORD 1. In June 2018 sold to *Frazer Ferries*. In March 2019 renamed the FRAZER STRANGFORD. Used as a reserve vessel.

THE HIGHLAND COUNCIL

THE COMPANY *The Highland Council* is a Scottish local authority.

MANAGEMENT Area Roads Operations Manager Richard Porteous, **Ferry Foremen** Allan McCowan and Donald Dixon.

ADDRESS *Area Office* Lochybridge Depot, Carr's Corner Industrial Estate, Fort William PH33 6TQ, ***Ferry Office*** Ferry Cottage, Ardgour, Fort William PH33 7AA.

TELEPHONE Administration *Area Office* +44 (0)1349 781083, ***Corran*** +44 (0)1855 841243.

INTERNET Email communityservices@highland.gov.uk

Website www.highland.gov.uk/info/1526/public_and_community_transport/812/

corran_ferry_timetable_and_fares *(English)*

ROUTES OPERATED Vehicle Ferries Corran - Ardgour (5 mins; ***CORRAN, MAID OF GLENCOUL***; half-hourly).

1	CORRAN	351t	01	10.0k	42.0m	150P	30C	2L	BA	UK	9225990
2	MAID OF GLENCOUL	166t	75	8.0k	32.0m	116P	16C	1L	BA	UK	7521613

Scillonian III *(Andrew Cooke)*

Renfrew Rose *(Brian Maxted)*

CORRAN Built by George Prior Engineering Ltd, Hull, UK for *The Highland Council* to replace the MAID OF GLENCOUL as main vessel.

MAID OF GLENCOUL Built by William McCrindle Ltd, Shipbuilders, Ardrossan, UK for *Highland Regional Council* for the service between Kylesku and Kylestrome. In 1984 the ferry service was replaced by a bridge and she was transferred to the Corran - Ardgour service. In April 1996, ownership transferred to *The Highland Council*. In 2001 she became the reserve vessel.

The *Highland Council* also supports both services operated by *Highland Ferries*.

HIGHLAND FERRIES

THE COMPANY *Highland Ferries* is a UK private sector operation. Services are operated under contract to *The Highland Council*.

MANAGEMENT Operator Dougie Robertson.

TELEPHONE Administration +44(0)7468 417137 **Reservations** Not applicable.

INTERNET Email southuist24@hotmail.co.uk

Facebook www.facebook.com/CamusnagaulFerry

1p	BHOY TAYLOR	15T	80	7.5k	9.8m	12P	0C	0L	-	UK
2	RENFREW ROSE	65t	84	7.6k	17.5m	12P	3C	0L	B	UK

ROUTES OPERATED Vehicle Ferry *1st June - 30th September* Cromarty - Nigg (Ross-shire) (10 mins; ***RENFREW ROSE***; half-hourly), **Passenger-only Ferry** Fort William - Camusnagaul (10 mins; ***BHOY TAYLOR***; up to 5 per day).

BHOY TAYLOR Built as the CAILIN AN AISEAG by Buckie Shipbuilders Ltd, Buckie, UK for *Highland Regional Council* and used on the Fort William - Camusnagaul passenger-only service. In 2006 the service transferred to *Geoff Ward* under contract with a different vessel. In 2013 the CAILIN AN AISEAG resumed service with *Highland Ferries* as contractor. In April 2013 she as renamed the BHOY TAYLOR.

RENFREW ROSE Built by MacCrindle Shipbuilding Ltd, Ardrossan for *Strathclyde PTE* (later *Strathclyde Partnership for Transport*). Built as a small car ferry but operated passenger only between Renfrew and Yoker (apart from occasionally carrying ambulances in earlier days before they became too heavy). In March 2010 laid up. In June 2012 sold to *Arranmore Fast Ferries* for use as a passenger/car ferry. In June 2016 sold to *Highland Ferries* to reopen the Cromarty - Nigg service.

INISHBOFIN ISLAND DISCOVERY

THE COMPANY *Inishbofin Island Discovery Ltd* is an Irish Republic private sector Company.

ADDRESS Cloonamore, Inishbofin Island, Co Galway, Republic of Ireland.

TELEPHONE Administration and Reservations +353 (0)95 45819, Mobile +353 (0)86 1718829 and +353 (0)87 3667185

FAX +353 (0)95 45984.

INTERNET Email info@inishbofinferry.ie **Website**

(English)

ROUTE OPERATED *Passenger Service* Cleggan, Co Galway - Inishbofin Island (30 mins, ***ISLAND ADVENTURE, ISLAND DISCOVERY***, ***ISLAND EXPLORER***; up to 3 per day. **Cargo Service** Cleggan, Co Galway - Inishbofin Island (30 mins, ***RAASAY***, 2 per week).

1p	ISLAND ADVENTURE	-	94	-	27.1m	250P	0C	0L	-	IR	
2p	ISLAND DISCOVERY	107t	91	10.9k	25.0m	99P	0C	0L	-	IR	8650851
3p	ISLAND EXPLORER	-	99	10.9k	15.0m	72P	0C	0L	-	IR	
4F	RAASAY	69t	76	8.0k	24.3m	12P	6C	1L -	B	IR	7340435

ISLAND ADVENTURE Previously the JOLIE FRANCE II of *Vedettes Jolie France*, France. Acquired by *Inishbofin Island Discovery Ltd* in 2018 and renamed the ISLAND ADVENTURE.

ISLAND DISCOVERY Built for *Inishbofin Island Discovery Ltd.*

RAASAY Built by James Lamont & Co Ltd, Port Glasgow, UK for and used primarily on the Sconser (Skye) - Raasay service. In 1997 she was replaced by the LOCH STRIVEN, became a spare/relief vessel and inaugurated in October 2003 the winter service between Tobermory (Mull) and Kilchoan (Ardnamurchan). From summer 2016 operated as second vessel on Oban - Lismore route. In March 2018 withdrawn and sold to *Humphrey O'Leary* of Clare Island, Co Mayo. In August sold to *Inishbofin Island Discovery* to operate the cargo service. Number is Lloyds Number, not IMO.

ISLES OF SCILLY STEAMSHIP COMPANY

THE COMPANY *Isles of Scilly Steamship Company* is a British private sector company.

MANAGEMENT Chief Executive Robert Goldsmith, **Marketing & Communications Manager** Sharon Sandercock, **Chief Operating Officer** Stuart Ried.

ADDRESS *Scilly* PO Box 10, Hugh Town, St Mary's, Isles of Scilly TR21 0LJ, ***Penzance*** Steamship House, Quay Street, Penzance, Cornwall, TR18 4BZ.

TELEPHONE Administration & Reservations +44 (0) 1736 334220.

INTERNET Email sales@islesofscilly-travel.co.uk **Website** www.islesofscilly-travel.co.uk *(English),*

ROUTES OPERATED *Passenger services:* Penzance - St Mary's (Isles of Scilly) (2 hrs 40 mins; ***SCILLONIAN III***; 1 per day), St Mary's - Tresco/St Martin's/St Agnes/Bryher; ***LYONESSE LADY, SWIFT LADY (inter-island boats)***; irregular), ***Freight service***: ***GRY MARITHA***; Freight from Penzance Monday, Wednesday and Fridays (weather dependant, all year round).

1F	GRY MARITHA	590t	81	10.5k	40.3m	6P	5C	1L	C	UK	8008462
2	LYONESSE LADY	40t	91	9.0k	15.5m	4P	1C	0L	AC	UK	
3F	MALI ROSE	968t	92	-	50.2m	6P	10C	1L	SC	UK	9065144
4	SCILLONIAN III	1346t	77	15.5k	67.7m	485P	5C	1L	C	UK	7527796
5F	SWIFT LADY	-	04	30.0k	8.4m	0P	0C	0L	-	UK	

GRY MARITHA Built by Moen Slip AS, Kolvereid, Norway for *Gjofor* of Norway. In design she is a coaster rather than a ferry. In 1990 she was sold to the *Isles of Scilly Steamship Company*. She operates a freight and passenger service all year (conveying most goods to and from the Islands). During the winter she provides the only sea service to the islands, the SCILLONIAN III being laid up.

LYONESSE LADY Built Lochaber Marine Ltd of Corpach, Fort William, Scotland, for inter-island ferry work.

MALI ROSE Pallet and deck cargo carrier built by Halsnøy Verft, Halsnøy, Norway. Passed through various hands until June 2016 when she was sold to *Isles of Scilly Steamship Company*.

SCILLONIAN III Built by Appledore Shipbuilders Ltd, Appledore, UK for the Penzance - St Mary's service. She operates from late March to November and is laid up in the winter. She is the last major conventional passenger/cargo ferry built for UK waters and probably Western Europe. Extensively refurbished during Winter 1998/99 and 2012/13. She can carry cars in her hold and on deck, as well as general cargo/perishables, boats, trailer tents and passenger luggage.

SWIFT LADY Stormforce 8.4 RIB (Rigid Inflatable Boat) built by Redbay Boats of Cushendall, Co Antrim, Northern Ireland for inter-island ferry work conveying mail and as back-up to the LYONESSE LADY.

Raasay *(Nick Widdows)*

Frazer Strangford *(Nick Widdows)*

MURPHY'S FERRY SERVICE

THE COMPANY *Murphy's Ferry Service* is privately operated.

MANAGEMENT Operator Brendan Murphy.

ADDRESS Lawrence Cove, Bere Island, Co Cork, Republic of Ireland.

TELEPHONE Landline + 353 (0)27 75988, **Mobile** +353 (0)87 2386095.

INTERNET Email info@murphysferry.com **Website** www.murphysferry.com *(English),*

ROUTE OPERATED Castletownbere (Pontoon - 3 miles to east of town centre) - Bere Island (Lawrence Cove, near Rerrin) (20 mins; ***IKOM K***; up to 8 per day).

1	IKOM K	55t	99	10.0k	16.0m	60P	4C	1L	B	IR	

IKOM K Built by Arklow Marine Services, Arklow, Republic of Ireland for *Murphy's Ferry Service*.

RATHLIN ISLAND FERRY

THE COMPANY *Rathlin Island Ferry Ltd* is a UK private sector company owned by Ciarán and Mary O'Driscoll of County Cork, Republic of Ireland.

MANAGEMENT Managing Director Ciarán O'Driscoll.

ADDRESS Ballycastle Ferry Terminal, 18 Bayview Road, Ballycastle, County Antrim BT54 6BT.

TELEPHONE Administration & Reservations +44 (0)28 2076 9299.

INTERNET Email info@rathlinballycastleferry.com **Website** www.rathlinballycastleferry.com *(English),*

ROUTE OPERATED Vehicle Ferry Ballycastle - Rathlin Island (45 min; ***SPIRIT OF RATHLIN***; up to 4 per day). **Passenger-only Fast Ferry** (20 min; ***RATHLIN EXPRESS***; up to 6 per day). The service is operated on behalf of the *Northern Ireland Department of Regional Development*.

1»p	RATHLIN EXPRESS	31t	09	18.0k	17.7m	98P	0C	0L	-	UK	
2	SPIRIT OF RATHLIN	105t	17	9.4k	25.0m	125P	5C	1L	B	UK	9780122

RATHLIN EXPRESS Built by Arklow Marine Services, Arklow, Republic of Ireland for *Rathlin Island Ferry Ltd.*

SPIRIT OF RATHLIN Built by Arklow Marine Services, Arklow, Irish Republic for *DRD (Northern Ireland)*, UK to replace the CANNA. Chartered to *Rathlin Island Ferry Ltd.*

SHANNON FERRY

THE COMPANY *Shannon Ferry Group Ltd* is a Republic of Ireland private company owned by eighteen shareholders on both sides of the Shannon Estuary.

MANAGEMENT Managing Director Eugene Maher.

ADDRESS Ferry Terminal, Killimer, County Clare, V15 FK09, Republic of Ireland.

TELEPHONE Administration +353 (0)65 9053124, **Reservations** Phone bookings not available; Online booking available at www.shannonferries.com

FAX Administration +353 (0)65 9053125, **Reservations** Fax bookings not available; Online booking available at www.shannonferries.com

INTERNET Email enquiries@shannonferries.com **Website** www.shannonferries.com *(English),*

ROUTE OPERATED Killimer (County Clare) - Tarbert (County Kerry) (20 mins; ***SHANNON BREEZE, SHANNON DOLPHIN***; hourly (half-hourly during June, July, August and September)).

1	SHANNON BREEZE	611t	00	10.0k	80.8m	350P	60C	-	BA	IR	9224910
2	SHANNON DOLPHIN	501t	95	10.0k	71.9m	350P	52C	-	BA	IR	9114933

Ikom K *(Brian Maxted)*

God Met Ons III *(Miles Cowsill)*

SHANNON BREEZE, SHANNON DOLPHIN Built by Appledore Shipbuilders, Appledore, UK for *Shannon Ferry Group Ltd.*

SHERKIN ISLAND FERRY

THE COMPANY The *Sherkin Island Ferry* is privately operated in the Republic of Ireland.

MANAGEMENT Operator: Vincent O'Driscoll.

ADDRESS Sherkin Ferry, The Cove, Baltimore, Skibbereen, Co Cork, P81 RW71, Republic of Ireland.

TELEPHONE Administration +353 (0)87 244 7828. **Ferry Boat** +353 (0)87 911 7377.

INTERNET Email info@sherkinferry.com **Website** www.sherkinferry.com *(English)*

ROUTE OPERATED Passenger only Baltimore (Co Cork) - Sherkin Island (10 minutes; ***MYSTIC WATERS***; ***YOKER SWAN***; up to 10 per day). **Note:** No vehicle service advertised.

1p	MYSTIC WATERS	100t	72		19.8m	99P	0C	0L	-	IR	8943038
2	YOKER SWAN	65t	84		21.9m	50P	3C	0L	B	IR	

MYSTIC WATERS Built by Ryton Marine Ltd, Wallsend, UK as the FREDA CUNNINGHAM for *Tyne & Wear PTE* and operated between North Shields and South Shields. Withdrawn in 1993 and sold to *Tyne Towage Ltd*, Newcastle and renamed the ANYA DEV. Later sold and renamed the LADY LAURA. In 2006 sold to *Sherkin Island Ferry* and renamed the MYSTIC WATERS.

YOKER SWAN Built by MacCrindle Shipbuilding Ltd, Ardrossan for *Strathclyde PTE* (later *Strathclyde Partnership for Transport*). Built as a small car ferry but operated passenger only between Renfrew and Yoker (apart from carrying ambulances in earlier days before they became too heavy). In March 2010 laid up. Later sold to *Sherkin Island Ferry* for use as a passenger/car ferry. She is used as required to convey vehicles and freight to and from the island, and sometimes conveys passengers. No public vehicle service is advertised.

SKYE FERRY

THE COMPANY The *Skye Ferry* is owned by the *Isle of Skye Ferry Community Interest Company*, a company limited by guarantee.

MANAGEMENT Ferry Development Manager Jo Crawford.

ADDRESS 6 Coulindune, Glenelg, Kyle, Ross-shire IV40 8JU.

TELEPHONE Administration +44 (0)7881 634726.

INTERNET Email info@skyeferry.co.uk **Website** skyeferry.co.uk *(English),*

ROUTE OPERATED *Easter - October only* Glenelg - Kylerhea (Skye) (10 mins; ***GLENACHULISH***; frequent service).

1	GLENACHULISH	44t	69	9.0k	20.0m	12P	6C	-	BSt	UK

GLENACHULISH Built by Ailsa Shipbuilding Company, Troon, UK for the *Ballachulish Ferry Company* for the service between North Ballachulish and South Ballachulish, across the mouth of Loch Leven. In 1975 the ferry was replaced by a bridge and she was sold to *Highland Regional Council* and used on a relief basis on the North Kessock - South Kessock and Kylesku - Kylestrome routes. In 1983 she was sold to *Murdo MacKenzie*, who had operated the Glenelg - Skye route as ferryman since 1959. The vessel was eventually bought by *Roddy MacLeod* and the service resumed in September 1990. The *Isle of Skye Ferry Community Interest Company* reached agreement with *Mr MacLeod* that he would operate the ferry in 2006. In 2007 she was sold to the Company. During winter 2012 she was chartered to *The Highland Council* to operate between North and South Strome following a road closure due to a rock fall. She is the last turntable ferry in operation.

STRANGFORD LOUGH FERRY SERVICE

THE COMPANY The *Strangford Lough Ferry Service* is operated by the *DFI Transport NI*, a Northern Ireland Government Department (formerly operated by *Department of the Environment (Northern Ireland)*).

MANAGEMENT Ferry Manager Tim Tew.

ADDRESS Strangford Lough Ferry Service, The Slip, Strangford, Co Down BT30 7NE.

TELEPHONE Administration +44 0300 200 7898, **Reservations** Not applicable.

INTERNET Email Strangfordferry@infrastructure-ni.gov.uk

Website www.nidirect.gov.uk/strangford-ferry-timetable *(English)*,

ROUTE OPERATED Strangford - Portaferry (County Down) (10 mins; ***PORTAFERRY II, STRANGFORD II***; half-hourly).

1	PORTAFERRY II	312t	01	12.0k	38.2m	260P	28C	-	BA	UK	9237436
2	STRANGFORD II	405t	16	12.0k	64.0m	260P	28C	-	BA	UK	9771561

PORTAFERRY II Built by McTay Marine, Bromborough, Wirral, UK for *DRD (Northern Ireland)*.

STRANGFORD II Built by Cammell Laird, Birkenhead for *DRD (Northern Ireland)*, UK to replace the STRANGFORD FERRY. Entered service February 2017.

C TOMS & SON LTD

THE COMPANY *C Toms & Son Ltd* is a British private sector company.

MANAGEMENT Managing Director Allen Toms.

ADDRESS East Street, Polruan, Fowey, Cornwall PL23 1PB.

TELEPHONE Administration +44 (0)1726 870232.

INTERNET Email enquiries@ctomsandson.co.uk **Website** www.ctomsandson.co.uk *(English)*

ROUTE OPERATED *Car Ferry* Fowey - Bodinnick (Cornwall) (5 mins; ***GELLAN, JENACK***; frequent), ***Passenger Ferry*** Fowey - Polruan (Cornwall) (5 mins; ***KALEY, LADY DIANA, LADY JEAN, TAMSIN, THREE COUSINS***; frequent).

1	GELLAN	50t	03	4.5k	36.0m	50P	10C	-	BA	UK
2	JENACK	60t	00	4.5k	36.0m	50P	15C	-	BA	UK
3p	KALEY	7.6t	03	-	9.5m	48P	0C	-	-	UK
4p	LADY DI	-	81	-	8.2m	36P	0C	-	-	UK
5p	LADY JEAN	-	-	-	-	12P	0C	-	-	UK
6p	THREE COUSINS	-	14	-	-	12P	0C	-	-	UK

GELLAN, JENACK Built by C Toms & Sons Ltd, Fowey, UK.

KALEY, LADY DIANA, LADY JEAN, THREE COUSINS Built by C Toms & Sons Ltd, Fowey, UK.

VALENTIA ISLAND CAR FERRY

THE COMPANY *Valentia Island Car Ferry* is the trading name of *Valentia Island Ferries Ltd*, an Republic of Ireland private sector company.

MANAGEMENT Manager Richard Foran.

ADDRESS Valentia Island, County Kerry, Republic of Ireland.

TELEPHONE Administration +353 (0)87 241 8973, **Reservations** Not applicable.

FAX Administration +353 (0)66 76377, **Reservations** Not applicable.

INTERNET Email reforan@indigo.ie **Website** www.valentiaisland.ie/life-business/valentia-island-car-ferry/

Jenack *(Brian Maxted)*

Dame Vera Lynn *(John Bryant)*

ROUTE OPERATED Reenard (Co Kerry) - Knightstown (Valentia Island) (5 minutes; ***GOD MET ONS III***; frequent service, 1st April - 30th September).

1	GOD MET ONS III	95t	63	-	43.0m	95P	18C	-	BA	IR	

GOD MET ONS III Built by BV Scheepswerven Vh HH Bodewes, Millingen, The Netherlands for *FMHE Res* of The Netherlands for a service across the River Maas between Cuijk and Middelaar. In 1987 a new bridge was opened and the service ceased. She was latterly used on contract work in the Elbe and then laid up. In 1996 acquired by *Valentia Island Ferries* and inaugurated a car ferry service to the island. **Note** This island never had a car ferry service before. A bridge was opened at the south end of the island in 1970; before that a passenger/cargo service operated between Reenard Point and Knightstown.

WOOLWICH FREE FERRY

THE COMPANY The *Woolwich Free Ferry* is operated by *Briggs Marine*, a British private sector company on behalf of *Transport for London*.

ADDRESS New Ferry Approach, Woolwich, London SE18 6DX.

TELEPHONE Administration +44 (0)20 8853 9400, **Reservations** Not applicable.

FAX Administration +44 (0)20 8316 6096, **Reservations** Not applicable.

INTERNET Website www.tfl.gov.uk/modes/river/woolwich-ferry *(English)*,

ROUTE OPERATED Woolwich - North Woolwich (free ferry) (5 mins; ***BEN WOOLLACOTT***, ***DAME VERA LYNN***; every 10 mins (weekdays - two ferries in operation), every 15 mins (weekends - one ferry in operation)).

1	BEN WOOLLACOTT	1538t	18	8.0k	62.2m	150P	42C	12L	BA	UK	9822011
2	DAME VERA LYNN	1539t	18	8.0k	62.2m	150P	42C	12L	BA	UK	9822023

BEN WOOLLACOTT, DAME VERA LYNN Built by Remontowa Shipbuilding, Gdansk, Poland. They are diesel electric battery hybrid vessels.

Ben Woollacott *(John Bryant)*

YASMINE

***Yasmine* at Rotterdam.** *(Rob de Visser)*

SECTION 3 - GB & IRELAND - FREIGHT ONLY FERRIES

CLDN/COBELFRET FERRIES

THE COMPANIES *CLdN Cobelfret SA* is a Luxembourg private sector company. There are a number of subsidiary companies. *CLdN* stands for *Compagnie Luxembourgouise de Navigation*.

MANAGEMENT CLdN Ro-Ro SA (Luxembourg) Caroline Dubois, **Cobelfret Waterways SA (Vlissingen)** Geert Bogaerts, **CLdN ro-ro Agencies Ltd (UK)** Karla Fairway.

ADDRESSES *Luxembourg* CLdN Cobelfret SA & CLdN ro-ro SA, 3-7 rue Schiller, 2519 Luxembourg, ***UK*** CLdN ro-ro UK Ltd, Long Reach House, London Road, Purfleet, Essex RM19 1RP UK, ***UK - Irish Republic*** CLdN ro-ro SA, Port Centre, 2nd Floor, Alexandra Road, Dublin Port, Dublin 1, D01 H4C6, Republic of Ireland.

TELEPHONE *Luxembourg* CLdN Cobelfret SA +352 (0)26 44 631, **CLdN ro-ro SA** +352 (0)26 44 661 ***UK*** +44 (0)1708 865522, ***Irish Republic*** +353 (0)1 856 1608.

FAX *Luxembourg* CLdN Cobelfret SA +352 (0)26 44 63 298, **CLdN ro-ro SA** +352 (0)26 44 66 299 ***UK*** +44 (0)1708 866419, ***Irish Republic*** +353 (0)1 704 0164.

INTERNET Email admin.roro@cldn.com **Website** www.cldn.com *(English)*

ROUTES OPERATED Cobelfret Ferries Services Zeebrugge - Purfleet (9 hrs; 2/3 per day), Zeebrugge - Killingholme (13 hrs; 6 per week), **CLdN Services** Rotterdam - Purfleet (14 hrs 30 mins); 6 per week), Rotterdam - Killingholme (14 hrs; 6 per week), Zeebrugge - Esbjerg (24hrs; 1 per week), Zeebrugge - Dublin (35-41 hrs; 2 per week), Rotterdam - Dublin (41-47 hrs; 3 per week), Rotterdam - Leixoes (Portugal) (64-69 hrs; 3 per week), Zeebrugge - Santander (50 hrs; 3 per week, Zeebrugge - Göteborg (32-33 hrs; 4 per week (1 weekly call at Hirtshals in both directions), ***CLdN Container service*** Rotterdam - Dublin (43/47 hrs; ***ARX*** ; 1 per week). NOTE: Because vessels are so often moved between routes it is impossible to say which ro-ro vessels will be on which routes. ***Contract Services for Ford Motor Company*** Vlissingen - Dagenham (11 hrs; ***CELESTINE, CYMBELINE, UNDINE***; 2 per day).

1	ADELINE	21020t	12	15.8k	150.0m	12P	-	170T	A	MT	9539092
2	AMANDINE	33960t	11	18.5k	195.4m	12P	-	270T	A	MT	9424871
3	ARX	6901t	05	13.8k	139.8m	0P		707 TEU	C	MT	9328625
4	CAPUCINE	16342t	11	16.0k	150.0m	12P	-	140T	A	MT	9539066
5	CATHERINE	21287t	02	18.0k	182.2m	12P	-	200T	A2	MT	9209453
6	CELANDINE	23987t	00	17.9k	162.5m	12P	630C	157T	A	MT	9183984
7	CELESTINE	23986t	96	17.8k	162.5m	12P	630C	157T	A	MT	9125372
8	CELINE	74273t	17	17.9k	235.0m	12P	8000C	580T	A2	MT	9789233
9	CLEMENTINE	23986t	97	17.8k	162.5m	12P	630C	157T	A	BE	9125384
10	CYMBELINE	11866t	92	17.0k	147.4m	8P	350C	100T	A2	MT	9007764
11	DELPHINE	74273t	18	17.9k	235.0m	12P	8000C	580T	A2	MT	9789245
12	HERMINE	50443t	19	17.6k	211.6m	12P	-	400T	A2	MT	9831177
13	LAURELINE	50443t	19	18.0k	212.0m	12P	-	400T	A	MT	9823352
14	MAZARINE	25593t	09	18.5k	195.4m	12P	-	180T	A	MT	9376696
15	MELEQ	32770t	17	21.0k	209.6m	12P	-	262T	A2	TR	9809112
16	MELUSINE	23987t	99	17.8k	162.5m	12P	630C	157T	A	BE	9166637
17	OPALINE	33960t	10	18.5k	195.4m	12P	-	270T	A	MT	9424869
18	PALATINE	25593t	09	18.5k	195.4m	12P	-	180T	A	MT	9376701
19	PAULINE	49166t	06	21.7k	200.0m	12P	656C	258T	A	MT	9324473
20	PEREGRINE	25235t	10	18.5k	195.4m	12P	-	180T	A	MT	9376725
21	SEVERINE	16342t	12	16.0k	150.0m	12P	-	140T	A	MT	9539078
22	SIXTINE	50443t	19	17.6k	211.6m	12P	-	400T	A2	MT	9831165
23	UNDINE	11854t	91	15.0k	147.4m	8P	350C	100T	A2	MT	9006112
24	VALENTINE	23987t	99	18.0k	162.5m	12P	630C	157T	A	BE	9166625
25	VESPERTINE	25235t	10	18.5k	195.4m	12P	-	180T	A	MT	9376713
26	VICTORINE	23987t	00	17.8k	162.5m	12P	630C	157T	A	BE	9184029
27	YASMINE	49166t	07	21.7k	200.0m	12P	656C	258T	A	MT	9337353

28	YSALINE	50443t	19	18.0k	212.0m	12P	-	400T	A	MT	9823364

ADELINE Built by the Kyokuyo Shipyard, Shimonoseki, Japan. After competition, an additional deck and sponsons were retro-fitted at the Chengxi Shipyard, Jiangyin, China.

AMANDINE Built by Flensburger Schiffbau-Gesellschaft, Flensburg, Germany. Operates mainly between Rotterdam and Killingholme and Rotterdam/Zeebrugge and Dublin.

ARX Container ship built as the LUPUS 1 by Detlef Hegemann Rolandwerft, Berne, Germany. In June 2005 chartered to *C2C Line* operating between Zeebrugge and Dublin and renamed the C2C LUPUS. In July 2007 renamed the C2C AUSTRALIS. In June 2010 purchased by an associated company of *CLdN* and renamed the ARX.

CAPUCINE, SEVERINE Built by the Kyokuyo Shipyard, Shimonoseki, Japan for *CLdN*. Initially operated on their Ipswich - Rotterdam service. This service was suspended in August 2012. In September, they were chartered to *Stena Line* and placed on the Harwich - Rotterdam service. Charter ended in January 2018. In February 2018 the CAPUCINE was chartered to the *Italian Ministry of Defence* and in June 2018 the SEVERINE was chartered to *GNV* of Italy. The SEVERINE returned in September 2018.

CATHERINE Built as the ROMIRA by Zhonghua Shipyard, Zhonghua, China for *Dag Engström Rederi* of Sweden. For six months engaged on a number of short-term charters, including *Cobelfret Ferries* who used her on both the Rotterdam - Immingham and Zeebrugge - Purfleet routes. In September 2002 purchased by *Cobelfret Ferries* and, in November 2002, renamed the CATHERINE and placed on the Rotterdam - Immingham service. In Spring 2003 chartered to the *US Defense Department* to convey materials to the Persian Gulf. Returned in late summer and operated thereafter on the Rotterdam - Immingham service. In January 2009 chartered to *CoTuNav* of Tunisia. In February 2010 returned to *Cobelfret* service and operated on the Rotterdam - Purfleet service. In March 2010 again chartered to *CoTuNav*. In March 2011 chartered to *RMR Shipping* to operate between Western Europe and Antwerpen, Eemshaven, Harwich and Dublin to Lagos (Nigeria). In May 2011 returned to *Cobelfret Ferries*. Now operates mainly on the Zeebrugge - Göteborg route.

CELANDINE, VALENTINE, VICTORINE Built by Kawasaki Heavy Industries, Sakaide, Japan for *Cobelfret*. The CELANDINE was originally to be called the CATHERINE and the VICTORINE the CELANDINE. The names were changed before delivery. In May 2011 the CELANDINE was chartered to *RMR Shipping*. Returned in November 2013.

CELESTINE Built by Kawasaki Heavy Industries, Sakaide, Japan as the CELESTINE. In 1996 chartered to the *British MoD* and renamed the SEA CRUSADER. She was originally expected to return to *Cobelfret Ferries* in early 2003 and resume the name CELESTINE; however, the charter was extended because of the Iraq war. Returned in September 2003 and placed on the Zeebrugge - Immingham service. In November 2006 moved to the Zeebrugge - Purfleet route. In November 2008 moved to the Oostende - Dartford service. In April 2009 the route became Oostende - Purfleet. In April 2010 chartered to *RMR Shipping*. In May 2014 returned to *Cobelfret Ferries* and in May 2016 transferred to the Dagenham - Vlissingen service.

CELINE, DELPHINE Built by Hyundai Mipo Dockyard, Ulsan, South Korea. They are convertible to LPG propulsion and designed to be useable on deep sea ro-ro services as well as *CLdN's* current short sea routes. They mainly operate between Zeebrugge and Killingholme and Zeebrugge and Dublin.

CLEMENTINE Built by Kawasaki Heavy Industries, Sakaide, Japan for *Cobelfret Ferries*. Mainly used on the Zeebrugge - Immingham service. In 2007 moved to the Zeebrugge - Purfleet route. In March 2013 chartered to *RMR Shipping*. In July 2013 chartered to *DFDS Seaways* and placed on the Immingham - Cuxhaven service. In November 2014 returned to *Cobelfret Ferries*. In January 2015 she retuned to charter with *DFDS Seaways* for four weeks.

CYMBELINE, UNDINE Built by Dalian Shipyard, Dalian, China for *Cobelfret Ferries*. Currently mainly used on the Dagenham - Vlissingen route. They were occasionally used on a weekend Southampton - Vlissingen service but this ceased in 2012 following the closure of the

Valentine *(Nick Widdows)*

Finnhawk *(Uwe Jakob)*

Southampton Ford Transit factory. Occasional weekend trips are made to Middlesbrough (Teesport).

HERMINE, LAURALINE, SIXTINE, YSALINE Built by Hyundai Mipo Dockyard, Ulsan, South Korea. Used on a variety of routes.

MAZARINE, PALATINE, PEREGRINE, VESPERTINE Built by Flensburger Schiffbau-Gesellschaft, Flensburg, Germany.

MELEQ Built by Flensburger Schiffbau-Gesellschaft, Flensburg, Germany for *Alternative Transport (Ekol)* of Turkey. In January 2019 chartered to *CLdN*. Now used mainly on the Rotterdam - Leixoes route.

MELUSINE Built by Kawasaki Heavy Industries, Sakaide, Japan for *Cobelfret*. Similar to the CLEMENTINE.

OPALINE Built by Flensburger Schiffbau-Gesellschaft, Flensburg, Germany. Operates mainly between Rotterdam and Killingholme and Rotterdam and Dublin.

PAULINE, YASMINE Built by Flensburger Schiffbau-Gesellschaft, Flensburg, Germany. to operate on the Zeebrugge - Killingholme route. They now operate mainly on the Rotterdam - Killingholme service.

CLdN also own the SOMERSET on charter to *Stena Line* and the WILHELMINE on charter to *P&O Ferries*.

Under Construction

29	NEWBUILDING 1	50443t	22	18.0k	212.0m	12P	-	400T	A	-	-
30	NEWBUILDING 2	50443t	22	18.0k	212.0m	12P	-	400T	A	-	-

NEWBUILDING 1, NEWBUILDING 2 Undr constrction by Hyundai Mipo Dockyard, Ulsan, South Korea.

FINNLINES

THE COMPANY *Finnlines PLC* is a Finnish private sector company owned by Grimaldi of Italy. Services to the UK are marketed by *Finnlines UK Ltd*, a British private sector company.

MANAGEMENT President & CEO Emanuele Grimaldi, **Head of Group Marketing North Sea ro-ro** Staffan Herlin.

ADDRESS *Finland* PO Box 197, 00181 Helsinki, Finland, ***UK*** Finnlines UK Ltd, Finhumber House, Queen Elizabeth Dock, Hedon Road, HULL HU9 5PB.

TELEPHONE Administration & Reservations *Finland* +358 (0)10 343 50, ***UK*** +44 (0)1482 377 655.

INTERNET *Email Finland* info.fi@finnlines.com ***UK*** info.uk@finnlines.com ***Website*** www.finnlines.com *(English, Finnish, German, Polish, Swedish)*

ROUTES OPERATED Irregular service from St Petersburg, Helsinki, Rauma and Kotka to Hull, Immingham, Amsterdam, Antwerpen and Bilbao. For details see website. In view of the fact that ships are liable to be transferred between routes, the following is a list of all Finnlines Cargo Service ro-ro vessels, including those which currently do not serve the UK. Ro-pax vessels on Baltic services are listed in Section 6.

1	FINNBREEZE	33816t	12	21.0k	217.8m	12P	600C	320T	A	FI	9468889
2	FINNHAWK	11530t	01	20.0k	162.2m	12P	-	140T	A	FI	9207895
3	FINNKRAFT	11530t	00	20.0k	162.2m	12P	-	140T	A	FI	9207883
4	FINNMASTER	12251t	98	20.0k	154.5m	12P	-	124T	A2	FI	9132014
5	FINNMERCHANT	23235t	03	21.0k	193.0m	12P	-	180T	A	FI	9234082
6	FINNMILL	25732t	02	20.0k	184.8m	12P	-	190T	A	FI	9212656
7	FINNPULP	25732t	02	20.0k	184.8m	12P	-	190T	A	FI	9212644
8	FINNSEA	33816t	12	21.0k	217.8m	12P	600C	320T	A	FI	9468891
9	FINNSKY	33816t	12	21.0k	217.8m	12P	600C	320T	A	FI	9468906

10	FINNSUN	33816t	12	21.0k	217.8m	12P	600C	320T	A	FI	9468918
11	FINNTIDE	33816t	12	21.0k	217.8m	12P	600C	320T	A	FI	9468920
12	FINNWAVE	33816t	12	21.0k	217.8m	12P	600C	320T	A	FI	9468932

FINNBREEZE, FINNSEA, FINNSKY, FINNSUN, FINNTIDE, FINNWAVE Built by Jinling Shipyard, Nanjing, China for *Finnlines*. The vessels were lengthened by approximately 30 metres at Remontowa Shipyard, Gdansk, Poland between November 2017 and December 2018.

FINNHAWK Built by Jinling Shipyard, Nanjing, China for the *Macoma Shipping Group* and chartered to *Finnlines*. In April 2008 purchased by *Finnlines*. Currently operates used on service between Finland and The Netherlands, Belgium, the UK and Spain.

FINNKRAFT Built by Jinling Shipyard, Nanjing, China for the *Macoma Shipping Group* and chartered to *Finncarriers*. In April 2008 purchased by *Finnlines*. Currently operates on services between Finland and Germany.

FINNMASTER Built as the UNITED TRADER by Fosen Mekaniske Verksteder A/S, Rissa, Norway for *United Shipping* (a subsidiary of *Birka Shipping*) of Finland and chartered to *Transfennica*. During 2000 used on their Kemi - Oulu - Antwerpen - Felixstowe service. In 2001 the route was transferred to *Finnlines* and the vessels used sub-chartered to them (charter later transferred to *Finnlines*). In 2002 *United Shipping* was renamed *Birka Cargo* and she was renamed the BIRKA TRADER. In 2006 the service ceased and she was transferred to other *Finnlines* routes. In 2008 the charter was extended a further four years. In January 2013 chartered to *Transfennica*. In July 2013 renamed the TRADER. In January 2015 sold to *Finnlines* but not delivered until the end of the year, when the charter ended. In January 2016 renamed the FINNMASTER. In November 2016 chartered to *DFDS Seaways*. Operated mainly between Immingham and Rotterdam. In July 2017 charter ended and she returned to *Finnlines*, operating on a new service between Oxelösund (Sweden) and Naantali (Finland). Now used on all *Finnlines* services.

FINNMERCHANT Built as the LONGSTONE by Flensburger Schiffbau-Gesellschaft, Flensburg, Germany for *AWSR Shipping* (later Foreland Shipping). Chartered to *Transfennica* and operated between Hanko (Finland) and Lübeck (Germany). In January 2009 chartered to *Finnlines* and placed on the Helsinki - Aarhus route. In January 2012 chartered to *North Sea RoRo*. In March 2013 the operation ceased and the charter was taken over by *DFDS Seaways* and she was placed on the Immingham - Cuxhaven route. In May took over the Zeebrugge - Rosyth route. In October 2013 sold to *C Bulk NV* of Belgium, an associated company of *CLdN/Cobelfret Ferries*. In April 2014 charter to *DFDS* ended and she was chartered to an Australian operator. In November 2014 renamed the DORSET. In December 2014 the charter ended and she returned to *CLdN*. In early January 2015 placed on the Zeebrugge - Purfleet service. Later in the month sold to *Finnlines* and renamed the FINNMERCHANT.

FINNMILL, FINNPULP Built by Jinling Shipyard, Nanjing, China for the *Macoma Shipping Group* and chartered to *Finnlines*. In 2008 purchased by *Finnlines*. During Winter 2008/09 extra ramps were added at STX Europe Helsinki shipyard to enable ro-ro traffic to be conveyed on the weather deck.

Under construction

14	NEWBUILDING	64000t	20	-	238.0m	12P	-	410T	A	FI	-
15	NEWBUILDING	64000t	21	-	238.0m	12P	-	410T	A	FI	-
16	NEWBUILDING	64000t	21	-	238.0m	12P	-	410T	A	FI	-

NEWBUILDING 1, NEWBUILDING 2, NEWBUILDING 3 Grimaldi Green 5th Generation (GG5G) Class hybrid vessels under construction by Jinling Shipyard, Nanjing, China. As well as the trailer deck capacity, there will be 5,600 square metres of car decks and space for 300 TEU of containers on the weather deck.

MANN LINES

THE COMPANY *Mann Lines* are owned by *Mann & Son (London) Ltd* of Great Britain. They replaced in 2001 *ArgoMann Ferry Service*, a joint venture between *Argo Reederei* of Germany and *Mann & Son*.

MANAGEMENT CEO Bill Binks, **General Manager (UK)** David Brooks.

ADDRESS Mann & Son (London) Ltd, The Naval House, Kings Quay Street, Harwich CO12 3JJ.

TELEPHONE Administration & Reservations *UK* +44 (0)1255 245200, ***Germany*** +49 (0)421 1638 50, ***Finland*** +358 (0)2 275 0000, ***Estonia*** +372 (0)679 1450.

FAX Administration & Reservations *UK* +44 (0)1255 245219, ***Germany*** + 49 (0)421 1638 520, ***Finland*** +358 (0)2 253 5905, ***Estonia*** +372 (0)679 1455.

INTERNET Email enquiry@manngroup.co.uk **Website** www.mannlines.com *(English, Finnish, Estonian, German, Russian)*

ROUTES OPERATED Harwich (Navyard) - Cuxhaven (Germany) - Paldiski (Estonia) - Turku (Finland) - Bremerhaven (Germany) – Harwich (***ML FREYJA***; weekly).

1	ML FREYJA	23000t	17	19.0k	190.8m	12P	-	180T	A	IT	9799977

ML FREYJA Built by CN Visentini, Donada, Italy and chartered to *Mann Lines*. In June 2017 sub-chartered to *SOL Continent Line* for six months. In December 2017 entered service with *Mann Lines*.

SEA-CARGO

THE COMPANY *Sea-Cargo AS* of Norway is a subsidiary of *Seatrans AS* of Norway.

MANAGEMENT Managing Director Ole Saevild, **Director Business Development** Erik A Paulsen, **General Manager (Immingham)** Mark Brighton, **General Manager (Aberdeen)** Ian Shewan.

ADDRESS *Norway* Wernersholmvegen 5, 5232 Paradis, Norway, ***Immingham*** Sea-Cargo UK, West Riverside Road, Immingham Dock, Immingham DN40 2NT, ***Aberdeen*** Sea-Cargo Aberdeen Ltd, Matthews Quay, Aberdeen Harbour, Aberdeen, AB11 5PG.

TELEPHONE Administration & Bookings *Bergen* +47 55 10 84 84, ***Immingham*** +44 (0)1469 577119, ***Aberdeen*** +44 (0)1224 596481.

FAX Administration & Reservations *Bergen* +47 85 02 82 16, ***Immingham*** 44 (0)1469 577708, ***Aberdeen*** +44 (0)1224 582360.

INTERNET Email mail@sea-cargo.no **Website** www.sea-cargo.no *(English)*

ROUTES OPERATED *Sea-Cargo* operate a network of services from West Norway to Amsterdam, Aberdeen, Immingham and Esbjerg. The schedule varies from week to week and is shown on the company website. The ***SC ASTREA*** and ***SC CONNECTOR*** are generally used on the twice-weekly Immingham - Tanager, Haugesund, Bergen and Odda service and the ***SEA-CARGO EXPRESS*** on the weekly Aberdeen - Tanager, Haugesund, Bergen, Florø, Ålesund, Kristiansund, Trondheim and Molde service.

1	SC AHTELA	8610t	91	14.8k	139.5m	12P	-	92T	AS	MT	8911736
2	SC ASTREA	9528t	91	13.5k	129.1m	0p	-	58T	A	BS	8917895
3	SC CONNECTOR	12251t	97	15.0k	154.5m	12P	-	124T	AS	MT	9131993
4	SEA-CARGO EXPRESS	6693t	12	16.0k	117.4m	0P	-	35T	A	MT	9358060
5	TRANS CARRIER	9953t	94	14.5k	144.5m	0P	-	94T	AS	BS	9007879
6	TRANSFIGHTER	20851t	01	14.5k	178.6m	0P	-	100T	AS	MT	9216626

SC AHTELA Built as the AHTELA by Brodogradiliste "Sava", Macvanska Mitrovica, Yugoslavia, completed by Fosen Mekaniske Verksteder, Rissa, Norway for *Rederi AB Gustav Erikson* of Finland. Chartered to *Transfennica*. In 1995 chartered to *DFDS Tor Line*. In 1996 chartered to *Finncarriers Oy* of Finland and in 1997 renamed the FINNOAK. In 2007 sold to *Hollming Oy* of

SECTION 3 - FREIGHT ONLY FERRIES

Finland and in 2008 the charter ended and she was renamed the AHTELA. Chartered to *Navirail* of Estonia to operate between Helsinki and Muuga (Estonia). Between February and May 2011 chartered to *Sea-Cargo* to operate between Esbjerg (Denmark) and Egersund (Norway). In October 2012 purchased by *Sea-Cargo* and renamed the SC AHTELA.

SC ASTREA Built as the ASTREA by Tangen Verft Kragerø A/S, Kragerø, Norway for *Finncarriers* of Finland. Operated between Finland and Spain - Portugal via Antwerpen. In 2006 chartered to *Danish MoD*. In 2007 chartered to *Sea-Cargo*. In August 2011 purchased by *Sea-Cargo* and renamed the SC ASTREA. Until early 2016 used primarily for moving windfarm equipment. In February placed on the Norway - Immingham service.

SC CONNECTOR Built as the UNITED EXPRESS by Fosen Mekaniske Verksteder A/S, Rissa, Norway for *United Shipping* (a subsidiary of *Birka Shipping*) of Finland and chartered to *Transfennica*. During 2000 used on their Kemi - Oulu - Antwerpen - Felixstowe service. In 2001 the route was transferred to *Finnlines* and the vessel used sub-chartered to them (charter later transferred to *Finnlines*). In 2002 *United Shipping* was renamed *Birka Cargo* and she was renamed the BIRKA EXPRESS. In 2008 the charter was extended a further four years. In June 2013 renamed the EXPRESS. In November 2013 chartered to *Transfennica*. In April 2014 sold to *Sea-Cargo* but initially continued to operate for *Transfennica*. During winter 2015 re-engined and modified to allow to side loading. In February 2015 renamed the SC CONNECTOR. Entered service in late April.

SEA-CARGO EXPRESS One of two vessels ordered in 2005 from Bharati Ratnagiri Ltd, Mumbai, India for *Sea-Cargo*. The order for the second ship was cancelled. Trailers are carried on the main deck only. Containers are carried on the weather deck and pallets on the lower decks. A crane is provided for the containers and a side door for pallets. She operates on the Aberdeen - Norway service.

TRANS CARRIER Built as the KORSNÄS LINK by Brodogradiliste Kraljevica, Kraljevica, Croatia for *SeaLink AB* of Sweden and due to be time-chartered to *Korsnäs AB*, a Swedish forest products company. However, due to the war in Croatia, delivery was seriously delayed and she was offered for sale. In 1994 sold to the *Swan Group* and renamed the SWAN HUNTER. She was placed on the charter market. In 1997 she was chartered to *Euroseabridge* and renamed the PARCHIM. In 1999 the charter ended and she resumed the name SWAN HUNTER. In 1999 she was sold to *SeaTrans* and renamed the TRANS CARRIER. She operated for *Sea-Cargo*. In 2005 chartered to *Finnlines* and used on the Finland to Spain/Portugal service. In 2006 returned to *Sea-Cargo*. In January and February 2009 lengthened by 18.9 metres in Poland.

TRANSFIGHTER Built as the FINNFIGHTER by Stocznia Gdynia, S.A. Gdynia, Poland for *B & N Nordsjöfrakt* of Sweden and chartered to F-Ships to operate between Finland and the USA. In 2004 Sold to *Gorthons Lines* of Sweden and in 2005 chartered to *Rederi AB Transatlantic* of Sweden. She continued to be operated between Scandinavia and North America. In 2006 extended by Blohm & Voss, Hamburg, Germany. In February 2009 she was renamed the TRANSFIGHTER. In November 2016 sold to *Seatrans AS* of Norway and chartered to *Sea-Cargo*. Initially used on a service Norwegian ports to Rotterdam and Sheerness. Sheerness is no longer served.

SEATRUCK FERRIES

THE COMPANY *Seatruck Ferries Ltd* is a British private sector company. It is part of the *Clipper Group*.

MANAGEMENT Chairman Peter Lybecker, **CEO** Alistair Eagles.

ADDRESSES *Heysham (HQ)* North Quay, Heysham Port, Heysham, Morecambe, Lancs LA3 2UH, ***Warrenpoint*** Seatruck House, The Ferry Terminal, Warrenpoint, County Down BT34 3JR, ***Liverpool:*** Seatruck Ferry Terminal, Brocklebank Dock, Port of Liverpool, L20 1DB, ***Dublin***: Seatruck Dublin, Terminal 5, Alexandra Road, Dublin 1 Irish Republic.

TELEPHONE Administration +44 (0)1524 855377, **Reservations *Heysham*** +44 (0)1524 853512. ***Warrenpoint*** +44 (0)28 754400, ***Liverpool*** + (0)151 9333660, ***Dublin*** + (0) 353 18230492.

Opaline *(Nick Widdows)*

Seatruck Progress *(Miles Cowsill)*

FAX Administration +44 (0)28 4175 4545, **Reservations *Warrenpoint*** +44 (0)28 4177 3737, ***Heysham*** +44 (0)1524 853549.

INTERNET Email aje@seatruckgroup.co.uk **Website** www.seatruckferries.com *(English)*

ROUTES OPERATED Heysham - Warrenpoint (9 hrs; ***SEATRUCK PERFORMANCE, SEATRUCK PRECISION***; 2 per day), Heysham - Dublin (9 hrs; ***SEATRUCK PANORAMA***; 1 per day), Liverpool - Dublin (9 hrs; ***CLIPPER POINT***, ***SEATRUCK PACE, SEATRUCK POWER, SEATRUCK PROGRESS***; up to 4 per day).

1	CLIPPER PENNANT	14759t	09	22.0k	142.0m	12P	-	120T	A	CY	9372688
2	CLIPPER POINT	14759t	08	22.0k	142.0m	12P	-	120T	A	CY	9350666
3	CLIPPER RANGER	7606t	98	17.0k	122.3m	12P	-	84T	A	IM	9119402
4	SEATRUCK PACE	14759t	09	22.0k	142.0m	12P	-	120T	A	CY	9350678
5	SEATRUCK PANORAMA	14759t	09	22.0k	142.0m	12P	-	120T	A	CY	9372676
6	SEATRUCK PERFORMANCE	19722t	12	21.0k	142.0m	12P	-	151T	A	IM	9506227
7	SEATRUCK POWER	19722t	11	21.0k	142.0m	12P	-	151T	A	IM	9506215
8	SEATRUCK PRECISION	19722t	12	21.0k	142.0m	12P	-	151T	A	IM	9506239
9	SEATRUCK PROGRESS	19722t	11	21.0k	142.0m	12P	-	151T	A	IM	9506203

CLIPPER PENNANT Built by Astilleros Sevilla SA, Sevilla, Spain for *Seatruck Ferries*. In November 2018 chartered to *Canary Bridge Seaways,* a joint venture between *Fred. Olsen Express* and *Balearia* to operate between the Spanish mainland and the Canary Islands.

CLIPPER POINT Built by Astilleros de Huelva SA, Huelva, Spain for *Seatruck Ferries*. In May 2012 chartered to *DFDS Seaways* and placed on the Immingham-Cuxhaven route. In April 2013 chartered to the organisers of the 'SATA Rally Azores 2013' car rally to take cars from Portugal to the Azores. In May began operating for *DFDS Seaways* in the Baltic. In October transferred to the Immingham - Cuxhaven route. In June 2015 the charter ended. In July she was chartered to *InterShipping*, of Morocco to operate between Algeciras and Tangiers. In September 2016 the charter ended and she returned to *Seatruck Ferries*.

CLIPPER RANGER Built as the LEMBITU by Astilleros de Huelva SA, Huelva, Spain for the *Estonian Shipping Company*. On completion chartered to *P&O European Ferries (Irish Sea)* and placed on their Liverpool - Dublin route. In Autumn 1998 she was chartered to *Dart Line* and placed on the Dartford - Vlissingen route. In 1999 she was renamed the DART 7. In Autumn 1999 the charter was ended and she was chartered to *Cetam* of France, resumed the name LEMBITU and was used on services between Marseilles and Tunis. In 2000 she was chartered to *P&O European Ferries (Irish Sea)* and renamed the CELTIC SUN; she operated between Liverpool and Dublin. In 2001 the charter ended; she then reverted to the name LEMBITU and was chartered to *NorseMerchant Ferries* and placed on the Heysham - Dublin service. In late 2001 the charter ended and she returned to *ESCO* service in the Baltic. In 2003 chartered to *Scandlines AG* and placed on their Rostock - Helsinki - Muuga service. This service finished in December 2004 and she was chartered to *Channel Freight Ferries* in January 2005. In March 2005 chartered to *NorseMerchant Ferries* again and operated between Heysham and Belfast. Later purchased by *Elmira Shipping* of Greece and renamed the RR CHALLENGE. In June 2005 chartered to *Seatruck Ferries*. In October 2007 sold to *Attica Group* of Greece and renamed the CHALLENGE. She continued to be chartered to *Seatruck Ferries*. In January 2008 she was transferred to the Liverpool - Dublin route and in April sold to *Seatruck Ferries*. In July renamed the CLIPPER RANGER. In June 2009 replaced the SHIELD (now the HILDASAY) until the new CLIPPER PENNANT took over in October. In May 2010 inaugurated a new Heysham - Larne service. In October 2013 chartered to *Caledonian MacBrayne* to replace the MUIRNEAG. The charter ended in May 2015. In November 2015 placed on the Liverpool - Dublin route as third ship. In March 2016 transferred to the Heysham - Dublin service. In September 2016 moved to the Liverpool - Dublin routes as fourth vessel. In August 2018 laid up. In July 2019 bare-boat chartered to *CTMA* of Canada for one year, with an option to buy.

SEATRUCK PACE Built as the CLIPPER PACE by Astilleros Sevilla SA, Sevilla, Spain for *Seatruck Ferries*. In March 2012 renamed the SEATRUCK PACE. In January 2013 chartered to *Blue Water Shipping* of Denmark to carry wind turbine parts between Mostyn (Wales) and Esbjerg. Now operates on the Liverpool - Dublin route.

SEATRUCK PANORAMA Built by Astilleros de Huelva SA, Huelva Spain for *Seatruck Ferries*. Launched as the CLIPPER PENNANT and renamed the CLIPPER PANORAMA before delivery. In December 2011 renamed the SEATRUCK PANORAMA.

SEATRUCK PERFORMANCE Built as the SEATRUCK PERFORMANCE by Flensburger Schiffbau-Gesellschaft, Flensburg, Germany for *Seatruck Ferries*. In September 2012 chartered to *Stena Line* and renamed the STENA PERFORMER. She operated on both the Heysham - Belfast and Birkenhead - Belfast services. In August 2018 returned to *Seatruck Ferries*, renamed the SEATRUCK PERFORMANCE and placed on the Heysham - Warrenpoint service.

SEATRUCK POWER, SEATRUCK PROGRESS Built by Flensburger Schiffbau-Gesellschaft, Flensburg, Germany for *Seatruck Ferries*.

SEATRUCK PRECISION Built as the SEATRUCK PRECISION by Flensburger Schiffbau-Gesellschaft, Flensburg, Germany for *Seatruck Ferries*. In September 2012 chartered to *Stena Line* and renamed the STENA PRECISION. She operated on the Heysham - Belfast service. In September 2015 moved to the Birkenhead - Belfast route. In August 2018 returned to *Seatruck Ferries*, renamed the SEATRUCK PRECISION and placed on the Heysham - Warrenpoint service.

Seatruck Ferries also own the ARROW, currently on charter to *Isle of Man Steam Packet Company*.

WALLENIUS SOL

THE COMPANY *Wallenius SOL* is a joint venture *Wallenius Lines* and *Swedish Orient Line*, both Swedish private sector companies.

MANAGEMENT Managing Director Ragnar Johansson, **Head of Communications** Richard Jeppsson.

ADDRESSES Klippan 1A, 414 51 Gothenburg, Sweden.

TELEPHONE +46 31 354 40 00.

FAX +46 (0)31-354 40 01.

INTERNET Email info@wallenius-sol.com **Website** wallenius-sol.com *(English)*

ROUTES OPERATED Oulu - Kemi - Husum - Lübeck - Göteborg - Zeebrugge - Tilbury - Zeebrugge - Oxelosund - Oulu (***THULELAND***, ***TUNDRALAND***; 1 per week), Kemi - Oulu - Antwerpen - Zeebrugge - Göteborg - Kemi (***BALTICA, VASALAND***; 1 per week).

1	BALTICA	21224t	90	19.0k	157.7m	0P	-	163T	A	FI	8813154
2	THULELAND	23128t	06	16.0k	190.7m	12P	-	200T	A	SE	9343261
3	TUNDRALAND	23128t	07	16.0k	190.7m	12P	-	200T	A	SE	9343273
4	VASALAND	20203t	84	19.5k	155.0m	12P	-	150T	A	UK	8222111

BALTICA Built by Hyundai Heavy Industries, Ulsan, South Korea as the AHLERS BALTIC for *Ahlers Line* and chartered to *Finncarriers*. In 1995 acquired by *Poseidon Schiffahrt AG* of Germany and renamed the TRANSBALTICA. She continued to be chartered to *Finncarriers* and was acquired by them when they purchased *Poseidon Schiffahrt AG* (now *Finnlines Deutschland AG*) in 1997. In 2003 sold to Norwegian interests and chartered back; She was renamed the BALTICA. In recent years she operated on the Helsinki - St Petersburg - Hamina - Helsinki - Zeebrugge - Tilbury – Amsterdam - Antwerpen - service with the MERCHANT. During 2007 she operated Helsinki - Turku - Antwerpen on a one-week cycle. In January 2008 moved to Baltic services. In April 2011 chartered to *Power Line* to operate between Helsinki and Travemünde. In January 2013 returned to *Finnlines*. In October 2015 sold to *Godby Shipping* of Finland. In November chartered to *SOL Continent Line*.

THULELAND Built as the TRANSPULP by Aker Finnyards, Rauma, Finland for *Baltic Container Shipping* of the UK and chartered to *Rederi AB Transatlantic* of Sweden. Operated on service operated for Stora Enso Paper Group, mainly in the Baltic. In early 2011 transferred to the Göteborg - Tilbury (once weekly) and Göteborg - Zeebrugge (*CLdN* service) (once weekly) services. In January 2013 began operating twice weekly to Tilbury, replacing the SELANDIA

SECTION 3 – FREIGHT ONLY FERRIES

SEAWAYS of *DFDS Seaways*. In January 2015 chartered to *SOL Continent Line*. In December 2016 renamed the THULELAND.

TUNDRALAND Built as the TRANSTIMBER by Aker Finnyards, Rauma, Finland for *Baltic Container Shipping* of the UK and chartered to *Rederi AB Transatlantic* of Sweden. Operated on service operated for Stora Enso Paper Group, mainly in the Baltic. In January 2015 chartered to *SOL Continent Line*. In August 2017 she was renamed the TUNDRALAND.

VASALAND Built as the OIHONNA by Rauma Repola OY, Rauma, Finland for *Effoa-Finska Ångfartygs Ab*, of Finland. In December 1986 sold to *Fincarriers Ab* of Finland. In November 2003 sold to *Stena RoRo* of Sweden and renamed the VASALAND. Over the ensuing years, chartered to a number of companies including *Finnlines* and *Transfennica*. In September 2009 chartered to *SOL Continent Line*, initially operating purely in the Baltic but since 2016 used on their North Sea service.

Under construction

5	NEWBUILDING 1	-	21	20.0k	242.0m	12P	-	420T	A	-	-
6	NEWBUILDING 2	-	21	20.0k	242.0m	12P	-	420T	A	-	-
7	NEWBUILDING 3	-	21	20.0k	242.0m	12P	-	420T	A	-	-
8	NEWBUILDING 4	-	21	20.0k	242.0m	12P	-	420T	A	-	-

NEWBUILDING 1, NEWBUILDING 2, NEWBUILDING 3, NEWBUILDING 4 Under construction by Yantai CIMC Raffles Shipyard, Yantai, China. To run on LNG.

FLOTA SUARDIAZ

THE COMPANY *Flota Suardiaz SL* is owned by *Grupo Suardiaz,* a Spanish private sector logistics company which operates divisions in ports, bunkering, warehousing, haulage, freight forwarding and shipping.

MANAGEMENT Presidente Don Juan Riva, **Director General** Alfredo Menendez Garcia.

ADDRESSES Spain Calle Ayala, 6 28001 Madrid, Spain, **UK** Suardiaz Shipping Ltd, Suardiaz House, 193 Shirley Road, Southampton SO15 3FG.

TELEPHONE Spain +34 914 31 66 40, **UK** +44 (0) 2380 211 981.

FAX Spain + 34 914 36 46 74, **UK** +44 (0) 2380 335309.

INTERNET Email infoweb@suardiaz.com, **Website** www.suardiaz.com *(English, Spanish).*

ROUTES OPERATED Northern Europe/Spain/Canaries/Med Lines Emden - Sheerness - Zeebrugge - Santander - Vigo - Las Palmas - Tenerife - Casablanca - Mostaganem - Barcelona (weekly with up to two sailings per week on some sections including Emden - Sheerness and Las Palmas - Tenerife - Barcelona). **Atlantic Line** Zeebrugge - St Nazaire - Vigo - Tanger Med (twice weekly with St Nazaire - Vigo four sailings per week). **Algeria Line** Barcelona - Marseille - Alger - Mostagenem (weekly).

Services listed carry unaccompanied ro-ro cargo together with large volumes of trade cars for vehicle manufacturers and distributors and interwork between routes. Occasional irregular calls are made at North Shields, Vlissingen, Le Havre and Southampton and sailings can sometimes omit scheduled ports. The Atlantic Line is operated with European Union funding from the TEN-T Programme and supported by a GEFCO car carrying contract between St Nazaire and Vigo. Vessels are regularly transferred between routes and are often chartered out for short periods to other operators and vehicle manufacturers. In view of this, the following is a list of all vessels in the *Flota Suardiaz* fleet including those not currently serving the UK.

1	BOUZAS	15224t	02	18.5k	149.4m	12P	1265C	105T	A	ES	9249996
2	GALICIA	16361t	03	15.0k	149.4m	12P	1390C	110T	A	PT	9268409
3	GRAN CANARIA CAR	9600t	01	18.0k	132.5m	0P	1150C	42T	AS	PT	9218014
4	IVAN	8191t	96	14.6k	102.5m	0P	853C	73T	A	PT	9112040
5	L'AUDACE	15222t	99	18.5k	149.4m	12P	1233C	105T	A	ES	9187318
6	LA SURPRISE	15222t	00	18.5k	149.4m	12P	1233C	105T	A	PT	9198719

Clipper Point *(Miles Cowsill)*

Pulpca *(Julian Jager)*

7	SUAR VIGO	16361t	03	18.5k	149.4m	12P	1356C	110T	A	ES	9250000
8	TENERIFE CAR	13122t	02	20.0k	149.4m	12P	1354C	54T	AS	PT	9249984
9	VERONA	37237t	00	20.5k	176.7m	0P	3HU919C	400T	QRS	HK	9190858
10	VIKING CONSTANZA	20216t	09	18.0k	139.9m	0P	2000C	65T	AQR	SG	9407689

BOUZAS, GALICIA, L'AUDACE, LA SURPRISE, SUAR VIGO Built by Hijos de J. Barreras SA, Vigo, Portugal for *Flota Suardiaz* of Spain for use on services in the Mediterranean and to the Canaries, U.K. and Benelux. The vessels are highly flexible with a 12-driver capacity and three full height freight decks, each fitted with a mezzanine deck for cars, together with a further dedicated car deck. In addition to operating for *Flota Suardiaz* a number of vessels have spent periods on charter to *UECC*. The L'AUDACE was chartered to *P&O Ferries* to operate between Hull and Zeebrugge in early 2015. Since early 2017 she has been on charter to *Priority Ro-Ro Services* in the Caribbean sailing between Santo Domingo, Dominican Republic and San Juan, Puerto Rico.

GRAN CANARIA CAR Built as HARALD FLICK by Hijos de J. Barreras SA, Vigo, Portugal for *Naviera del Odiel*, one of the shareholders in Barreras and placed on 10 year charter to *Flota Suardiaz* of Spain for use on services in the Mediterranean and to the Canaries, U.K. and Benelux. Renamed GRAN CANARIA CAR before entering service. In 2008 ownership passed to *Navicar SA* a subsidiary of *Flota Suardiaz*. In addition to operating for *Flota Suardiaz* has been chartered to *UECC* on several occasions.

IVAN Built by Astilleros De Murueta, Vizcaya, Spain for *Adamastor - Sociedade de Navegação, Lda* a subsidiary of *Flota Suardiaz* for use on short sea services. For many years she operated a now ceased service from Sheerness and Grimsby to Calais.

TENERIFE CAR Built by Hijos de J. Barreras SA, Vigo, Portugal for *Navicar SA* a subsidiary of *Flota Suardiaz* for use on services in the Mediterranean and to the Canaries, UK and Benelux.

VERONA Built by Uljanik Shipbuilding Industries, Pula, Croatia for Montagu Bay Shipping, Monrovia, Liberia for charter to *Wallenius Wilhelmsen*. In 2002 sold to *Siem Car Carriers* of Panama. Of deep-sea ocean-going ro-ro design with a quarter ramp, she was chartered by *Suardiaz* from early 2016 onwards.

VIKING CONSTANZA Built by Kyokuyo Shipyard Corporation, Japan for *Gram Car Carriers*, Norway for operation on the charter market as part of a series of four vessels. Of short sea PTCC design the vessels have both stern and quarter ramps. In 2015 chartered by *UECC*. In 2017 chartered by *Suardiaz*.

TRANSFENNICA

THE COMPANY *Transfennica Ltd* is a Finnish private sector company wholly owned by *Spliethoff Bevrachtingskantoor* of The Netherlands.

MANAGEMENT Managing Director Dirk P. Witteveen, **Sales Director (UK)** Andrew Clarke.

ADDRESSES *Finland* Eteläranta 12, 00130 Helsinki, Finland, ***UK*** Finland House, 47 Berth, Tilbury Port, Tilbury, Essex RM18 7EH.

TELEPHONE Administration & Reservations *Finland* +358 (0)9 13262, ***UK*** +44 (0)1375 363 900.

FAX Administration & Reservations *Finland* +358 (0)9 652377, ***UK*** +44 (0)1375 840 888.

INTERNET Email *Finland* info@transfennica.com ***UK*** info.uk@transfennica.com

Website www.transfennica.com *(English, Finnish, Russian)*

ROUTES OPERATED Tilbury (weekly) to various destinations in Finland and Russia. Please see the website. All *Transfennica* ships are listed below as ships are sometimes moved between routes.

1	BORE BANK	10585t	96	20.0k	138.8m	12P	-	105T	A2	FI	9160774
2	BORE SEA	25586t	11	18.5k	195.0m	12P	-	210T	A2	NL	9443554
3	CORONA SEA	25609t	08	20.0k	184.8m	12P	-	250T	AS	UK	9357597
4	GENCA	28301t	07	22.0k	205.0m	12P	-	200T	A2	NL	9307372

5	HAFNIA SEA	25609t	08	20.0k	184.8m	12P	-	250T	AS	UK	9357602
6	KRAFTCA	28301t	06	22.0k	205.0m	12P	-	200T	A2	NL	9307360
7	PLYCA	28301t	09	22.0k	205.0m	12P	-	200T	A2	NL	9345398
8	PULPCA	28301t	08	22.0k	205.0m	12P	-	200T	A2	NL	9345386
9	SEAGARD	10488t	99	21.0k	153.5m	12P	-	134T	A2	FI	9198977
10	TIMCA	28301t	06	22.0k	205.0m	12P	-	200T	A2	NL	9307358
11	TRICA	28301t	07	22.0k	205.0m	12P	-	200T	A2	NL	9307384

BORE BANK Built as the SERENADEN by Umoe Sterkoder AS, Kristiansund, Norway for *Rederi AB Engship* of Finland and chartered to *Transfennica*. In 2006 *Rederi AB Engship* was taken over by *Rettig Group Bore*. In 2007 converted at COSCO Shipyard, Nantong, China to add a garage on top of the weather deck, renamed AUTO BANK and placed on long-term charter to *UECC*. Generally used on the Baltic or Iberian services. In December 2016 converted back to a conventional ro-ro freighter by Öresundwerft, Landskrona, Sweden and renamed the BORE BANK. Chartered to *Transfennica*.

BORE SEA Built by Flensburger Schiffbau-Gesellschaft, Flensburg, Germany for *Bore Shipowners (Rettig Group Bore)* of Finland. In May 2011 chartered to *Transfennica* and operated between Zeebrugge and Bilbao. In January 2013 chartered for three years to *Fret Cetam* of France and used for the conveyance of parts for Airbus aircraft. In September 2016 chartered to *CLdN/Cobelfret Ferries*. Initially used mainly on the Zeebrugge - Purfleet service but later also used on the Iberian routes. In January 2018 chartered to *Transfennica*.

CORONA SEA Built as the TOR CORONA by Jinling Shipyard, Nanjing, China for *Macoma Shipping Ltd* of the UK and time-chartered to *DFDS Tor Line* for ten years. Used on the Fredericia – København - Klaipėda service. In April 2012 renamed the CORONA SEAWAYS. In January 2018 chartered to *Transfennica* and, in February, renamed the CORONA SEA.

GENCA, KRAFTCA, PLYCA, PULPCA, TIMCA, TRICA Built by New Szczecin Shipyard (SSN), Szczecin, Poland for *Spliethoff Bevrachtingskantoor*, owners of *Transfennica*.

HAFNIA SEA Built as the TOR HAFNIA by Jinling Shipyard, Nanjing, China for *Macoma Shipping Ltd* of the UK and time-chartered to *DFDS Tor Line* for ten years. Until 2013, mainly operated on the Immingham - Esbjerg route. In March 2011 renamed the HAFNIA SEAWAYS. In January 2015 chartered to *Cobelfret Ferries* for four weeks. In January 2018 chartered to *Transfennica* and in March 2018 renamed the HAFNIA SEA.

SEAGARD Built by J J Sietas KG, Hamburg, Germany for *Bror Husell Chartering* of Finland (later acquired by *Bore Shipowning* of Finland) and chartered to *Transfennica*.

UECC

THE COMPANY *United European Car Carriers AS* is a Norwegian private sector company jointly owned in equal shares by *Nippon Yusen Kabushiki Kaisha (NYK)* of Japan and *Wallenius Lines* of Sweden. *UECC* consists of companies in Norway, Germany, Spain, France, Portugal and the UK. The fleet technical and ship management department is based in Grimsby (UK).

MANAGEMENT Chief Executive Officer Glenn Edvardsen.

ADDRESSES Norway Karenlyst Allè 57, 0277 Oslo, **UK** Units 5B & 5C Appian Way, Europa Park, Grimsby, DN31 2UT.

TELEPHONE Norway +47 21 00 98 00, **UK** +44 (0)1472 269429.

FAX Norway +47 21 00 98 01, **UK** +44 (0)207 628 2858.

INTERNET Email marketing@uecc.com, **Website** www.uecc.com *(English)*.

ROUTES OPERATED

Atlantic Service Vigo – Le Havre – Zeebrugge – Sheerness – Vigo (***CITY OF OSLO***; weekly), Vigo – Zeebrugge – Bremerhaven – Drammen – Wallhamn – Cuxhaven – Southampton – Vigo (***RCC PRESTIGE, PROMETHEUS LEADER***; weekly), **Baltic Service** Southampton – Zeebrugge – Bremerhaven – Malmo – Hanko – St Petersburg – Gdynia – Southampton (***AUTO ECO, AUTO***

ENERGY; weekly), **Bristol Service** Portbury - Pasajes (***AUTOSUN***; weekly), **Biscay Services** Santander – Pasajes – Zeebrugge – Southampton – Santander (***AUTOSTAR***; weekly), Santander – Pasajes – Rotterdam - Zeebrugge – Santander (***AUTOSKY,*** weekly), Pasajes – Zeebrugge – Southampton – Le Havre – Pasajes (***AUTOPROGRESS***; ***AUTOPRESTIGE, AUTOPREMIER,*** weekly), **Norway Service** Bremerhaven – Oslo – Drammen – Bremerhaven (***AUTOPRIDE***; twice weekly), **North – South Service** Bremerhaven – Zeebrugge – Portbury – Vigo – Sagunto – Tarragona – Livorno – Pireaus – Autoport – Yenikoy – Vigo – Bremerhaven (***CORAL LEADER, EMERALD LEADER, OPAL LEADER, VEGA LEADER, VIKING LEADER***; weekly).

Services listed carry unaccompanied ro-ro cargo together with large volumes of trade cars and often call at additional ports for an inducement and these have included Cork, Dublin, Immingham, Liverpool, Tilbury, and Newcastle. In addition, ad-hoc short-sea contract sailings for vehicle manufacturers and distributors are also operated throughout Northern Europe. Vessels are regularly transferred between routes and contracts and the following is a list of all owned and long term chartered vessels currently in the *UECC* fleet including those not presently serving the UK. The fleet is regularly supplemented by occasional voyages made by vessels of *Flota Suardiaz* and *LDA Seaplane* (the *Louis Dreyfus Armateurs* Airbus ro-ro operation*)* and by deep sea ocean-going ro-ro vessels long term chartered from parent companies *NYK Line* and *Wallenius Lines* and Eukor (which is 40% owned by Wallenius*)*. Long term chartered vessels at the time of preparation and considered out of the scope of this book were the PROMETHEUS LEADER, CORAL LEADER, EMERALD LEADER, OPAL LEADER, VEGA LEADER AND VICTORY LEADER all of which belong to parent *NYK Line* and the RCC PRESTIGE of *Ray Car Carriers*.

1	AUTO ECO	43424t	16	18.6k	181.0m	0P	3800C	-	QRS	PT	9736365
2	AUTO ENERGY	43424t	16	18.6k	181.0m	0P	3800C	-	QRS	PT	9736377
3	AUTOPREMIER	11591t	97	20.0k	128.8m	0P	1220C	-	AS	PT	9131943
4	AUTOPRESTIGE	11596t	99	20.0k	128.8m	0P	1220C	-	AS	PT	9190157
5	AUTOPRIDE	11591t	97	20.0k	128.8m	0P	1220C	-	AS	PT	9131955
6	AUTOPROGRESS	11591t	98	20.0k	128.8m	0P	1220C	-	AS	PT	9131967
7	AUTOSKY	21010t	00	20.9k	140.0m	0P	2080C	-	AS	PT	9206774
8	AUTOSTAR	21010t	00	20.9k	140.0m	0P	2080C	-	AS	PT	9206786
9	AUTOSUN	21094t	00	20.9k	140.0m	0P	1220C	-	AS	PT	9227053
10	CITY OF OSLO	20209t	10	18.0k	139.9m	0P	2000C	65T	AQR	SG	9407677

AUTO ECO, AUTO ENERGY Designated as E-Class both are Dual fuel LNG Ice Class 1A pure car and truck carriers with side and quarter ramps built by Kawasaki Heavy Industries at NACKS shipyard, Nantong, China for *UECC*. Used on Baltic services, the vessels are refuelled by a specialist barge in Zeebrugge. Both vessels are used on the Baltic service.

AUTOPREMIER, AUTOPRESTIGE, AUTOPROGRESS, AUTOPRIDE Built by Frisian Shipyard, Harlingen, the Netherlands for *UECC*. Designated P-class, they are an enlarged version of the now scrapped R-class and built to a 'Grimsby-Max' specification with greater capacity for ro-ro cargo. Generally used on scheduled sailings between Iberia and the Benelux and UK or between Germany and Norway.

AUTOSKY, AUTOSTAR, AUTOSUN Built by Tsuneishi Zosen, Tadotsu, Japan for *UECC* Designated S-class, they are a further enlargement of the P-class and R-class designs and are normally used on Biscay routes.

CITY OF OSLO Built by Kyokuyo Shipyard Corporation, Japan for Gram Car Carriers, Norway. Of short sea PTCC design she features a stern and quarter ramp. In 2016 she was chartered by Suardiaz. In 2019 chartered to UECC for use on Biscay routes.

Under Construction

11	NEWBUILDING 1	-	21	-	169.0m	0P	3600C	-	QRS	-	-
12	NEWBUILDING 2	-	21	-	169.0m	0P	3600C	-	QRS	-	-

NEWBUILDING 1 & NEWBUILDING 2 Dual fuel LNG Battery Hybrid Ice Class 1A pure car and truck carriers with side and quarter ramps being built by China Ship Building Trading Co Ltd and Jiangnan Shipyard Group Co. Ltd. Vessels smaller than the E-Class and there is an option for two further vessels.

SECTION 4 - RO-RO OPERATORS CONVEYING PRIVATE TRAFFIC

The following operators employ ro-ro freight ships for the conveyance of their own traffic or traffic for a limited number of customers and do not normally solicit general traffic from hauliers or shippers.

FORELAND SHIPPING

THE COMPANY *Foreland Shipping Limited* (formerly *AWSR Shipping Limited*) is a UK private sector company. The principal shareholder in *Foreland Shipping* is *Hadley Shipping Group.*

MANAGEMENT Chairman Peter Morton, **Managing Director** Paul Trudgeon, **Operations Director** Stuart Williams.

ADDRESS 117-119 Houndsditch, London EC3A 7BT.

TELEPHONE +44 (0)20 7480 4140.

FAX +44 (0)20 7280 8790.

INTERNET Email enquiries@foreland-shipping.co.uk **Website** www.foreland-shipping.co.uk *(English)*

ROUTES OPERATED No routes are operated. Ships are for charter to the *UK Ministry of Defence* for their 'Strategic Sealift Capability'.

1	ANVIL POINT	23235t	03	17.1k	193.0m	12P	-	180T	A	UK	9248540
2	EDDYSTONE	23235t	02	17.1k	193.0m	12P	-	180T	A	UK	9234070
3	HARTLAND POINT	23235t	03	17.1k	193.0m	12P	-	180T	A	UK	9248538
4	HURST POINT	23235t	02	17.1k	193.0m	12P	-	180T	A	UK	9234068

ANVIL POINT, HARTLAND POINT Built by Harland & Wolff, Belfast, UK for *AWSR Shipping.*

EDDYSTONE, HURST POINT Built by Flensburger Schiffbau-Gesellschaft, Flensburg, Germany for *AWSR Shipping.*

HOLMEN CARRIER

THE COMPANY *Holmen Carrier* is the branding of ships operated for *Holmen Paper AB*, an international company based in Sweden.

MANAGEMENT President and CEO Henrik Sjölund.

ADDRESS Holmen AB, P.O. Box 5407, SE-114 84 Stockholm, Sweden.

TELEPHONE +46 8 666 21 00.

INTERNET Email info@holmen.com **Website** www.holmen.com/en *(English, Swedish)*

ROUTES OPERATED Norrköping (Sweden) - Travemünde - Sheerness - Hull - Norrköping (2 weeks; ***EXPORTER***, ***SHIPPER***; 1 per week).

1	EXPORTER	6620t	91	16.5k	122.0m	0P	-	90T	A	FI	8820860
2	SHIPPER	6620t	91	16.5k	122.0m	0P	-	90T	A	FI	8911748

EXPORTER Built as the GRANÖ by Brodogradiliste "Sava", Macvanska Mitrovica, Yugoslavia (fitted out by Fosen Mekaniske Verksteder of Rissa, Norway) for *Rederi AB Gustav Erikson* of Finland and chartered to *Transfennica* for service between Finland and Germany. In 1995 the owning company became *United Shipping* and in 2002 *Birka Cargo AB*. In 2000 she was chartered to the *Korsnäs Paper Group* to carry their traffic from Gävle (Sweden) to Chatham and Terneuzen (The Netherlands). In 2002 she was renamed the BIRKA EXPORTER. In 2005 the charter and operation of the services were taken over by *DFDS Tor Line*. The northbound Terneuzen - Gävle section became a ferry route marketed as part of the *DFDS Tor Line* network. This arrangement ceased in 2006. In 2008 chartered to *Finnlines*. In January 2010 chartered to *Holmen Paper AB*. In June 2013 renamed the EXPORTER.

SHIPPER Built as the STYRSÖ and renamed the BIRKA SHIPPER in 2002 and the SHIPPER in June 2013. Otherwise all details as the EXPORTER.

LD SEAPLANE

THE COMPANY *LD Seaplane* (formerly *Fret-CETAM*) is a French private sector company, 100% owned by *Louis Dreyfus Armateurs SAS*.

MANAGEMENT General Manager Jean-Louis Cadoret.

ADDRESS LD Seaplane, 21 Quai Gallieni - 92158, Suresnes Cedex, France.

TELEPHONE +33 (0)5 3459 1339.

INTERNET Email contact@lda.fr **Website** www.lda.fr/ld-seaplane-145 *(English, French)*

ROUTES OPERATED Mostyn (Wales) - Bordeaux (France) ***CIUDAD DE CADIZ***, Tunis – Tangiers Med – Cadiz (Spain) – Bordeaux ***VILLE DE BORDEAUX***, Hamburg - St Nazaire – Bordeaux ***CITY OF HAMBURG***. Vessels are used for conveying Airbus materials under contract. Spare capacity and light ship sailings are regularly used for conveying trailers, heavy rolling cargo and trade cars and calls are often made at other ports for such cargos and regularly include Pasajes, Santander, Portbury, Sheerness and Zeebrugge. In addition vessels are regularly chartered out for short periods when idle.

1	CITY OF HAMBURG	15643t	08	180k	126.5m	4P	853C	31T	A	FR	9383558
2	CIUDAD DE CADIZ	15643t	09	180k	126.5m	4P	853C	31T	A	FR	9383560
3	VILLE DE BORDEAUX	21528t	04	210k	154.3m	12P	658C	123T	A	FR	9270842

CITY OF HAMBURG, CIUDAD DE CADIZ Built by Singapore Technologies Marine Ltd, Singapore for *Louis Dreyfus Armateurs* of France. Able to operate as a conventional ro-ro or as a car carrier using portable mezzanine decks and a dedicated car deck.

VILLE DE BORDEAUX Built by JinLing Shipyard, Nanjing, China for *Louis Dreyfus Armateurs* of France. Able to operate as a conventional ro-ro or as a car carrier using portable mezzanine decks. Short periods have been previously been spent on charter to *Trasmediterranea*, *UECC*, *Cobelfret*, *LD Lines* and *P&O North Sea Ferries*. In 2009 laid up for a year in St Nazaire when Airbus production was temporarily reduced.

SCA

THE COMPANY *SCA* is a Swedish company.

MANAGEMENT Managing Director (UK) Hugo Heij.

ADDRESS *Sweden* Box 805, 851 23, Sundsvall, Sweden**, *UK*** Interforest Terminal London Ltd, 44 Berth, Tilbury Dock, Essex RM18 7HP.

TELEPHONE Administration & Reservations *Sweden* +46 (0)60 19 30 00, ***UK*** +44 (0)1375 488500.

FAX Administration & Reservations *Sweden* +46 (0)60-19 35 65, ***UK*** +44 (0)1375 488503.

INTERNET Email info@sca.com **Website** www.sca.com/en/logistics *(English)*

ROUTE OPERATED Umeå - Sundsvall - Sheerness - Rotterdam (Eemhaven) - Helsingborg - Oxelösund - Umeå (8/9 day round trip; ***SCA OBBOLA, SCA ORTVIKEN, SCA ÖSTRAND***; 1 per week).

1	SCA OBBOLA	20168t	96	16.0k	170.6m	0P	-	-	A	SE	9087350
2	SCA ORTVIKEN	20154t	97	16.0k	170.4m	0P	-	-	A	SE	9087374
3	SCA ÖSTRAND	20171t	96	16.0k	170.6m	0P	-	-	A	SE	9087362

SCA OBBOLA, SCA ORTVIKEN, SCA ÖSTRAND Built as the OBBOLA, ORTVIKEN and ÖSTRAND by Astilleros Españoles, Sevilla, Spain for *Gorthon Lines* and chartered to *SCA Transforest*. They are designed for the handling of forest products in non-wheeled 'cassettes' but can also accommodate trailers. The ORTVIKEN was lengthened during Autumn 2000 and the others during 2001. In June 2001 purchased by *SCA Transforest*. In spring 2016 renamed the SCA OBBOLA, SCA ORTVIKEN and SCA ÖSTRAND.

SMURFIT KAPPA GROUP

THE COMPANY *Smurfit Kappa Group* is an international company registered in the Irish Republic.

MANAGEMENT Group CEO Tony Smurfit.

ADDRESS Ballymount Road, Walkinstown 12, Dublin, Ireland.

TELEPHONE +353 (0)1 409 0000.

INTERNET Website www.smurfitkappa.com *(English)*

ROUTE OPERATED Södertälje (Sweden) - Harraholmen (Sweden) - Bremen (Germany)- Sheerness - Terneuzen (Netherlands) - Cuxhaven (Germany) - - Sodertalje (12 days; ***BALTICBORG, BOTHNIABORG***; 1 per week).

1	BALTICBORG	12460t	04	16.5 k	153.1m	OP	-	104T	A	NL	9267716
2	BOTHNIABORG	12460t	04	16.5 k	153.1m	OP	-	104T	A	NL	9267728

BALTICBORG, BOTHNIABORG Built by Bodewes Volharding, Volharding, The Netherlands (hull built by Daewoo Mangalia Heavy Industries SA, Mangalia, Romania) for *Wagenborg Shipping* of The Netherlands. Time-chartered to *Kappa Packaging* (now *Smurfit Kappa Group)*. Placed on service between Piteå and Northern Europe. Northbound journeys (Terneuzen - Piteå) marketed as *RORO2 Stockholm*, with a call at Södertälje (Sweden (near Stockholm)) and, from 2005, the section Bremen - Sheerness - Terneuzen marketed as *RORO2 London*. In 2007 these arrangements ceased and *Mann Lines* took over the marketing of northbound traffic, a northbound call at Harwich (Navyard) being introduced and the Södertälje call being replaced by a call at Paldiski in Estonia. This arrangement ceased in 2013 and they reverted to their previous schedules.

NORDIC
NASSAU

Pride of the Tyne **is passed by the car carrier *Nordic Ace.*** *(George Holland)*

SECTION 5 - GB & IRELAND - CHAIN, CABLE ETC FERRIES

CUMBRIA COUNTY COUNCIL

Address Resources Directorate, Highways Transportation and Fleet, County Offices, Kendal, Cumbria LA9 4RQ **Tel** +44 (0)1539 713040, **Fax** +44 (0)1539 713035.

Internet Email peter.hosking@cumbria.gov.uk *(English)*

Website www.cumbria.gov.uk/roads-transport/highways-pavements/windermereferry.asp *(English)*

Route Bowness-on-Windermere - Far Sawrey.

1	MALLARD	-	90	-	25.9m	140P	18C	-	BA

MALLARD Chain ferry built by F L Steelcraft, Borth, Dyfed for *Cumbria County Council*.

DARTMOUTH – KINGSWEAR FLOATING BRIDGE CO LTD

Address DKFBC Ltd, Dart Marina, Sandquay Road, Dartmouth, Devon TQ6 9PH. **Tel** +44 (0)7866 531687.

Internet Website www.dartmouthhigherferry.com *(English)*

Route Dartmouth - Kingswear (Devon) across River Dart (higher route) (forms part of A379).

1	HIGHER FERRY	540t	09	-	52.7m	240P	32C	-	BA

HIGHER FERRY Built by Ravestein BV, Deest, The Netherlands under contract to Pendennis Shipyard, Falmouth, who fitted the vessel out between January and June 2009.

ISLE OF WIGHT COUNCIL (COWES FLOATING BRIDGE)

Address Ferry Office, Medina Road, Cowes, Isle of Wight PO31 7BX. **Tel** +44 (0)1983 293041. **Internet Website** www.iwfloatingbridge.co.uk/timetable **Route** Cowes - East Cowes. ***Note*** the service is unable to operate at times of very low tide; a passenger service by launch is operated. Details are shown on the website.

1	FLOATING BRIDGE NO 6	-	17	-	38.0m	-	20C	-	BA
2●	NO 5	-	76	-	33.5m	-	15C	-	BA

FLOATING BRIDGE NO 6 Chain ferry built by Mainstay Marine Solutions Ltd, Pembroke Dock, UK.

NO 5 Chain ferry built by Fairey Marine, East Cowes, UK for *Isle of Wight County Council*, now *Isle of Wight Council*. In January 2017 withdrawn for sale. Laid up at Gosport.

KING HARRY FERRY AND CORNWALL FERRIES

Address 2 Ferry Cottages, Feock, Truro, Cornwall TR3 6QJ. **Tel** +44 (0)1872 862 312.

Internet Email info@ falriver.co.uk **Website** www.falriver.co.uk *(English)*

Route Philliegh - Feock (Cornwall) (across River Fal)

1	KING HARRY FERRY	500t	06	-	55.2m	150P	34C	-	BA	UK	9364370

KING HARRY FERRY Chain ferry built by Pendennis Shipyard, Falmouth (hull constructed at Ravestein Shipyard, Deest, The Netherlands) to replace the previous ferry. Number is Lloyd's number, not IMO.

LUSTY BEG ISLAND FERRY

Address Lusty Beg, Boa Island, Kesh, County Fermanagh BT93 8AD.

Tel +44 (0)28 686 33300 **Fax** +44 (0)28 686 32033

Internet Email info@lustybegisland.com **Website** www.lustybegisland.com *(English)*

Route Boa Island, County Fermanagh - Lusty Beg Island (Lower Lough Erne).

1	CORLOUGHAROO	-	-	-	10.0m	30P	2C	-	BA		

CORLOUGHAROO Cable ferry, built for *Lusty Beg Island*.

REEDHAM FERRY

Address Reedham Ferry, Ferry Inn, Reedham, Norwich NR13 3HA. **Tel** +44 (0)1493 700429.

Internet Email info@reedhamferry.co.uk **Website** www.reedhamferry.co.uk *(English)*

Route Acle - Reedham - Norton (across River Yare, Norfolk).

1	REEDHAM FERRY	-	84	-	11.3m	20P	3C	-	BA		

REEDHAM FERRY Chain ferry built by Newsons, Oulton Broad, Lowestoft, UK for *Reedham Ferry*. Maximum vehicle weight: 12 tons.

SANDBANKS FERRY

Address ***Company*** Bournemouth-Swanage Motor Road and Ferry Company, Shell Bay, Studland, Swanage, Dorset BH19 3BA. **Tel** +44 (0)1929 450203, ***Ferry*** Floating Bridge, Ferry Way, Sandbanks, Poole, Dorset BH13 7QN. **Tel** +44 (0)1929 450203.

Internet Email email@sandbanksferry.co.uk **Website** www.sandbanksferry.co.uk *(English)*

Route Sandbanks - Shell Bay (Dorset).

1	BRAMBLE BUSH BAY	625t	93	-	74.4m	400P	48C	-	BA	UK	9072070

BRAMBLE BUSH BAY Chain ferry, built by Richard Dunston (Hessle) Ltd, Hessle, UK for the *Bournemouth-Swanage Motor Road and Ferry Company*. Number is Lloyd's number, not IMO.

SOUTH HAMS DISTRICT COUNCIL

Address Lower Ferry Office, The Square, Kingswear, Dartmouth, Devon TQ6 0AA. **Tel** +44 (0)1803 861234.

Internet Website www.southhams.gov.uk/DartmouthLowerFerry *(English)*

Route Dartmouth - Kingswear (Devon) across River Dart (lower route).

1	THE TOM AVIS	-	94	-	33.5m	50P	8C	-	BA		
2	THE TOM CASEY	-	89	-	33.5m	50P	8C	-	BA		

THE TOM AVIS Float (propelled by tugs) built by C Toms & Sons, Fowey, UK for *South Hams District Council*.

THE TOM CASEY Float (propelled by tugs) built by Cosens, Portland, UK for *South Hams District Council*.

TORPOINT FERRY

Address 2 Ferry Street, Torpoint, Cornwall PL11 2AX. **Tel** +44 (0)1752 812233.

Internet Website www.tamarcrossings.org.uk *(English)*

Route Devonport (Plymouth) - Torpoint (Cornwall) across the Tamar. The three ferries operate in parallel, each on her own 'track'. Pre-booking is not possible and the above number cannot be used for that purpose.

1	LYNHER II	748t	06	-	73.0m	250P	73C	-	BA	-	9310941
2	PLYM II	748t	04	-	73.0m	250P	73C	-	BA	-	9310927
3	TAMAR II	748t	05	-	73.0m	250P	73C	-	BA	-	9310939

LYNHER II, PLYM II, TAMAR II Chain ferries built by Ferguson Shipbuilders Ltd, Port Glasgow, UK to replace 1960s-built ships. Number is Lloyds number, not IMO.

WATERFORD CASTLE RESORT

Address The Island, Waterford, Irish Republic. **Tel** +353 (0)51 878203, Fax: + 353 (0)51 879 316.

Internet Email info@waterfordcastleresort.com **Website** www.waterfordcastleresort.com *(English)*

Route Grantstown - Little Island (in River Suir, County Waterford).

1	MARY FITZGERALD	122t	72	10.0k	35.0m	100P	14C	-	BA	IR	8985531

MARY FITZGERALD Built as the STEDINGEN by Abeking & Rasmussen, Lemwerder, Germany for *Schnellastfähre Berne-Farge GmbH* (from 1993 *Fähren Bremen-Stedingen GmbH*) to operate across the River Weser (Vegesack - Lemwerder and Berne - Farge). In 2004 sold to the *Lough Foyle Ferry Company Ltd* and renamed the FOYLE RAMBLER. Generally used on the Buncrana - Rathmullan (Lough Swilly) service, which did not resume in summer 2014. In 2014 sold to *Waterford Castle Hotel* and renamed the MARY FITZGERALD. Modified to be cable guided. Number is Lloyds number, not IMO.

SECTION 6 - GB & IRELAND - MAJOR PASSENGER-ONLY FERRIES

There are a surprisingly large number of passenger-only ferries operating in the British Isles, mainly operated by launches and small motor boats. There are, however, a few 'major' operators who operate only passenger vessels (of rather larger dimensions) and have not therefore been mentioned previously.

Appledore Instow Ferry LIZZIE M 2010, 6.7m, 12 passengers, SHEILA M 2019, 7.6m, 12 passengers. **Route operated** Appledore (Devon) - Instow (Devon) (across River Torridge). **Website** www.appledoreinstowferry.com *(English)*

Aran Island Ferries BANRÍON NA FARRAIGE (117t, 27.4m, 1984, 195 passengers, IMO 8407709) (ex ARAN EXPRESS 2007), CEOL NA FARRAIGE (234t, 2001, 37.4m, 294 passengers, IMO 9246750), DRAÍOCHT NA FARRAIGE (318t, 1999, 35.4m, 294 passengers, IMO 9200897), GLÓR NA FARRAIGE (170t, 1985, 33.5m, 244 passenger, IMO 8522391) (ex ARAN FLYER 2007). **Routes operated** Rossaveal (Co Galway) – Inishmor, Rossaveal - Inis Meáin, Rossaveal - Inisheer. **Tel** +353 (0)91 568903 (572050 after 19.00), **Fax** +353 (0)91 568538, **Email** info@aranislandferries.com **Website** www.aranislandferries.com *(English)*

Blue Funnel Cruises HYTHE SCENE (66t, 1992, 21.3m, 162 passengers - catamaran) (ex GREAT EXPECTATIONS 2017), JENNY ANN (1979, 11.6m, 50 passengers) (ex PUFFIN BELLE 2017, ex FALDORE III 2015, ex JENNY ANN 1998), JENNY BLUE (ex OSSIAN OF STAFFA 2017) (1993, 13.7m, 65 passengers), JENNY R* (12t, 1984, 13.7m, 75 passengers), OCEAN SCENE (279t, 1994, 29.0m, 350 passengers - catamaran, IMO 8633865), OLIVER B* (21t, 1988, 12.2m, 62 passengers) (ex SOLENT PRINCE 2001, JENNY ANN 1999, FINGAL OF STAFFA). Note: The HYTHE SCENE is the regular ferry. Other vessels in the fleet (which are used for charters and excursions) can cover as necessary. **Route Operated** Southampton - Hythe, **Tel** +44 (0)2380 239800 **Email** office@bluefunnel.co.uk **Website** www.bluefunnel.co.uk *(English)*. *The JENNY R is owned by *Blue Funnel* but operated by *Solent and Wightline Cruises Ltd*, the OLIVER B is owned by *Solent and Wightline Cruises Ltd* but operated by *Blue Funnel Cruises*.

Carmarthen Bay Ferries GLANSTEFFAN (2018, 8.0m, 10 passengers (amphibian)). **Route Operated** Ferryside - Llanstephan (Carmarthenshire, Wales). **Tel** +44 (0)1237 874000. **Email** info@carmarthenbayferries.co.uk **Website** www.carmarthenbayferries.co.uk *(English, Welsh)*

Clydelink ISLAND TRADER (12 passengers), SILVER SWAN (12 passengers) **Route operated** Renfrew - Yoker (operated on behalf of *Strathclyde Partnership for Transport*). **Tel** +44 (0)871 705 0888, **Website** www.clydelink.co.uk *(English)*.

Cremyll Ferry (Plymouth Boat Trips) EDGCUMB BELLE (35t, 1957, 17.6m, 128 passengers) (ex HUMPHREY GILBERT 1978) **Route operated** Stonehouse, Plymouth, Devon - Cremyll,

Cornwall. **Note:** River craft owned by this operator are also used for the ferry service on some occasions. **Tel** +44 (0)1752 253153 or +44 (0)7971 208381 **Email** info@plymouthboattrips.co.uk **Website** www.plymouthboattrips.co.uk/ferries/cremyll-ferry *(English)*

Dartmouth Steam Railway & Riverboat Company DARTMOUTH PRINCESS (ex DEVON BELLE II 2000) (22t, 1990, 18.3m, 156 passengers), KINGSWEAR PRINCESS (27t, 1978, 19.1m, 150 passengers) (ex TWIN STAR II 2010). **Route operated** Dartmouth - Kingswear. **Note:** River craft owned by this operator are also used for the ferry service on some occasions. **Tel** +44 (0)1803 555872, **Website** www.dartmouthrailriver.co.uk/tours/dartmouth-to-kingswear-passenger-ferry *(English)*

Doolin2Aran Ferries DOOLIN DISCOVERY (2009, 15.2m, 72 passengers), HAPPY HOOKER (77t, 1989, 19.8m, 96 passengers), JACK B (2005, 15.2m, 67 passengers), ROSE OF ARAN (113t, 1976, 20.1m, 96 passengers. IMO 7527916), STAR OF DOOLIN (2018, 24.0m, 200 passengers). **Routes operated** Doolin - Inisheer, Doolin - Inishmore, Doolin - Inishmaan. Also Cliffs of Moher Cruise. **Tel** +353 (0)65 707 5555, **Email** info@doolin2aranferries.com **Website** www.doolin2aranferries.com *(English)*

Doolin Ferry (O'Brien Line) DOOLIN EXPRESS , (161t, 2010, 24.5m, 250 passengers), (ex BLANCHE HERMINE 2016, ex SAINT VINCENT DE PAUL 2014), GALWAY GIRL (99t, 1967, 24.1m, 200 passengers), TRANQUILITY (62t, 1988, 15.8m, 100 passengers). **Routes operated** Doolin - Inisheer, Doolin - Inishmaan, Doolin - Inishmore. Also cruises to Cliffs of Mohr. **Tel** +353 (0)65 707 5555, +353 (0)65 707 5618, **Email** info@doolinferry.com **Website** www.doolinferry.com *(English)*

Exe2Sea Cruises MY QUEEN (1929, 37t, 18m, 127 passengers) (ex GONDOLIER QUEEN) (reserve), ORCOMBE (23t, 1954, 14.3m, 90 passengers), PRINCESS MARINA (1936, 15.8m, 60 passengers). **Route operated** Exmouth - Starcross. **Tel** +44 (0)7974 022536 / +44 (0)7779 157280. **Email** info@exe2sea.co.uk **Website** www.exe2sea.co.uk (diverts to Facebook page) *(English)*

Fleetwood - Knott End Ferry (operated by *Wyre Marine Services Ltd*) WYRE ROSE (2005, 10.0m length, 32 passengers). **Route operated** Fleetwood - Knott End. **Tel** +44 (0)1253 871113, **Ferry mobile** +44 (0) 7793 270934, **Email** info@wyremarine.co.uk **Website** www.wyre.gov.uk (search for ferry) *(English)*

Gosport Ferry HARBOUR SPIRIT (293t, 2015, 32.8m, 297 passengers, IMO 9741669), SPIRIT OF GOSPORT (300t, 2001, 32.6m, 300 passengers, IMO 8972089), SPIRIT OF PORTSMOUTH (377t, 2005, 32.6m, 300 passengers, IMO 9319894). **Route operated** Gosport - Portsmouth. **Tel** +44 (0)23 9252 4551, **Fax:** +44(0)23 9252 4802, **Email** admin@gosportferry.co.uk **Website** www.gosportferry.co.uk *(English)*

Gravesend - Tilbury Ferry (operated by the *JetStream Tours*) THAMES SWIFT (25.6t, 1995, 18.3m, 50 passengers (tri-maran)), (ex MARTIN CHUZZLEWIT 2001), JACOB MARLEY (29t, 1985, 15.5m, 98 passengers) (ex SOUTHERN BAY ROSE 2016, ex SEAWAYS EXPRESS 2006, ex CONDOR KESTREL), URIAH HEEP (25.6t, 1999, 18.3m, 60 passengers, (tri-maran) - undergoing major restoration). **Note** the THAMES SWIFT is the regular ferry; the JACOB MARLEY may substitute on occasions and also the URIAH HEEP (possibly renamed) when restoration (following an accident when used on the Southampton - Hythe service in 2016) is complete. **Route operated** Gravesend (Kent) - Tilbury (Essex), **Tel** +44 (0)1634 525202, **Email** bookings@jetstreamtours.com **Website** www.jetstreamtours.com *(English)*

Hamble - Warsash Ferry CLAIRE (2.1t, 1985, 7.3m, 12 passengers), EMILY (3.7t, 1990, 8.5m, 12 passengers. **Route operated** Hamble - Warsash (across Hamble River). **Tel** +44 (0)23 8045 4512, **Mobile** +44 (0)7720 438402 Duty Ferryman +44 (0) 7827 157154. **Email** mike@hambleferry.co.uk, **Website** www.hambleferry.co.uk *(English)*

Harwich Harbour Foot & Bicycle Ferry HARBOUR FERRY (8t, 1969, 11.4m, 58 passengers) (ex lifeboat from the liner CANBERRA, ex TAURUS 2012, ex PUFFIN BILLI, 2016). **Routes operated** Harwich (Ha'penny Pier) - Shotley (Marina), Harwich - Felixstowe (Landguard Point)

(Easter to end of September). **Tel** +44 (0)1728 666329, **Email** chris@harwichharbourferry.com **Website** www.harwichharbourferry.com *(English)*

Hayling Ferry (operated by **Baker Trayte Marine Ltd**). PRIDE OF HAYLING 1989, 11.9m, 63 passengers), **Route operated** Eastney - Hayling Island. **Tel/Fax:** +44(0)23 9229 4800, +44(0)23 9266 2942, **Mobile** +44(0)7500 194854, **Website** www.haylingferry.net *(English)*

Hovertravel ISLAND FLYER (161t, 2016, 22.4m, 80 passengers, IMO 9737797, Griffon Hovercraft 12000TD/AP), SOLENT FLYER (161t, 2016, 40.0k, 22.4m, 80 passengers, IMO 9737785, Griffon Hovercraft 12000TD/AP), FREEDOM 90 (1990, 25.4m, 95 passengers, BHC AP1-88/100S hovercraft, converted from AP1-88/100 in 1999), ISLAND EXPRESS (1985, 25.4m, 95 passengers, BHC AP1-88/100S hovercraft, converted from BHC AP1-88/100 in 2001) (ex FREJA VIKING, 2002). **Route operated** Southsea - Ryde. **Tel** +44 1983 717700, **Email** info@hovertravel.com **Website** www.hovertravel.co.uk *(English)*

Isle of Sark Shipping Company BON MARIN DE SERK (118t, 1983, 20.7m, 131 passengers, IMO 8303056), SARK BELLE (50t, 1979, 26.2m, 180 passengers) (ex BOURNEMOUTH BELLE 2011), SARK VENTURE (133t, 1986, 21.3m, 122 passengers, IMO 8891986), SARK VIKING (Cargo Vessel) (104t, 2007, 21.2m, 12 passengers, IMO 8648858). **Route operated** St Peter Port (Guernsey) - Sark. **Tel** +44 (0) 1481 724059, **Email** info@sarkshipping.gg **Website** www.sarkshippingcompany.com *(English)*

John O'Groats Ferries PENTLAND VENTURE (186t, 1987, 29.6m, 250 passengers, IMO 8834122). **Route operated** John O'Groats – Burwick (Orkney). **Tel** +44 (0)1955 611353, **Email** Office@jogferry.co.uk **Website** www.jogferry.co.uk *(English)*

Kintyre Express KINTYRE EXPRESS V (2012, 12.5m, 12 passengers), **Routes operated** Campbeltown - Ballycastle, Port Ellen (Islay) - Ballycastle. **Tel** +44 (0) 1586 555895, **Email** info@kintyreexpress.com **Website** www.kintyreexpress.com *(English)*

Lundy Company OLDENBURG (294t, 1958, 43.6m, 267 passengers, IMO 5262146). **Routes operated** Bideford - Lundy Island, Ilfracombe - Lundy Island. Also North Devon coastal cruises and River Torridge cruises. **Tel** +44 (0)1237 470074, **Fax** +44 (0)1237 477779, **Email** info@lundyisland.co.uk **Website** www.lundyisland.co.uk *(English)*

Manche Iles Express (trading name of Société Morbihannaise de Navigation) GRANVILLE (325t, 2006, 41.0m, 245 passengers, IMO 9356476 - catamaran) (ex BORNHOLM EXPRESS 2014), VICTOR HUGO (387t, 1997, 35.0m, 195 passengers, IMO 9157806 - catamaran) (ex SALTEN 2003). **Routes operated** Jersey - Guernsey, Granville – Jersey - Sark - Guernsey, Portbail or Carteret – Jersey, Guernsey and Sark, Diélette - Alderney - Guernsey. **Tel *France*** +33 0825 131 050, **Guernsey** +44 (0)1481 701316, ***Jersey*** +44 (0)1534 880756, **Website** www.manche-iles-express.com *(French, English)*

MBNA Thames Clippers (trading name of Collins River Enterprises Ltd) AURORA CLIPPER (181t, 2007, 37.8m, 27.5k, 220 passengers, IMO 9451824), CYCLONE CLIPPER (181t, 2007, 37.8m, 27.5k, 220 passengers, IMO 9451880), GALAXY CLIPPER (155t, 2015, 34.0m, 155 passengers, IMO 9783784), HURRICANE CLIPPER (181t, 2002, 37.8m, 27.5k, 220 passengers, IMO 9249702), JUPITER CLIPPER (155t, 2017, 35.0 m, 28.0k, 170 passengers, IMO 9223796), MERCURY CLIPPER (155t, 2017, 35.0 m, 28.0k, 170 passengers, IMO 9223801), METEOR CLIPPER (181t, 2007, 37.8m, 27.5k, 220 passengers, IMO 9451812), MONSOON CLIPPER (181t, 2007, 37.8m, 27.5k, 220 passengers, IMO 9451795), MOON CLIPPER (98t, 2001, 32.0m, 25.0k, 138 passengers, IMO 9245586) (ex DOWN RUNNER 2005), NEPTUNE CLIPPER (155t, 2015, 34.0m, 155 passengers, IMO 9783796), SKY CLIPPER (60t, 1992, 25.0m, 62 passengers) (ex VERITATUM 1995, SD10 2000), STAR CLIPPER (60t, 1992, 25.0m, 62 passengers) (ex CONRAD CHELSEA HARBOUR 1995, SD9 2000), STORM CLIPPER (60t, 1992, 25.0m, 62 passengers) (ex DHL WORLDWIDE EXPRESS 1995, SD11 2000), SUN CLIPPER (98t, 2001, 32.0m, 25.0k, 138 passengers, IMO 9232292) (ex ANTRIM RUNNER 2005), TORNADO CLIPPER (181t, 2007, 37.8m, 27.5k, 220 passengers, IMO 9451783), TWIN STAR (45t, 1974, 19.2m, 120 passengers), TYPHOON CLIPPER (181t, 2007, 37.8m, 27.5k, 220 passengers, IMO 9451771, (2015, 34.0m, 154 seats), VENUS CLIPPER (172t, 2019, 38.0m, 25.0k, 220 passengers, IMO 9867736) The 'Typhoon', 'Tornado', 'Cyclone' and 'Monsoon', 'Aurora' and 'Meteor' Clippers were designed by

Galway Girl *(Miles Cowsill)*

Star of Doolin *(Miles Cowsill)*

Oldenburg *(Nick Widdows)*

Sun Clipper *(Andrew Cooke)*

AIMTEK and built by Brisbane Ship Constructions in Australia in 2007. 'Galaxy' and 'Neptune' were designed by One2three Naval Architects and built by Incat Tasmania, Hobart, Australia. 'Jupiter', 'Mercury' and 'Venus' were also designed by One2three Naval Architects but were built by Wight Shipyard, East Cowes, Isle of Wight. **Routes operated** Embankment - Waterloo - Blackfriars – Bankside - London Bridge - Tower - Canary Wharf – Greenland - Masthouse Terrace - Greenwich - North Greenwich – Woolwich, Bankside – Millbank - St George (Tate to Tate Service), Putney - Wandsworth - Chelsea Harbour - Cardogan - Embankment - Blackfriars, Canary Wharf - Rotherhithe DoubleTree by Hilton Docklands Hotel (TWIN STAR).**Tel** +44 (0)870 781 5049, **Fax** +44 (0)20 7001 2222, **Email** web@thamesclippers.com **Website** www.thamesclippers.com *(English)*

Mersey Ferries ROYAL IRIS OF THE MERSEY (464t, 1960, 46.3m, 650 passengers, IMO 8633712) (ex MOUNTWOOD 2002), SNOWDROP (670t, 1960, 46.6m, 650 passengers, IMO 8633724) (ex WOODCHURCH 2004). **Routes operated** Liverpool (Pier Head) - Birkenhead (Woodside), Liverpool - Wallasey (Seacombe) with regular cruises from Liverpool and Seacombe to Salford along the Manchester Ship Canal. **Tel *Admin*** +44 (0)151 639 0609, ***Bookings and Enquiries*** +44 (0)151 330 10003, **Twitter** @merseyferries, **Facebook** Mersey Ferries **Website** www.merseyferries.co.uk *(English)*

Mudeford Ferry (Derham Marine) FERRY DAME (4t, 1989, 9.1m, 48 passengers), JOSEPHINE (10.5t, 1997, 10.7m, 70 passengers - catamaran), JOSEPHINE II (10.5t, 2013, 11.0m, 86 passengers - catamaran). **Route operated** Mudeford Quay - Mudeford Sandbank. **Tel** +44 (0)7968 334441 **Email** information@mudefordferry.co.uk **Website** www.mudefordferry.co.uk *(English)*

Nexus (trading name of Tyne & Wear Integrated Transport Authority) PRIDE OF THE TYNE (222t, 1993, 24.0m, 240 passengers, IMO 9062166), SPIRIT OF THE TYNE (174t, 2006, 25.0m, 200 passengers). **Route operated** North Shields - South Shields. Also cruises South Shields - Newcastle. **Tel** +44 (0)191 2020747, **Website** www.nexus.org.uk/ferry *(English)*

O'Malley Ferries, Clare Island NAOMH CIARAN II (35t, 1982, 17.7m, 97 passengers, TORMORE (67t, 1992, 17.7m, 75 passengers), TRUE LIGHT (19t, 2002, 12.8m, 38 passengers). **Routes Operated** Roonagh (Co Mayo) - Inishturk, (50 mins), Roonagh - Clare, Island. **Tel** +353(0) 98 25045, **Mobiles** +353(0)87 660 0409, +353(0)86 887 0814, **Email** www.omalleyferries.com **Website** www.omalleyferries.com *(English)*

The Little Ferry Company SPIKE ISLANDER (13.0m, 20.3k, 12 passengers), **Route Operated** St Peter Port (Guernsey) - Alderney. **Tel** +44 (0)1481 822828 **Email** office@thelittleferrycompany.com **Website** www.thelittleferrycompany.com *(English)*

Travel Trident HERM TRIDENT V (79t, 1989, 25.9m, 250 passengers), TRIDENT VI (79t, 1992, 22.3m, 250 passengers). **Route operated** St Peter Port (Guernsey) - Herm. **Tel** +44 (0)1481 721379, **Fax** +44 (0)1481 700226, **Email** peterwilcox@cwgsy.net **Website** www.traveltrident.com *(English)*

Waverley Excursions WAVERLEY (693t, 1946, 73.13m, 860 passengers, IMO 5386954). **Routes operated** Excursions all round British Isles. However, regular cruises in the Clyde, Bristol Channel, South Coast and Thames provide a service which can be used for transport purposes and therefore she is in a sense a ferry. She is the only seagoing paddle steamer in the world. NOTE: Due to the need to replace boilers the WAVERLEY did not operate in 2019. It is hoped to resume sailings in 2020. **Tel** +44 (0)845 130 4647, **Fax** +44 (0)141 243 2224, **Email** info@waverleyexcursions.co.uk **Website** www.waverleyexcursions.co.uk *(English)*

Western Isles Cruises Ltd LARVEN (21t, 2017, 14.2m, 42 passengers (catamaran)), WESTERN ISLES (54t, 1960, 18.0m, 82 passengers). **Route Operated** Mallaig - Inverie (Knoydart) - Tarbet Loch Nevis - Inverie and Tarbet, **Tel** +44 (0)1687 462233, **Email** info@westernislescruises.co.uk, **Website** www.westernislescruises.co.uk *(English)*

Western Lady Ferry Service WESTERN LADY VI (ex TORBAY PRINCESS ex DEVON PRINCESS II) (50t, 1981, 19.2m, 145 passengers), WESTERN LADY VII (ex TORBAY PRINCESS II, ex BRIXHAM BELLE II, ex DEVON PRINCESS III) (46t, 1984, 19.8m, 150 passengers). **Route Operated** Torquay - Brixham. **Tel** +44 (0)1803 293797, **Website** www.westernladyferry.com

Star Clipper *(Andrew Cooke)*

Solent Flyer *(Andrew Cooke)*

(English) Note: The service is now part of *Dartmouth Steam Railway & Riverboat Company* but is marketed separately.

White Funnel BALMORAL (735t, 1949, 62.2m, 800 passengers, IMO 5034927) Excursions in Bristol Channel, North West, South Coast, Thames and Clyde. However, no services operated in 2018 or 2019. Services may resume in 2020. **Email** balmoral@whitefunnel.co.uk **Website** www.whitefunnel.co.uk *(English)*

Pride of the Tyne *(George Holland)*

STENA BALTICA
Stena Line

Stena Baltica **leaving Gdańsk.** *(Frank Lose)*

SCANDINAVIAN AND NORTHERN EUROPE REVIEW 2018/19

The following geographical review again takes the form of a voyage along the coast of the Netherlands and Germany, round the Southern tip of Norway, down the Kattegat, through the Great Belt and into the Baltic, then up to the Gulf of Finland and Gulf of Bothnia.

FRISIAN ISLANDS & ELBE

Rederij Doeksen's new twin catamarans *Willem Barentsz* and *Willem de Vlamingh* have continued to experience lengthy delays but were moved from Vietnam to Harlingen during April 2019 for completion. Although the vessels were then anticipated to enter service during September 2019, on arrival at Harlingen, it was discovered that the craft had been damaged due to water ingress during the voyage from the Far East which would necessitate further works and a subsequent slippage in completion date to early 2020. They will serve the routes from Harlingen to Vlieland and Terschelling.

A further attempt to restart the Elbe crossing between Cuxhaven and Brunsbüttel was announced during 2019 with a new outfit called Elbeferry which was reported to be purchasing the redundant Fjord1 vessel *Fanafjord* for the route. However, despite announcing a May 2019 start date, the plans came to nothing although local authorities remain hopeful that a service can recommence in due course.

NORWEGIAN DOMESTIC

Bastø-Fosen have placed an order for a fourth vessel to join the three introduced in 2016 and 2017. The new vessel will be built at the Sefine shipyard in Turkey. The vessel will be electric powered. Providing sufficient investment is made in shoreside recharging facilities, the company has stated its intention to convert some of the earlier vessels to electric operation in the future.

Havila has announced that it's four new vessels, currently under construction at Norwegian and Spanish shipyards will be given the name *Havila Capella*, *Havila Castor*, *Havila Polaris* and *Havila Pollux*.

Hurtigruten's new *Roald Amundsen* entered service in July 2019 will be officially named in a ceremony in Antarctica in the Autumn, becoming the first cruise ship to be named in that continent. A third vessel in the class has been ordered from the Kleven Verft shipyard, due for delivery in 2021.

SKAGERRAK & KATTEGAT

Color Line's new *Color Hybrid* entered service in August 2019 on the Sandefjord – Strömstad service, replacing *Bohus* which was sold for further service in the Mediterranean. The company is also to retain *Color Viking* in service following the decision of the municipal authorities in Sandefjord to award a two-ship contract to rivals Fjord Line. The latter had been unable to procure a second vessel so will retain a single-ship operation with *Oslofjord* whilst Color Line continues with its two ferries.

Color Line also introduced a dedicated freight-only vessel on its flagship Oslo – Kiel service. The *Color Carrier* was acquired from Finnlines, for whom it had previously served as *Finncarrier*, and placed onto the route in early January, providing additional capacity and removing some freight traffic from the cruise ferries. The ship undertakes three return sailings each week.

Stena Line's new ro-pax for the Göteborg – Frederikshavn service was introduced as *Stena Vinga* in September 2018. Formerly the *Hammerodde*, she was purchased from Danske Færger following the loss of that company's concession to operate the Bornholm services.

The HH-Ferries operation between Helsingør and Helsingborg was rebranded as ForSea during November 2018. It had previously continued to trade as Scandlines, following the purchase of the route from that company in 2015. All four vessels adopted a new teal livery when the new

Baltic Princess *(Uwe Jakob)*

Robin Hood *(Frank Lose)*

brand was rolled out on the official inauguration of *Tycho Brahe* and *Aurora af Helsingborg* as fully battery powered vessels.

DANISH DOMESTIC

Molslinjen took delivery of its new Austal ships catamaran *Express 4* in late January 2019. The vessel was deployed on the Sjællands Odde – Århus service, joining *Express 2* and *Express 3*. The company also took over the operation of the Danske Færger fleet following its purchase of the company and the services were rebranded and ships re-liveried. The 'færgen' part of the previous trading names was replaced by 'linjen' so Samsöfærgen became Samsölinjen, a pattern repeated for Alslinjen, Fanølinjen and Langelandslinjen. The conventional ships in the fleet are gradually adopting a light grey hull colour.

Ærøfærgerne took delivery of the electric powered *Ellen* in July 2019 and she was introduced onto the services from Søby and Faaborg/Fynshav during the summer.

Samsø Rederi has placed an order for a new 35 metre passenger catamaran to establish a new service between the island and Århus. The vessel will offer capacity for 296 passengers and 60 bicycles.

SOUTHERN BALTIC

TT-Lines has placed an order for a large, new, LNG-powered ro-pax ferry with the Jinling shipyard in China. The vessel will be delivered in 2022 and will measure 230 metres in length and offer capacity for 800 passengers and 4,600 metres of vehicle space. An option for a second vessel is believed to be in place.

Molslinjen took over the contract for services to Rønne from Køge and Ystad in September 2018, operating as Bornholmslinjen. The company's new Rauma-built ro-pax *Hammershus* was joined on the services by *Express 1* and *Max Mols* (redeployed from the Kattegat services) as well as the *Povl Anker*, acquired as part of the takeover of Danske Færger.

Unity Line purchased Moby Line's *Puglia* and introduced her as the *Copernicus* during Summer 2018 operating between Świnoujscie and Trelleborg, replacing the elderly *Kopernik* which was initially sold for breaking but is now looking likely to enter service in the Mediterranean.

Polferries finally introduced its chartered *Nova Star* between Gdańsk and Nynäshamn in September 2018, following six months of refit disputes with its owners ST Marine. The vessel joined *Wawel* on the service, making it a daily operation in the peak season.

NORTHERN BALTIC

Destination Gotland's new *Visborg* was delivered from China over the New Year and entered service in February. Sistership *Thjelvar* remains under construction.

Tallink has placed an order with Rauma Marine Construction for another large, LNG-powered, day ferry for the Tallinn – Helsinki service which will join *Megastar* on delivery in late 2021. Although the overall specifications will be largely the same as *Megastar*, the ship will be designed from scratch. The new vessel will carry 2,800 passengers.

Tallink has also completed an extensive refurbishment programme across much of its fleet with both the Stockholm – Helsinki flagships *Silja Serenade* and *Silja Symphony* as well as *Galaxy* and *Baltic Princess* receiving significant investment in their public spaces.

Eckerö Line introduced a second vessel on its Helsinki – Tallinn operation, purchasing P&O's Irish Sea ro-pax *European Endeavour*, which was refitted, re-liveried and renamed *Finbo Cargo*. She inaugurated a new route between the port of Vuosaari (in the eastern suburbs of Helsinki) with Muuga (20 kilometres east of Tallinn), to focus on freight traffic, whilst also taking motorists and their vehicles. At the same time, Tallink started to allow car passenger traffic on its own ship serving that route, the *Seawind*.

The trio of double-ended ferries previously operated by Saaremaa Laevakompanii to the Estonian Islands (and two subsequently across the River Elbe between 2015 and 2017) were

Viking Grace *(Uwe Jakob)*

SPL Princess Anastasia *(Darren Holdaway)*

Cracovia *(Frank Lose)*

sold to the Woodward Group for conversion and operation within Canada. The *Saaremaa*, *Hiiumaa* and *Grete* were placed into service on Canada's east coast during Spring 2019 although only *Grete* was renamed, as *Qajaq W*. Praamid, the current operators of the services to the Estonian islands, chartered ForSea's *Mercandia VIII* for both the summer 2018 and 2019 seasons to provide additional capacity.

Viking Line's new Stockholm – Turku cruiseferry commenced construction in China in June 2019 and she is to be given the name *Viking Glory* following a public competition.

Kvarken Link, the consortium behind the Wasaline operation placed an order for the design and construction of a new vessel for the Vaasa – Umeå service with Raume Marine Construction. The order is worth €120 million. The new ship will carry 800 passengers and offer 1,500 metres of lane capacity and will be powered by LNG. She will replace *Wasa Express*, which re-opened the service in 2013, when she arrives in 2021.

A new jointly-owned shipping company formed in April 2019 by Wallenius and Swedish Orient Lines under the name of Wallenius SOL. The new operation inherited SOL's existing vessels and Baltic network which links the Finnish ports of Kemi, Oulu, Pietarsaari and Kaskinen, along with the Swedish port of Husum with the ports of Göteborg, Zeebrugge, Lübeck, Antwerpen and Tilbury. The operation commenced on April 12 utilising the ro-ro vessels *Baltica*, *Tavastland*, *Thuleland*, *Tundraland* and *Wasaland*. The new company also announced a major investment in four new ro-ro vessels to be constructed by CIMC in China and delivered in 2021. The vessels will measure 241 metres in length, offer 5,800 lane metres of capacity and will be LNG-powered.

Matthew Punter

SECTION 7 - NORTHERN EUROPE

ÆRØFÆRGERNE

THE COMPANY *Ærøfærgerne* is a Danish company, owned by the municipality of Ærø.

MANAGEMENT Managing Director Kelda Møller, **Marketing Coordinator** Jeanette Erikson.

ADDRESS Vestergade 1, 5970 Ærøskøbing, Denmark.

TELEPHONE Administration & Reservations +45 62 52 40 00.

FAX Administration & Reservations +45 62 52 20 88.

INTERNET Email info@aeroe-ferry.dk **Website** www.aeroe-ferry.dk *(Danish, English, German)*

ROUTE OPERATED Ærøskøbing (Ærø) - Svendborg (Funen) (1hr 15mins; ***ÆRØSKØBING, MARSTAL***; every 1/2 hours), Søby (Ærø) - Faaborg (Funen) (1hr; ***SKJOLDNÆS***; 3 per day), Søby (Ærø) - Funenshav (Als) (1hr 10mins; ***SKJOLDNÆS***; 3 per day).

1	ÆRØSKØBING	1617t	99	12.0k	49.0m	395P	42C	-	BA	DK	9199086
2	ELLEN	1000t	18	13.0k	59.4m	198P	31C		BA	DK	9805374
3	MARSTAL	1617t	99	12.0k	49.0m	395P	42C	-	BA	DK	9199074
4	SKJOLDNÆS	986t	79	11.0k	47.1m	245P	31C	-	BA	DK	7925649

ÆRØSKØBING, MARSTAL Built by EOS, Esbjerg, Denmark for *Ærøfærgerne*.

ELLEN Built by Søby Vaerft, Søby, Ærø, Denmark for *Ærøfærgerne*. Hybrid electric powered. Expected to enter service Autumn 2019.

SKJOLDNÆS Built as the SAM-SINE by Søren Larsen & Sønner Skibsværft A/S, Nykøbing Mors, Denmark for *Hou-Sælvig Ruten Aps* of Denmark. Operated between Hou (Jylland) and Sælvig (Samsø). In 1995 she was taken over by *Samsø Linien*. In 2001 she was lengthened by Ørskov Christensen's Staalskibsværft, Frederikshavn, Denmark. In 2009 sold to *Ærøfærgerne* and renamed the SKJOLDNÆS. To be replaced by the ELLEN.

BASTØ FOSEN

THE COMPANY *Bastø Fosen* is a Norwegian private sector company, a subsidiary of *Torghatten ASA - Brønnøysund*.

MANAGEMENT Managing Director May Kristin Salberg.

ADDRESS PO Box 94, 3191 Horten, Norway.

TELEPHONE Administration +47 33 03 17 40, **Reservations** +47 33 03 17 40 (buses only).

INTERNET Email bastohorten@fosen.no **Website** basto-fosen.no *(Norwegian, English)*

ROUTE OPERATED Moss - Horten (across Oslofjord, Norway) (30 mins; ***BASTØ I, BASTØ II, BASTØ III, BASTØ IV***, ***BASTØ V, BASTØ VI***; up to every 15 mins).

1	BASTØ I	5505t	97	14.0k	109.0m	550P	200C	18L	BA	NO	9144081
2	BASTØ II	5505t	97	14.0k	109.0m	550P	200C	18L	BA	NO	9144093
3	BASTØ III	7310t	05	18.0k	116.2m	540P	212C	18L	BA	NO	9299408
4	BASTØ IV	7700t	16	16.0k	142.9m	600P	200C	30L	BA	NO	9771420
5	BASTØ V	7700t	17	16.0k	142.9m	600P	200C	30L	BA	NO	9771432
6	BASTØ VI	7870t	16	16.0k	142.9m	600P	200C	30L	BA	NO	9769219

BASTØ I, BASTØ II Built by Fosen Mekaniske Verksteder, Frengen, Norway.

BASTØ III Built by Stocznia Remontowa, Gdańsk, Poland.

BASTØ IV, BASTØ V Built by Sefine Shipyard, Yalova, Turkey.

BASTØ VI Built by Cemre Shipyard, Yalova, Turkey.

Under construction

7	NEWBUILDING	7870t	20	14.0k	142.9m	600P	200C	18L	BA	NO	-

NEWBUILDING Under construction by Sefine Shipyard, Yalova, Turkey. Hybrid diesel/electric but will be able to operate in 100% electric mode when shore infrastructure is completed.

COLOR LINE

THE COMPANY *Color Line ASA* is a Norwegian private sector stock-listed limited company. The company merged with *Larvik Scandi Line* of Norway (which owned *Larvik Line* and *Scandi Line*) in 1996. In 1997 the operations of *Larvik Line* were incorporated into *Color Line*; *Scandi Line* continued as a separate subsidiary until 1998, when it was also incorporated into *Color Line*. The marketing name *Color Scandi Line* was dropped at the end of 2000.

MANAGEMENT CEO Trond Kleivdal.

ADDRESS *Commercial* Postboks 1422 Vika, 0115 Oslo, Norway, ***Technical Management*** Color Line Marine AS, PO Box 2090, 3210 Sandefjord, Norway.

TELEPHONE Administration +47 22 94 44 00, **Reservations *Germany*** +49 04 31/73 00 - 100, ***Denmark*** +45 99 56 10 00, **Norway** 810 00 811.

INTERNET Email kundeservice@colorline.no **Website** www.colorline.com *(English, Danish, German, Norwegian, Swedish)*

ROUTES OPERATED Conventional Ferries Oslo (Norway) - Kiel (Germany) (19 hrs 30 mins; ***COLOR FANTASY, COLOR MAGIC***; 1 per day), Kristiansand (Norway) - Hirtshals (3 hrs 15 mins; ***SUPERSPEED 1***; 4 per day), Larvik (Norway) - Hirtshals (Denmark) (3 hrs 45 mins; ***SUPERSPEED 2***; up to 2 per day), Sandefjord (Norway) - Strömstad (Sweden) (2 hrs 30 mins; ***COLOR HYBRID, COLOR VIKING***; up to 4 per day). **Freight ferry** Oslo - Kiel (21 hrs; ***COLOR CARRIER***; 3 per week).

1F	COLOR CARRIER	12433t	98	20.0k	154.5m	12P	-	124T	A2	NO	9132002
2	COLOR FANTASY	74500t	04	22.3k	224.0m	2605P	750C	90T	BA	NO	9278234
3	COLOR HYBRID	27000t	19	25.3k	160.0m	2000P	500C	-	BA	NO	9824289
4	COLOR MAGIC	75100t	07	22.3k	224.0m	2812P	550C	90T	BA	NO	9349863
5	COLOR VIKING	19763t	85	16.4k	137.0m	1773P	370C	40T	BA2	NO	8317942
6	SUPERSPEED 1	36822t	08	27.0k	211.3m	2400P	750C	121T	BA2	NO	9374519
7	SUPERSPEED 2	33500t	08	27.0k	211.3m	2000P	764C	121T	BA2	NO	9378682

COLOR CARRIER Built as the UNITED CARRIER by Fosen Mekaniske Verksteder A/S, Rissa, Norway for *United Shipping* (a subsidiary of *Birka Shipping*) of Finland and chartered to *Transfennica*. During 2000 she was used on their Kemi - Oulu - Antwerpen - Felixstowe service. In 2001 the route was transferred to *Finnlines* and the vessel used sub-chartered to them (charter later transferred to *Finnlines*). In 2002 *United Shipping* was renamed *Birka Cargo* and the ship was renamed the BIRKA CARRIER. In 2006 the service ceased. In 2008 the charter was extended a further four years. In January 2013 chartered to *Transfennica*. In June 2013 she was renamed the CARRIER. In January 2015 sold to *Finnlines* but not delivered until the end of the year, when the charter ended. In January 2016 renamed the FINNCARRIER. In July 2018 sold to *Color Line* and chartered back to *Finnlines*. In January 2019 renamed the COLOR CARRIER and entered service between Oslo and Kiel.

COLOR FANTASY Built by Kværner Masa-Yards, Turku, Finland for *Color Line* to replace the PRINSESSE RAGNHILD on the Oslo - Kiel service.

COLOR HYBRID Built by Ulstein Verft A/S, Ulsteinvik, Norway, to replace the BOHUS on the Sandefjord - Strömstad route in August 2019. She is a hybrid vessel, operating in both battery and diesel-electric mode.

COLOR MAGIC Built by Aker Yards, Turku, Finland (hull construction) and Rauma, Finland (fitting out), for the Oslo - Kiel route.

Color Carrier *(Peter Therkildsen)*

Gotland *(Uwe Jakob)*

COLOR VIKING Built as the PEDER PAARS by Nakskov Skibsværft A/S, Nakskov, Denmark for *DSB (Danish State Railways)* for their service between Kalundborg (Sjælland) and Århus (Jylland). In 1990 purchased by *Stena Line* of Sweden for delivery in 1991. In that year renamed the STENA INVICTA and entered service on the *Sealink Stena Line* Dover - Calais service. She was withdrawn from the route in February 1998, before the formation of *P&O Stena Line,* but ownership was transferred to that company. In Summer 1998, she was chartered to *Silja Line* to operate between Vaasa and Umeå under the marketing name 'WASA JUBILEE'. In Autumn 1998 she was laid up at Zeebrugge. She remained there until Autumn 1999 when she was chartered to *Stena Line* to operate between Holyhead and Dublin. In 2000 she was chartered to *Color Line*, renamed the COLOR VIKING and in April entered service on the Sandefjord - Strömstad service. In 2002 purchased by *Color Line*.

SUPERSPEED 1, SUPERSPEED 2 Built by Aker Yards, Rauma, Finland for the Kristiansand - Hirtshals and Larvik - Hirtshals routes. In January 2011, the SUPERSPEED 1 was modified to provide additional facilities and increase passenger capacity.

DESTINATION GOTLAND

THE COMPANY *Destination Gotland AB* is a Swedish private sector company owned by *Rederi AB Gotland*.

MANAGEMENT Managing Director Christer Bruzelius, **Marketing Manager** Adam Jacobsson.

ADDRESS PO Box 1234, 621 23 Visby, Gotland, Sweden.

TELEPHONE Administration +46 (0)498-20 18 00, **Reservations** +46 (0)771-22 33 00.

FAX Administration +46 498 20 18 90 **Reservations** +46 (0)498-20 13 90.

INTERNET Email info@destinationgotland.se **Website** www.destinationgotland.se *(Swedish, English, German)*

ROUTES OPERATED Fast Conventional Ferries Visby (Gotland) - Nynäshamn (Swedish mainland) (3 hrs 15 mins; ***GOTLAND, VISBORG, VISBY***; up to 7 per day), Visby - Oskarshamn (Swedish mainland) (2 hrs 55 mins; ***GOTLAND, VISBORG, VISBY***; up to 3 per day). **Fast Ferries (Summer only)** Visby (Gotland) - Nynäshamn (3 hrs 15 mins; ***GOTLANDIA II***; 1 per week), Visby - Vastervik (2 hrs 30 mins; ***GOTLANDIA II***; 1 per day).

1	GOTLAND	29746t	03	28.5k	195.8m	1500P	500C	118T	BAS2	SE	9223796
2»	GOTLANDIA	5632t	99	35.0k	112.5m	700P	140C	-	A	SE	9171163
3»	GOTLANDIA II	6554t	06	36.0k	122.0m	780P	160C	-	A	SE	9328015
4	THJELVAR	32000t	19	28.5k	200.0m	1650P	500C	110L	BAS2	SE	9783071
5	VISBORG	32000t	18	28.5k	200.0m	1650P	500C	110L	BAS2	SE	9763655
6	VISBY	29746t	03	28.5k	195.8m	1500P	500C	118T	BAS2	SE	9223784

GOTLAND, VISBY Built by Guangzhou Shipyard International, Guangzhou, China for *Rederi AB Gotland* for use on *Destination Gotland* services.

GOTLANDIA Alstom Leroux Corsair 11500 monohull vessel built as the GOTLAND at Lorient, France for *Rederi AB Gotland* and chartered to *Destination Gotland*. In 2003 renamed the GOTLANDIA. Now laid up.

GOTLANDIA II Fincantieri SF700 monohull fast ferry built at Riva Trigoso, Italy for *Rederi AB Gotland* for use by *Destination Gotland*.

VISBORG, THJELVAR Built by Guangzhou Shipyard International, Guangzhou, China for *Rederi AB Gotland* for use on *Destination Gotland* services. LNG powered.

DFDS SEAWAYS

THE COMPANY *DFDS Seaways* is a division of *DFDS A/S*, a Danish private sector company.

MANAGEMENT CEO DFDS A/S Niels Smedegaard, **Executive Vice-President Shipping Division** Peder Gellert Pedersen, **Head of Baltic Sea Business Area** Anders Refsgaard.

ADDRESS *København* Sundkrogsgade 11, 2100 København Ø, Denmark.

TELEPHONE Administration +45 33 42 33 42, **Reservations *Denmark*** +45 78 79 55 36, ***Germany*** +49 (0)40-389030, ***Lithuania*** +370 46 393616, ***Sweden*** +46 454 33680

FAX Administration +45 33 42 33 41. **INTERNET Administration** incoming@dfdsseaways.dk, **Reservations *Denmark*** incoming@dfdsseaways.dk ***Germany*** service.de@dfds.com ***Lithuania*** booking.lt@dfds.com, ***Sweden*** pax@dfds.com

Website www.dfdsseaways.com *(English, Danish, Dutch, German, Italian, Japanese, Norwegian, Polish, Swedish)*

ROUTES OPERATED *Passenger services* København - Oslo (Norway) (16 hrs 30 mins; ***CROWN SEAWAYS, PEARL SEAWAYS***; 1 per day), Klaipėda (Lithuania) - Kiel (Germany) (21 hrs; ***REGINA SEAWAYS, VICTORIA SEAWAYS***; 7 per week), Klaipėda - Karlshamn (Sweden) (14 hrs; ***ATHENA SEAWAYS, OPTIMA SEAWAYS, PATRIA SEAWAYS,***; 10 per week), Paldiski (Estonia) - Kapellskär (Sweden) (10 hrs; ***LIVERPOOL SEAWAYS***; 6 per week), Paldiski - Hanko (Finland) (3 hrs; ***SAILOR***; 2 per day). ***Freight only service*** Fredericia - København - Klaipėda (***ARK FUTURA***; 2 per week).

See Section 1 for services operating to Britain and Mediterranean services.

1F	ARK FUTURA	18725t	96	19.7k	183.3m	12P	-	164T	AS	DK	9129598
2	ATHENA SEAWAYS	24950t	07	23.0k	199.1m	500P	-	190T	A	LT	9350680
3F	BOTNIA SEAWAYS	11530t	00	20.0k	162.2m	12P	-	140T	A	LT	9192129
4	CROWN SEAWAYS	35498t	94	22.0k	169.4m	1940P	450C	50T	BA	DK	8917613
5	LIVERPOOL SEAWAYS	21856t	97	20.0k	186.0m	320P	100C	135T	A	LT	9136034
6	OPTIMA SEAWAYS	25206t	99	21.5k	186.3m	327P	164C	150T	A	LT	9188427
7	PATRIA SEAWAYS	18332t	92	17.0k	154.0m	242P	-	114T	BA2	LT	8917390
8	PEARL SEAWAYS	40039t	89	21.0k	178.4m	2090P	350C	70T	BA	DK	8701674
9	REGINA SEAWAYS	25518t	10	24.0k	199.1m	600P	-	190T	A	LT	9458535
10	SAILOR	20921t	87	19.0k	157.6m	119P	50C	82L	A2	EE	8401444
11	VICTORIA SEAWAYS	24950t	09	23.0k	199.1m	600P	-	190T	A	LT	9350721

ARK FUTURA Built as the DANA FUTURA by C N Visentini di Visentini Francesco & C, Donada, Italy for *DFDS*. In 2001 she was renamed the TOR FUTURA. Initially operated mainly between Esbjerg and Harwich, but latterly operated mainly between Esbjerg and Immingham. In 2004 chartered to *Toll Shipping* of Australia. Later time-chartered to the *Danish MoD* for 5.5 years. However, when not required for military service she has been chartered to other operators such as *P&O Ferries*, *Cobelfret Ferries* and *Van Uden Ro-Ro* and used on *DFDS Tor Line* services. In 2006 sold to *DFDS Lys Line Rederi A/S* of Norway, a *DFDS* subsidiary and chartered back. In April 2011 renamed the ARK FUTURA. Currently operating on the Fredericia - København - Klaipėda service.

ATHENA SEAWAYS Built as the CORAGGIO by Nuovi Cantieri Apuani, Marina di Carrara, Italy. First of an order of eight vessels for *Grimaldi Holdings* of Italy. Used on *Grimaldi Lines* Mediterranean services. In September 2010, bare-boat chartered to *Stena Line* to operate between Hoek van Holland and Killingholme. In November 2011 replaced by the new STENA TRANSIT and returned to Mediterranean service. In December 2013 renamed the ATHENA SEAWAYS, chartered to *DFDS* and replaced the LIVERPOOL SEAWAYS on the Klaipėda - Kiel service. In May 2016 purchased by *DFDS*.

BOTNIA SEAWAYS Built as the FINNMASTER by Jinling Shipyard, Nanjing, China for the *Macoma Shipping Group* and chartered to *Finncarriers*. In 2008 sold to *DFDS Lisco* and in January 2009 delivered, chartered to *DFDS Tor Line* and renamed the TOR BOTNIA. Operated on the Immingham - Rotterdam route until December 2010. In January 2011 moved to the Kiel - St

Petersburg route. In January 2013 renamed the BOTNIA SEAWAYS. Currently operating on the Marseilles - Tunis service.

CROWN SEAWAYS Launched as the THOMAS MANN by Brodogradevna Industrija, Split, Croatia for *Euroway AB* for their Lübeck - Travemünde - Malmö service. However, political problems led to serious delays and, before delivery, the service had ceased. She was purchased by *DFDS*, renamed the CROWN OF SCANDINAVIA and introduced onto the København - Oslo service. In January 2013 renamed the CROWN SEAWAYS.

LIVERPOOL SEAWAYS Built as the LAGAN VIKING by CN Visentini, Donada, Italy for *Levantina Trasporti* of Italy and chartered to *Norse Irish Ferries*, operating between Liverpool and Belfast. In 1999 the charter was taken over by *Merchant Ferries*. Purchased by *NorseMerchant Ferries* in 2001. In 2002 the service transferred to Twelve Quays River Terminal, Birkenhead. In January 2005 renamed the LIVERPOOL VIKING and in December moved to the Birkenhead – Dublin route. In August 2010 renamed the LIVERPOOL SEAWAYS. In February 2011 moved to the Klaipėda - Karlshamn service. In January 2014 chartered to *NaviRail*. In January 2015 returned to *DFDS* and placed on the Paldiski - Kapellskär service.

OPTIMA SEAWAYS Ro-pax vessel built as the ALYSSA by C N Visentini di Visentini Francesco & C Donada, Italy for *Levantina Trasporti* of Italy for charter. Initially chartered to *CoTuNav* of Tunisia for service between Marseilles, Génova and Tunis and in 2000 to *Trasmediterranea* of Spain for service between Barcelona and Palma de Mallorca. In 2001 chartered to *Stena Line Scandinavia AB*, renamed the SVEALAND and placed as second vessel on the *Scandlines AB* freight-only Trelleborg - Travemünde service. In 2003 sub-chartered to *Scandlines AG* and placed on the Kiel - Klaipėda route, replacing the ASK and PETERSBURG. In 2004 sold to *Rederia AB Hornet*, a *Stena* company. In late 2005 the *Scandlines* Kiel - Klaipėda service ended. In early 2006 she was chartered to *TT-Line* to cover for the rebuilding of the engines of their four newest vessels. Later sold to *DFDS*, renamed the LISCO OPTIMA. In April 2012 renamed the OPTIMA SEAWAYS. Currently operates on the Karlshamn - Klaipėda route.

PATRIA SEAWAYS Ro-pax vessel built as the STENA TRAVELLER by Fosen Mekaniske Verksteder, Trondheim, Norway for *Stena RoRo*. After a short period with *Stena Line* on the Hoek van Holland - Harwich service, she was chartered to *Sealink Stena Line* for their Southampton - Cherbourg route, initially for 28 weeks. At the end of the 1992 summer season she was chartered to *TT-Line* to operate between Travemünde and Trelleborg and was renamed the TT-TRAVELLER. In late 1995, she returned to *Stena Line*, resumed the name STENA TRAVELLER and inaugurated a new service between Holyhead and Dublin. In Autumn 1996 she was replaced by the STENA CHALLENGER (18523t, 1991). In early 1997 she was again chartered to *TT-Line* and renamed the TT-TRAVELLER. She operated on the Rostock - Trelleborg route. During Winter 1999/2000 her passenger capacity was increased to 250 and passenger facilities renovated. In early 2002 the charter ended and she was renamed the STENA TRAVELLER, chartered to *Stena Line* and placed on their Karlskrona - Gdynia service. This charter ended in May 2003 and she was sold to *Lisco Baltic Service* and renamed the LISCO PATRIA. Placed on the Klaipėda - Karlshamn service. In January 2006 transferred to the Klaipėda - Kiel service to replace the *Scandlines* vessel SVEALAND following that company's withdrawal from the joint route. In Spring 2006 returned to the Klaipėda – Karlshamn route. In May 2011 chartered to *Baltic Scandinavia Lines* and placed on their Paldiski - Kapellskär service. In September 2011 a controlling interest in this service was acquired by *DFDS Seaways*. In January 2012 renamed the PATRIA SEAWAYS. In September 2014 replaced by the *Sirena Seaways* and became a relief vessel. In April 2015 chartered as a windfarm accommodation vessel off Esbjerg. In January 2016 chartered to *P&O Ferries* to cover for refits on the Hull routes. In April 2016 became third vessel on the Klaipėda – Karlshamn route.

PEARL SEAWAYS Built as the ATHENA by Wärtsilä Marine, Turku, Finland for *Rederi AB Slite* of Sweden (part of *Viking Line*) and used on 24-hour cruises from Stockholm to Mariehamn (Åland). In 1993 the company went into liquidation and she was sold to *Star Cruises* of Malaysia for cruises in the Far East. She was renamed the STAR AQUARIUS. Later that year she was renamed the LANGKAPURI STAR AQUARIUS. In February 2001 sold to *DFDS* and renamed the AQUARIUS. After rebuilding, she was renamed the PEARL OF SCANDINAVIA and introduced onto the København - Oslo service. In January 2011 renamed the PEARL SEAWAYS.

Athena Seaways *(Uwe Jakob)*

Patria Seaways *(Uwe Jakob)*

Crown Seaways *(Andrew Cooke)*

Ark Germania *(Uwe Jakob)*

REGINA SEAWAYS Built as the ENERGIA by Nuovi Cantieri Apuani, Marina di Carrara, Italy for *Grimaldi Holdings* of Italy. In August 2011 chartered to DFDS Seaways and moved to Klaipėda for modifications. In September 2011 renamed the REGINA SEAWAYS and placed on the Klaipėda - Kiel service.

SAILOR Built as the FINNSAILOR by Gdańsk Shipyard, Gdańsk, Poland for *Finnlines* of Finland for freight service between Finland and Germany. In 1996 converted to ro-pax format to inaugurate a new passenger/freight service between Helsinki and Norrköping (Sweden) for subsidiary *FinnLink*. In 1997 this service was transferred to the Kapellskär - Naantali route and passengers (other than lorry drivers) ceased to be conveyed. In 2000 she was chartered to *Nordö-Link* to operate between Travemünde and Malmö. In 2002 she returned to *FinnLink*. In 2004 transferred to *Nordö-Link*. In 2007 returned to *FinnLink* as fourth ship. In early 2009 transferred to *Finnlines'* freight service operating between Helsinki, Turku and Travemünde but in April transferred back. In March 2011 moved back to *Finnlines Nordö-Link*. In November 2013 chartered to *Navirail* of Estonia to operate between Paldiski and Hanko. In January 2014 returned to *Finnlines* and placed on the Naantali - Kapellskär route. In January 2015 time chartered again to *Navirail*. In February 2015 demise chartered to *Navirail* and renamed the SAILOR. In October 2016 time chartered to *DFDS Seaways*, following their take over of the Hanko and Paldiski route.

VICTORIA SEAWAYS Built by Nuovi Cantieri Apuani, Marina di Carrara, Italy. Launched as the FORZA. Fifth of an order of eight vessels for *Grimaldi Holdings* of Italy. Whilst under construction, sold to *DFDS Tor Line*. On delivery renamed the LISCO MAXIMA. In March/April 2012 renamed the VICTORIA SEAWAYS. Operates between Kiel and Klaipėda.

Under construction

12	NEWBUILDING 1	54900t	21	23.0k	230.0m	600P	-	270L	A2	-
13	NEWBUILDING 2	54900t	21	23.0k	230.0m	600P	-	270L	A2	-

NEWBUILDING 1, NEWBUILDING 2 Under construction by Guangzhou Shipyard International, Guangzhou, China. They will operate on Baltic routes from Klaipėda to Kiel and Karlshamn.

REDERIJ DOEKSEN

THE COMPANY *BV Rederij G. Doeksen en Zn BV* is a Dutch private sector company. Ferries are operated by subsidiary *Terschellinger Stoomboot Maatschappij*, trading as *Rederij Doeksen*.

MANAGEMENT Managing Director P J M Melles, **Manager Operations** R. de Vries, **Controller** R. Herrema, **Manager Hospitality** D Spoor, **Manager Marketing & Communications** A. van Brummelen-van Dam.

ADDRESS Waddenpromenade 5, 8861 NT Harlingen, The Netherlands.

TELEPHONE *In The Netherlands* 088 - 9000 888, ***From abroad*** +31 562 442 002.

FAX +31 (0)517 413303.

INTERNET Email info@rederij-doeksen.nl **Website** www.rederij-doeksen.nl *(Dutch, English, German))* **Facebook** www.facebook.com/rederijdoeksen **Twitter** www.twitter.com/rederijdoeksen **Instagram** www.instagram.com/rederijdoeksen **LinkedIn** www.LinkedIn.com/company/rederijdoeksen

ROUTES OPERATED Conventional Ferries Harlingen (The Netherlands) - Terschelling (Frisian Islands) (2 hrs; ***FRIESLAND, MIDSLAND, WILLEM BARENTSZ***, ***WILLEM DE VLAMINGH***; up to 6 per day), Harlingen - Vlieland (Frisian Islands) (1 hr 45 mins; ***VLIELAND***; 3 per day). **Fast Passenger Ferries** Harlingen - Terschelling (45 mins; ***KOEGELWIECK, TIGER***; 3 to 6 per day), Harlingen - Vlieland (45 mins; ***KOEGELWIECK, TIGER***; 2 per day), Vlieland - Terschelling (30 mins; ***KOEGELWIECK, TIGER***; 2 per day). **Freight Ferry** Harlingen - Terschelling (2 hrs; ***NOORD-NEDERLAND***), Harlingen - Vlieland (1hr 45 mins; ***NOORD-NEDERLAND***).

1	FRIESLAND	3583t	89	14.0k	69.0m	1100P	122C	12L	BA	NL	8801058
2»p	KOEGELWIECK	439t	92	33.0k	35.5m	315P	0C	0L	-	NL	9035527

3	MIDSLAND	1812t	74	15.5k	77.9m	700P	55C	6L	BA	NL	7393066
4F	NOORD-NEDERLAND	361t	02	14.0k	68.0m	12P	-	-	BA	NL	9269611
5»p	TIGER	660t	02	37.0k	52.0m	414P	0C	0L	BA	NL	9179191
6	VLIELAND	2726t	05	15.0k	64.1m	1950P	58C	4L	BA	NL	9303716

FRIESLAND Built by Van der Giessen-de Noord, Krimpen aan den IJssel, Rotterdam, The Netherlands for *Rederij Doeksen*. Used on the Harlingen - Terschelling route.

KOEGELWIECK Harding 35m catamaran built at Rosendal, Norway for *Rederij Doeksen* to operate between Harlingen and Terschelling, Harlingen and Vlieland and Terschelling and Vlieland.

MIDSLAND Built as the RHEINLAND by Werftunion GmbH & Co, Cassens-Werft, Emden, Germany for *AG Ems* of Germany. In 1993 purchased by *Rederij Doeksen* and renamed the MIDSLAND. Used mainly on the Harlingen - Terschelling route but also used on the Harlingen - Vlieland service. She is now a reserve vessel.

NOORD-NEDERLAND Catamaran built by ASB, Harwood, New South Wales, Australia for *Rederij Doeksen*. Used on freight services from Harlingen to Terschelling and Vlieland. In spring 2017 lengthened by 20 metres.

TIGER Catamaran built as the SUPERCAT 2002 by FBMA Babcock Marine, Cebu, Philippines for *SuperCat* of the Philippines. In 2007 purchased by *Rederij Doeksen* and renamed the TIGER. Operates from Harlingen to Terschelling and Vlieland.

VLIELAND Catamaran built by FBMA Babcock Marine, Cebu, Philippines for *Rederij Doeksen* to operate between Harlingen and Vlieland.

Under construction

7	WILLEM BARENTSZ	3744t	19	14.0k	70.0m	700P	66C	-	BA	NL	9807578
8	WILLEM DE VLAMINGH	3744t	19	14.0k	70.0m	700P	66C	-	BA	NL	9807580

WILLEM BARENTSZ, WILLEM DE VLAMINGH Built for *Rederij Doeksen* by Strategic Marine, Vung Tau, Vietnam and being fitted out at Nesta Shipping, Harlingen, Netherlands. They are aluminium catamarans and LNG powered. They arrived in the Netherlands in May 2019 but are not due to enter service until 2020. They will replace the MIDSLAND. These vessels will be the first single fuel LNG ferries in the Netherlands and the very first ships in the world where single fuel LNG engines directly drive a fixed propeller.

REDERI AB ECKERÖ

THE COMPANY *Rederi AB Eckerö* is an Åland Islands company. It operates two ferry companies, a cruise operation from Stockholm (*Birka Cruises*), a ro-ro time chartering company (*Eckerö Shipping*) and a bus company on Åland (*Williams*).

ADDRESS PO Box 158, AX-22101 Mariehamn, Åland, Finland.

TELEPHONE Administration +358 (0)18 28 030.

FAX Administration +358 (0)18 12 011.

INTERNET Email info@rederiabeckero.ax **Website** www.rederiabeckero.ax *(English, Swedish)*

ECKERÖ LINE

THE COMPANY *Eckerö Line Ab Oy* is a Finnish company, 100% owned by *Rederi Ab Eckerö* of Åland, Finland. Until January 1998, the company was called *Eestin-Linjat*.

MANAGEMENT Managing Director Taru Keronen, **Marketing Director** Ida Toikka-Everi.

ADDRESS PO Box 307, 00181 Helsinki, Finland.

TELEPHONE Administration & Reservations +358 9 (0) 6000 4300.

INTERNET Email info@eckeroline.fi **Website** www.eckeroline.fi www.finbocaro.com *(Swedish, Finnish, English)*

ROUTE OPERATED Passenger & Freight Service Helsinki (Jätkäsaari) - Tallinn (Estonia) (2 hrs 30 mins; ***FINLANDIA***; up to 2 per day), **Freight and Car Passengers only** Helsinki (Vuosaari Port) - Tallinn (Muuga); ***FINBO CARGO***; 2 per day.

1	FINBO CARGO	22152t	00	22.5k	180.0m	366P	-	120L	BA2	FI	9181106
2	FINLANDIA	36093t	01	27.0k	175.0m	1880P	665C	116T	BA	FI	9214379

FINBO CARGO Built as the MIDNIGHT MERCHANT by Astilleros Españoles SA, Sevilla, Spain for *Cenargo* (then owners of *NorseMerchant Ferries*). On delivery, chartered to *Norfolkline* to operate as second vessel on the Dover - Dunkerque (Ouest) service. In 2002 modified to allow two-deck loading. In 2006 chartered to *Acciona Trasmediterranea* of Spain and renamed the EL GRECO. Used on Mediterranean and Canary Island services. In 2007 sold to *P&O Ferries* and renamed the EUROPEAN ENDEAVOUR. Operated on The Dover - Calais route and as a re-fit relief vessel on Irish Sea routes. In May 2010 laid up. In February 2011 moved to the Liverpool - Dublin route. In May 2019 sold to *Rederi AB Eckerö*, renamed the FINBO CARGO and, in June 2019, placed on the new Helsinki - Muuga freight route.

FINLANDIA Built as the MOBY FREEDOM by Daewoo Shipbuilding & Heavy Machinery Ltd, Okpo, South Korea for *Moby SpA (Moby Line)* of Italy. Operated on their Génova/Civitavecchia/Livorno - Olbia routes. In March 2012 sold to *Eckerö Line*, and renamed the FREEDOM. Refitted at Landskrona and, in June, renamed the FINLANDIA. She entered service on 31st December 2012.

ECKERÖ LINJEN

THE COMPANY *Eckerö Linjen* is an Åland Islands company 100% owned by *Rederi AB Eckerö*.

MANAGEMENT Managing Director Tomas Karlsson, **Marketing Director** Maria Hellman.

ADDRESS Torggatan 2, Box 158, AX-22100 Mariehamn, Åland.

TELEPHONE Administration +358 (0)18 28 000, **Reservations** +358 (0)18 28 300.

FAX Administration +358 (0)18 28 380. **Reservations** +358 (0)18 28 230.

INTERNET Email info@eckerolinjen.ax **Website** www.eckerolinjen.se *(Swedish, Finnish, English)*

ROUTE OPERATED Eckerö (Åland) - Grisslehamn (Sweden) (2 hrs; ***ECKERÖ***; 3 per day).

1	ECKERÖ	12358t	79	19.5k	121.1m	1500P	265C	34T	BA	SE	7633155

ECKERÖ Built as the JENS KOFOED by Aalborg Værft A/S, Aalborg, Denmark for *Bornholmstrafikken*. Used on the Rønne - København, Rønne - Ystad and (until December 2002) Rønne - Sassnitz services. Rønne - København service became Rønne – Køge in September 2004. In October 2004 sold to *Eckerö Linjen* for delivery in May 2005. Renamed the ECKERÖ and substantially rebuilt before entering service in early 2006. In January 2009 transferred from the Finnish to the Swedish flag.

AG EMS

THE COMPANY *AG Ems* is a German public sector company.

MANAGEMENT Managing Director & Chief Executive Dr Bernhard Brons, **Marine Superintendent** Knut Gerdes, **Operations Manager** Hans-Jörg Oltmanns.

ADDRESS Am Aussenhafen, Postfach 1154, 26691 Emden, Germany.

TELEPHONE Administration & Reservations +49 (0)1805-180182.

FAX Administration & Reservations +49 (0)4921-890740.

INTERNET Email info@ag-ems.de **Website** www.ag-ems.de *(German)* www.borkumlijn.nl *(Dutch)* www.helgolandlinie.de *(German)*

ROUTES OPERATED Conventional Ferries Emden (Germany) - Borkum (German Frisian Islands) (2 hrs; ***GRONINGERLAND, MÜNSTERLAND, OSTFRIESLAND, WESTFALEN***; up to 4 per day), Eemshaven (The Netherlands) - Borkum (55 mins; ***GRONINGERLAND, MÜNSTERLAND, OSTFRIESLAND, WESTFALEN***; up to 4 per day). **Fast Ferry** Emden - Borkum (1 hr; ***NORDLICH***; up to 4 per day), Eemshaven - Borkum (30 mins; ***NORDLICHT***; 1 per week in summer).

1	GRONINGERLAND	1070t	91	12.0k	44.4m	621P	30C	-	BA	DE	9002465
2	MÜNSTERLAND	1859t	86	15.5k	78.7m	1200P	70C	10L	BA	DE	8601989
3p»	NORDLICHT	435t	89	33.0k	38.8m	272P	0C	0L	-	DE	8816015
4	OSTFRIESLAND	1859t	85	16.0k	78.7m	1200P	70C	10L	BA	DE	8324622
5p	WAPPEN VON BORKUM	287t	76	11.5k	42.8m	358P	0C	0L	-	DE	7525918
6	WESTFALEN	1812t	72	15.5k	77.9m	1200P	65C	10L	BA	DE	7217004

GRONINGERLAND Built by Husumer Schiffswerft, Husum, Germany as the HILLIGENLEI for *Wyker Dampfschiffs-Reederei Föhr-Amrum GmbH* of Germany. Operated Schlüttsiel - Halligen - Wittdün (North Frisian Islands). In 2004 laid up. In late 2005 sold to *AG Ems*. In 2006 renamed the GRONINGERLAND.

MÜNSTERLAND Built by Martin Jansen GmbH & Co KG Schiffswerft, Leer, Germany for *AG Ems*.

NORDLICHT Fjellstrand 38m passenger-only catamaran built at Mandal, Norway for *AG Ems*.

OSTFRIESLAND Built by Martin Jansen GmbH & Co KG Schiffswerft, Leer, Germany for *AG Ems*. In 2015 lengthened by 15.4 m by BVT Brenn-und Verformtechnik GmbH, Bremen, Germany.

WAPPEN VON BORKUM Built as the HANNOVER by Schiffswerft Schlömer GmbH & Co KG, Oldersum, Germany for *Friesland Fahrlinie* of Germany. In 1979 sold to *AG Ems* and renamed the STADT BORKUM. In 1988 sold to *ST-Line* of Finland, operating day trips from Rauma and renamed the PRINCESS ISABELLA. In 1994 returned to *AG Ems* and renamed the WAPPEN VON BORKUM.

WESTFALEN Built by as the WESTFALEN by C Cassens Schiffswerft, Emden, Germany for *AG Ems*. Rebuilt in 1994. In 2006 renamed the HELGOLAND and inaugurated a new Wilhelmshaven - Helgoland service for subsidiary *Helgoland Linie*. In January 2016 reverted to the name WESTFALEN and used on service from Borkum.

FINNLINES

THE COMPANY *Finnlines plc* is a Finnish private sector company. The Italian company *Grimaldi Compagnia de Navigazione SpA* has a controlling interest. It operates four passenger brands: *Finnlines HansaLink*, *Finnlines NordöLink* and *FinnLink* and *TransRussiaExpress*.

MANAGEMENT President and CEO Emanuele Grimaldi, **Head of Passenger Services and Line Manager HansaLink & Hanko–Rostock** Kielo Vesikko, **Line Manager NordöLink, Finnlink and Russia** Antonio Raimo.

ADDRESS PO Box 197, 00181 Helsinki, Finland.

TELEPHONE Administration +358 (0)10 343 50, **Passenger Reservations** +358 (0)9 231 43 100.

INTERNET *Finnlines* Email info.fi@finnlines.com **Website *Finnlines*** www.finnlines.com *(English, Finnish, German, Polish, Swedish)*

ROUTES OPERATED *Finnlines Hansalink branded routes* Helsinki (Vuosaari) - Travemünde (27 hrs; ***FINNLADY, FINNMAID, FINNSTAR***; 7 per week).

Finnlines NordöLink branded route Malmö - Travemünde (9 hrs; ***EUROPALINK, FINNPARTNER, FINNTRADER***; up to 3 per day).

FinnLink branded route Naantali (Finland) - Långnäs - Kapellskär (Sweden) (6 hrs; ***FINNFELLOW, FINNSWAN***; 2 per day).

1	EUROPALINK	45923t	07	25.0k	216.0m	500P	-	300T	BA2	SE	9319454

Finlandia *(Miles Cowsill)*

Bergensfjord *(Uwe Jakob)*

2	FINNFELLOW	33769t	00	22.0k	188.3m	452P	-	220T	BA	FI	9145164
3	FINNLADY	45923t	07	25.0k	216.0m	500P	-	300T	BA2	FI	9336268
4	FINNMAID	45923t	06	25.0k	216.0m	500P	-	300T	BA2	FI	9319466
5	FINNPARTNER	32534t	94	21.3k	183.0m	270P	-	236T	A2	SE	9010163
6	FINNSTAR	45923t	06	25.0k	216.0m	500P	-	300T	BA2	FI	9319442
7	FINNSWAN	45923t	07	25.0k	216.0m	500P	-	300T	BA2	FI	9336256
8	FINNTRADER	32534t	95	21.3k	183.0m	270P	-	220T	BA2	SE	9017769
9	ROSALIND FRANKLIN	29841t	99	22.0k	188.3m	440P	-	210T	BA2	CY	9137997

EUROPALINK Built by Fincantieri-Cantieri Navali Italiani SpA, Castellamare, Italy for *Finnlines* to operate for *Finnlines NordöLink* between Travemünde and Malmö. Launched as the FINNLADY but name changed before delivery. In April 2009 transferred to *Finnlines HansaLink*. In October 2012 sold to *Atlantica Navigazione* of Italy, another company within the *Grimaldi Group*, for Mediterranean service. In January 2018 repurchased by *NordöLink* (a subsidiary of *Finnlines*) and returned to the Travemünde and Malmö service.

FINNFELLOW 'Ro-pax' ferry built as the STENA BRITANNICA by Astilleros Españoles, Cadiz, Spain for *Stena RoRo* and chartered to *Stena Line BV* to operate between Hoek van Holland and Harwich. In 2003 replaced by a new STENA BRITANNICA, sold to *Finnlines*, renamed the FINNFELLOW and placed on the Helsinki - Travemünde route. In 2004 transferred to *FinnLink*.

FINNLADY, FINNMAID Built by Fincantieri-Cantieri Navali Italiani SpA, Ancona, Italy to operate between Helsinki and Travemünde.

FINNPARTNER 'Ro-pax' vessel built by Stocznia Gdańska SA, Gdańsk, Poland for *Finnlines Oy* of Finland to provide a daily service conveying both freight and a limited number of cars and passengers on the previously freight-only route between Helsinki and Travemünde. In February 2007 replaced by the FINNLADY and placed on the Turku - Travemünde freight service; in May sent to the Remontowa Shipyard in Gdańsk for rebuilding to increase passenger capacity and allow for two-deck through loading. Currently operating on the Travemünde - Malmö and Lübeck - St Petersburg services.

FINNSTAR Built by Fincantieri-Cantieri Navali Italiani SpA, Castellamare, Italy to operate between Helsinki and Travemünde.

FINNSWAN Built by Fincantieri-Cantieri Navali Italiani SpA, Castellamare, Italy as the NORDLINK for *Finnlines* to operate for *Finnlines NordöLink* between Travemünde and Malmö. In February 2018 renamed the FINNSWAN and in May moved to the Naantali - Långnäs - Kapellskär route.

FINNTRADER 'Ro-pax' vessel built by Stocznia Gdańska SA, Gdańsk, Poland for *Finnlines Oy* of Finland to provide a daily service conveying both freight and a limited number of cars and passengers on the previously freight-only route between Helsinki and Travemünde. In 2006/07 rebuilt to increase passenger capacity and allow for two-deck through loading. In 2007 transferred to the Malmö - Travemünde route.

ROSALIND FRANKLIN 'Ro-pax' ferry built by Astilleros Españoles, Cadiz, Spain. Ordered by *Stena RoRo* of Sweden and launched as the STENA SEAPACER 1. In 1998 sold, before delivery, to *Finnlines* and renamed the FINNCLIPPER. Entered service on the Helsinki - Travemünde route in 1999. During Winter 1999/2000 she was converted to double-deck loading. In 2003 transferred to *FinnLink*. In 2007 an additional freight deck was added. In May 2018 chartered to *Baleària* of Spain and renamed the ROSALIND FRANKLIN.

FJORD LINE

THE COMPANY *Fjord Line* is a Norwegian company. During 2007 most of the shares of the company were purchased by *Frode and Ole Teigen*. The company bought and merged with *Master Ferries* during December 2007 and all operations are branded as *Fjord Line*.

MANAGEMENT CEO Rickard Ternblom, **Communications Director** Eva Sørås Mellgren.

ADDRESS PO Box 513, 4379 Egersund, Norway.

TELEPHONE Administration & Reservations +47 51 46 40 00.

INTERNET Email info@fjordline.com freight@fjordline.com **Website** www.fjordline.com *(English, Danish, German, Dutch, Polish, Norwegian)*

ROUTES OPERATED Conventional Ferry Bergen (Norway) - Stavanger - Hirtshals (Denmark) (17 hrs; ***BERGENSFJORD, STAVANGERFJORD***; daily), Langesund (Norway) - Hirtshals (4 hrs 30 mins; ***BERGENSFJORD, STAVANGERFJORD***; daily), Sandefjord (Norway) - Strömstad (Sweden) (2 hrs 30 mins; ***OSLOFJORD***; 2 per day), **Fast Ferry *May-August*** Kristiansand (Norway) - Hirtshals (Denmark) (2 hrs 15 min; ***FJORD CAT***; up to 3 per day).

1	BERGENSFJORD	31678t	13	21.5k	170.0m	1500P	600C	90T	BA	DK	9586617
2»	FJORD CAT	5619t	98	43.0k	91.3m	663P	220C	-	A	DK	9176060
3	OSLOFJORD	16794t	93	19.0k	134.4m	882P	350C	44T	BA	DK	9058995
4	STAVANGERFJORD	31678t	13	21.5k	170.0m	1500P	600C	90T	BA	DK	9586605

BERGENSFJORD, STAVANGERFJORD Built by Bergen Group Fosen AS, Rissa, Norway for *Fjord Line*. They operate on LNG.

FJORD CAT Incat 91-metre catamaran, built speculatively at Hobart, Tasmania, Australia. In Spring 1998, following *Incat's* acquisition of a 50% share in *Scandlines Cat-Link A/S*, she was chartered by *Nordic Catamaran Ferries K/S* to that company, operating between Århus and Kalundborg and named the CAT-LINK V. She is the current holder of the Hales Trophy for fastest crossing of the Atlantic during her delivery voyage between the USA and Falmouth, UK (although this claim is disputed because it was not a genuine commercial service). In 1999 the charter was transferred to *Mols-Linien*, she was renamed the MADS MOLS and operated between Århus and Odden. Charter ended in July 2005. Laid up and renamed the INCAT 049. In 2006 sold to *Gabriel Scott Rederi (Master Ferries)* and renamed the MASTER CAT. In December 2008 purchased by *Fjord Line* renamed the FJORD CAT. Did not operate in 2009 but service resumed in 2010.

OSLOFJORD Built by Fosen Mekaniske Verksteder, Rissa, Norway for *Rutelaget Askøy-Bergen* as the BERGEN and used on the *Fjord Line* Bergen - Egersund - Hanstholm service. In April 2003 chartered to *DFDS Seaways*, renamed the DUCHESS OF SCANDINAVIA and, after modifications, introduced onto the Harwich - Cuxhaven service. In 2004 sold to *Bergensfjord KS* of Norway and chartered to *DFDS Seaways*. In 2005 sub-chartered to *Fjord Line* for 5 months (with *DFDS* officers and deck-crew) and renamed the ATLANTIC TRAVELLER. In 2006 chartered directly to *Fjord Line*. In March 2008 purchased by *Fjord Line* and renamed the BERGENSFJORD. In January 2014 renamed the OSLOFJORD, rebuilt as a day ferry by STX Finland, Rauma, Finland and, in June 2014, inaugurated a new service between Sandefjord and Strömstad.

Under Construction

5»	NEWBUILDING	-	20	40.0k	109.0m	1200P	410C	30L	A	DK	-

NEWBUILDING Austal 109m catamaran under construction by Austal Ships, Fremantle, Australia to replace the FJORD CAT.

FORSEA

THE COMPANY *ForSea* (formerly *Scandlines Helsingør - Helsingborg*) is the trading name of *HH Ferries Group*, a Swedish private sector company owned by First State Investments. Previously a joint venture between *Scandlines* and *Stena Line*, it was acquired by First State Investments in January 2015 and until 2018 operated as part of the *Scandlines* network.

ADDRESS Bredgatan 5, 252 25 Helsingborg, Sweden.

TELEPHONE Administration & Reservations +46 42 18 61 00.

INTERNET Email customerservice@forseaferries.com **Website** www.forsea.dk *(Danish)*, www.forseaferries.com *(English)*, www.forsea.se *(Swedish)*.

ROUTES OPERATED Helsingør (Sjælland, Denmark) - Helsingborg (Sweden) (20 mins; ***AURORA AF HELSINGBORG, MERCANDIA IV, MERCANDIA VIII, HAMLET, TYCHO BRAHE***; up to every 20 mins)

Havila Capella *(Havila Kystruten)*

Finnmarken *(Uwe Jakob)*

1	AURORA AF HELSINGBORG	10918t	92	14.0k	111.2m	1250P	225C	25Lr	BA	SE	9007128
2	HAMLET	10067t	97	13.5k	111.2m	1000P	244C	34L	BA	DK	9150030
3F	MERCANDIA IV	4296t	89	13.0k	95.0m	420P	170C	18L	BA	DK	8611685
4	MERCANDIA VIII	4296t	87	13.0k	95.0m	420P	170C	18L	BA	EE	8611623
5	TYCHO BRAHE	11148t	91	14.5k	111.2m	1250P	240C	35Lr	BA	DK	9007116

AURORA AF HELSINGBORG Train/vehicle ferry built by Langsten Verft A/S, Tomrefjord, Norway for *SweFerry* for *ScandLines* joint *DSB/SweFerry* service between Helsingør and Helsingborg. In autumn 2018 converted to full battery electric operation with shoreside power supply. She can also operate in hybrid and diesel electric mode, although the last is only used in emergency.

HAMLET Road vehicle ferry built by Finnyards, Rauma, Finland for *Scandlines* (50% owned by *Scandlines AG* and 50% owned by *Scandlines AB* of Sweden) for the Helsingør - Helsingborg service. Sister vessel of the TYCHO BRAHE but without rail tracks.

MERCANDIA IV Built as the SUPERFLEX NOVEMBER by North East Shipbuilders Ltd, Sunderland, UK for *Vognmandsruten* of Denmark. In 1989 sold to *Mercandia* and renamed the MERCANDIA IV. In 1990 she began operating on their *Kattegatbroen* Juelsminde - Kalundborg service. In 1996 she was transferred to their *Sundbroen* Helsingør - Helsingborg service. In 1997 the service and vessel were leased to *HH-Ferries*. In 1999 she was purchased by *HH-Ferries*. She has been equipped to carry dangerous cargo. From 1 September operates freight only

MERCANDIA VIII Built as the SUPERFLEX BRAVO by North East Shipbuilders Ltd, Sunderland, UK for *Vognmandsruten* of Denmark and used on their services between Nyborg and Korsør and København (Tuborg Havn) and Landskrona (Sweden). In 1991 she was chartered to *Scarlett Line* to operate on the København and Landskrona route. In 1993 she was renamed the SVEA SCARLETT but later in the year the service ceased and she was laid up. In 1996 she was purchased by *Mercandia*, renamed the MERCANDIA VIII and placed on their *Sundbroen* Helsingør - Helsingborg service. In 1997 the service and vessel were leased to *HH-Ferries*. In 1999 she was purchased by *HH-Ferries*. Now reserve vessel. Between April and July 2015 she operated between Puttgarden and Rødby for *Scandlines*, following damage sustained by the PRINSESSE BENEDIKTE at Gdańsk during a refit. In summer 2018 and summer 2019 chartered to *Praamid* of Estonia to act as spare vessel.

TYCHO BRAHE Train/vehicle ferry, built by Tangen Verft A/S, Tomrefjord, Norway for *DSB* for the *ScandLines* joint *DSB/SweFerry* service between Helsingør and Helsingborg.

HAVILA KYSTRUTEN

THE COMPANY *Havila Kystruten* is a trading name of *Havila Shipping ASA*, a Norwegian private sector company, In March 2018 it won a ten-year concession to operate, with *Hurtigruten,* the 'Kystruten' (coastal route) between Bergen and Kirkenes from 1st January 2021.

MANAGEMENT CEO Njål Sævik.

ADDRESS P.O.Box 215, N-6099 Fosnavaag, Norway.

TELEPHONE +47 70 08 09 00.

FAX +47 70 08 09 01.

INTERNET Email office@havila.no **Website** www.havila.no *(English, German, Norwegian)*

ROUTE OPERATED Bergen - Kirknes (from 1st January 2021).

Under Construction

1	HAVILA CAPELLA	-	20	18.0k	125.0m	700P	-	0L	S	NO	-
2	HAVILA CASTOR	-	20	18.0k	125.0m	700P	-	0L	S	NO	-
3	HAVILA POLARIS	-	20	18.0k	125.0m	700P	-	0L	S	NO	-
4	HAVILA POLLUX	-	20	18.0k	125.0m	700P	-	0L	S	NO	-

HAVILA CAPELLA, HAVILA CASTOR Hybrid vessel under construction by Tersan Shipyard, Yalova, Turkey. To run on LPG and they will be fitted with large battery packs.

HAVILA POLARIS, HAVILA POLLUX Hybrid vessel under construction by Barreras Shipyard, Vigo, Spain. Construction of one of the vessels will be sub-contracted to another shipyard in the wider Vigo area. To run on LPG and they will be fitted with large battery packs.

HURTIGRUTEN

THE COMPANY *Hurtigruten AS* is a Norwegian private sector company. The service was originally provided by a consortium of companies. By 2006, through mergers and withdrawal from the operation, there were just two companies - *Troms Fylkes D/S* and *Ofotens og Vesteraalens D/S* and in that year *Hurtigruten ASA* was formed. In September 2015 it was taken over by *Silk Bidco AS* of Norway and the company changed its name to *Hurtigruten AS*.

MANAGEMENT Chairman Trygve Hegnar, **Chief Executive Officer** Daniel Skjeldam.

ADDRESS Hurtigruten AS, Fredrik Lamges gate 14, Postboks 6144, 9291 Tromsø, Norway.

TELEPHONE Administration +47 970 57 030, **Reservations *Norway*** +47 810 03 030,

UK +44 (0)2036 037112, ***Ireland*** +353 (0)1607 4420.

INTERNET Email firmapost@hurtigruten.com uk.sales@hurtigruten.com

Websites www.hurtigruten.co.uk *(English)* www.hurtigruten.no *(Norwegian)* www.hurtigruten.de *(German)* www.hurtigruten.fr *(French)* www.hurtigruten.us *(US English)*

ROUTE OPERATED 'Hurtigruten' sail every day throughout the year from Bergen and calls at 34 ports up to Kirkenes and takes you along one of the world's most exciting coast lines, where you will find yourself close to nature, people and traditions. Daily departures throughout the year. The round trip takes just under 11 days.

1	FINNMARKEN	15539t	02	18.0k	138.5m	1000P	47C	0L	S	NO	9231951
2p	FRAM	11647t	07	18.0k	110.0m	500P	0C	0L	-	NO	9370018
3	KONG HARALD	11204t	93	18.0k	121.8m	691P	45C	0L	S	NO	9039119
4	LOFOTEN	2621t	64	16.0k	87.4m	410P	0C	0L	C	NO	5424562
5	MIDNATSOL	16151t	03	18.0k	135.7m	1000P	45C	0L	S	NO	9247728
6	NORDKAPP	11386t	96	18.0k	123.3m	691P	45C	0L	S	NO	9107772
7	NORDLYS	11204t	94	18.0k	121.8m	691P	45C	0L	S	NO	9048914
8	NORDNORGE	11384t	97	18.0k	123.3m	691P	45C	0L	S	NO	9107784
9	POLARLYS	11341t	96	18.0k	123.0m	737P	35C	0L	S	NO	9107796
10	RICHARD WITH	11205t	93	18.0k	121.8m	691P	45C	0L	S	NO	9040429
11p	ROALD AMUNDSEN	20889t	19	15k	140.0m	530P	0C	0L	S	NO	9813072
12p	SPITSBERGEN	7344t	09	16.0k	100.5m	335P	0C	0L	-	NO	9434060
13	TROLLFJORD	16140t	02	18.0k	135.7m	822P	45C	0L	S	NO	9233258
14	VESTERÅLEN	6262t	83	18.0k	108.6m	560P	35C	0L	S	NO	8019368

FINNMARKEN Built by Kværner Kleven Skeppsvarv, Ulsteinvik, Norway for *Ofotens og Vesteraalens D/S*. In October 2009 chartered as a support vessel for the Gorgon Project (natural gas) in Western Australia. In November 2011 returned to *Hurtigruten* and, in February 2012, returned to service. In January 2021 to be moved to the company's expedition fleet.

FRAM Built by Fincantieri-Cantieri Navali Italiani SpA at Trieste for *Hurtigruten Group ASA* (ordered by *OVDS*). Since 2007 she has operated cruises around Greenland and Svalbad during the summer period and in South America during the winter and this has been the pattern since. She is named after Fridtjof Nansen's expedition ship FRAM and has ice class 1A/1B.

KONG HARALD Built by Volkswerft, Stralsund, Germany for *Troms Fylkes D/S*.

LOFOTEN Built by A/S Aker Mekaniske Verksted, Oslo, Norway for *Vesteraalens D/S*. In 1988 she was sold to *Finnmark Fylkesrederi og Ruteselskap*. In 1996 she was sold to *Ofotens og Vesteraalens D/S*. In 2002 she was replaced by the FINNMARKEN but she then operated summer cruises and in the winter months substituted for the NORDNORGE when that vessel was sailing in the Chilean Fjords and Antarctica. Since 2008 she has operated on the main Hurtigruten roster.

MIDNATSOL Built by Fosen Mekaniske Verksteder, Rissa, Norway for *Troms Fylkes D/S*. From 2016 also used as an expedition ship in the Antarctic. In January 2021 to be moved to the company's expedition fleet.

NORDKAPP Built by Kværner Kleven Skeppsvarv, Ulsteinvik, Norway for *Ofotens og Vesteraalens D/S*. During the winters of 2005/06 and 2006/07 she operated cruises in South America but following the delivery of the FRAM she now remains on the Hurtigruten throughout the year.

NORDLYS Built by Volkswerft, Stralsund, Germany for *Troms Fylkes D/S*. In 2002 sold to *Kilberg Shipping KS* of Norway and leased back on 15 year bareboat charter with options to repurchase. She was laid up during winter 2008/09 until required to replace the damaged RICHARD WITH from the end of January. She now operates full-time on the Hurtigruten roster.

NORDNORGE Built by Kværner Kleven, Ulsteinvik, Norway for *Ofotens og Vesteraalens D/S*. During winters 2002/03 - 2007/08 she operated cruises in South America. During most of Winter 2008/09 she was used as an accommodation vessel for a liquefied natural gas field. Laid up at Bremerhaven during winter 2009/10.

POLARLYS Built by Ulstein Verft A/S, Ulsteinvik, Norway for *Troms Fylkes D/S*.

RICHARD WITH Built by Volkswerft, Stralsund, Norway for *Ofotens og Vesteraalens D/S*. In 2002 sold to *Kystruten KS*, of Norway and leased back on 15 year bareboat charter with options to re-purchase.

ROALD AMUNDSEN Built by Kleven Verft, Ulsteinvik, Norway. She is designed to cope with both polar waters (for cruising) and service on the regular routes along the Norwegian coastline. There is an option for two more vessels.

SPITSBERGEN Built as the ATLANTIDA by Estaleiros Navais de Viana do Castelo, Viana do Castelo, Portugal for *Atlanticoline* of Portugal as a ro-ro ferry to operate in the Azores. Although completed in 2009, she was never delivered because she did not meet the required specification. In June 2015 purchased by *Hurtigruten* and renamed the NORWAY EXPLORER. Taken to the Öresund Drydocks shipyard, Landskrona, Sweden for rebuilding to make her suitable for *Hurtigruten* service and cruising in polar waters. In May 2016 renamed the SPITSBERGEN and entered service on the *Hurtigruten*, running along-side the LOFOTEN. Unlike most other *Hurtigruten* vessels, no cars can be conveyed. In January 2021 to be moved to the company's expedition fleet.

TROLLFJORD Built by Fosen Mekaniske Verksteder, Rissa, Norway for *Troms Fylkes D/S*. In January 2021 to be moved to the company's expedition fleet.

VESTERÅLEN Built by Kaarbös Mekaniske Verksted A/S, Harstad, Norway for *Vesteraalens D/S*. From 1987 owned by *Ofotens og Vesteraalens D/S* and from 2006 by *Hurtigruten Group ASA*.

Under Construction

15p	FRIDTJOF NANSEN	20889t	20	15k	140.0m	530P	0C	0L	S	NO	9813084
16p	NEWBUILDING	20889t	21	15k	140.0m	530P	0C	0L	S	NO	-

FRIDTJOF NANSEN, NEWBUILDING Under construction by Kleven Verft, Ulsteinvik, Norway. Other details as ROALD AMUNDSEN.

FÆRGESELSKABET LÆSØ

THE COMPANY *Færgeselskabet Læsø K/S* is a Danish public sector company, 50% owned by the county of North Jylland and 50% by the municipality of Læsø.

MANAGEMENT Managing Director Lars Ricks, **Marketing Manager** Bente Faurholt.

ADDRESS Havnepladsen 1, Vesterø Havn, 9940 Læsø, Denmark.

TELEPHONE Administration & Reservations +45 98 49 90 22

INTERNET Email info@laesoe-line.dk **Website** www.laesoe-line.dk *(English, Danish, German)*

ROUTE OPERATED Læsø - Frederikshavn (Jylland) (1 hr 30 mins; ***ANE LÆSØ***, ***MARGRETE LÆSØ***; up 7 per day).

1	ANE LÆSØ	2208t	95	12.0k	53.8m	440P	72C	-	BA	DK	9107370
2	MARGRETE LÆSØ	3668t	97	13.5k	68.5m	586P	76C	12L	BA	DK	9139438t

ANE LÆSØ Built as the VESBORG by Ørskov Stålskibsværft, Ørskov, Denmark for *Samsø Linien*. In March2012 sold to *Læsø Færgen*. Rebuilt by Soby Yard, Aerø, Denmark and renamed the ANE LÆSØ. Between September 2014 and February 2015 she operated on the Hou - Sælvig (Samsø) service which had been taken over by *Samsø Rederi* before their new SAMSØ (now PRINSESSE ISABELLA) was delivered. She will continue to act as reserve vessel on this route.

MARGRETE LÆSØ Built as the LÆSØ FÆRGEN by A/S Norsdsøværftet, Ringkøbing, Denmark for *Andelsfærgeselskabet Læsø* of Denmark. In June 1997 renamed the MARGRETE LÆSØ. In July 1999 transferred to *Færgeselskabet Læsø*.

MOBY SPL

THE COMPANY *Moby SPL* is a joint venture between *Moby Lines* of Italy and *St. Peter Line*, a EU registered private sector company.

MANAGEMENT CEO Sergey Kotenev.

18/2 South Street, Valetta, VLT 1102, Malta; Representative office in St. Petersburg Russia – 199106, St. Petersburg, Martime Glory Plaza, 1.

TELEPHONE *Russia* +7 (812) 507 89 92, ***Finland*** +358 (0)9 6187 2000

INTERNET Email sales@stpeterline.com **Website** www.stpeterline.com *(Russian, Chinese, English, Estonian, Finnish, Swedish)*

ROUTES OPERATED St Petersburg - Tallinn - Stockholm - Helsinki - St Petersburg ***SPL PRINCESS ANASTASIA***; 1 per week), St Petersburg - Helsinki - St Petersburg. ***SPL PRINCESS ANASTASIA***; 1 per week).

1	SPL PRINCESS ANASTASIA	37583t	86	22.988k	176.8 m	2500P	318C	63L	BA2	IT	8414582

SPL PRINCESS ANASTASIA Built as the OLYMPIA by Oy Wärtsilä Ab, Turku, Finland for *Rederi AB Slite* of Sweden for *Viking Line* service between Stockholm and Helsinki. In 1993 she was chartered to *P&O European Ferries* to inaugurate a new service between Portsmouth and Bilbao. Renamed the PRIDE OF BILBAO. During the summer period she also operated, at weekends, a round trip between Portsmouth and Cherbourg. In 1994 she was purchased by the *Irish Continental Group* and re-registered in the Bahamas. In 2002 her charter was extended for a further five years and again for a further three years from October 2007. The Cherbourg service ended at the end of 2004. In September 2010 redelivered to *Irish Continental Group*. In October 2010 renamed the BILBAO. In November 2010 chartered to *St. Peter Line*, in February 2011 renamed the SPL PRINCESS ANASTASIA and in April 2011 inaugurated a new Stockholm - St Petersburg service. In February 2011 purchased by an associated company of *St. Peter Line*. During January and February 2014 she served as a floating hotel at the Winter Olympics in Sochi, Russia. In November 2016 sold to *Moby Lines* of Italy and chartered to *Moby SPL*.

MOLSLINJEN

THE COMPANY *Molslinjen A/S* (formerly *Mols-Linien A/S*) is a Danish private sector company. In October 2018 they were authorised to acquire all the vessels and services of *Danske Færger A/S*.

MANAGEMENT CEO Søren Jespersen, **Communications Manager** Jesper Maack, **Marketing Manager** Mikkel Hybel.

ADDRESS Hveensgade 4, 8000 Aarhus C, Denmark.

TELEPHONE Administration +45 89 52 52 00, **Reservations** +45 70 10 14 18 (press 1).

FAX Administration +45 89 52 53 93.

INTERNET **Email** molslinjen@molslinjen.dk **Websites** www.molslinjen.dk www.bornholmslinjen.com *(Danish)*

ROUTES OPERATED

Alslinjen Fynshav (Als) - Bøjden (Funen) (50 mins; ***FRIGG SYDFYEN, FYNSHAV***; hourly (summer) two-hourly (winter)),

Bornholmslinjen Rønne (Bornholm, Denmark) - Køge (5 hrs 30 mins; ***HAMMERSHUS***; 1 per day, Rønne – Sassnitz (Germany) (3 hrs 20 mins; ***HAMMERSHUS***; 1 per day). **Fast Ferry** Rønne - Ystad (Sweden) (1 hr 20 mins; ***EXPRESS 1, MAX***; up to 8 per day).

Fanølinjen Esbjerg (Jylland) - Nordby (Fanø) (12 mins; ***FENJA, MENJA, SØNDERHO***; every 20-40 mins),

Langelandslinjen Spodsbjerg (Langeland) - Tårs (Lolland) (45 mins; ***LANGELAND, LOLLAND***; hourly),

Molslinjen* (all service fast ferry) *All year Århus (Jylland) - Odden (Sjælland) (1 hr 5 mins; ***EXPRESS1***, ***EXPRESS 2, EXPRESS 3, EXPRESS 4***; up to 12 per day), ***April - October- weekends only*** Ebeltoft (Jylland) - Odden (45 mins; ***EXPRESS 2***; 1 per day).

Samsølinjen Kalundborg - Ballen (Samsø) (1 hr 15 min; ***SAMSØ***; up to 4 per day).

1»	EXPRESS 1	10504t	09	40.0k	112.6m	1200P	417C	34L	A	DK	9501590
2»	EXPRESS 2	10500t	13	40.0k	112.6m	1000P	417C	34L	A	DK	9561356
3»	EXPRESS 3	10842t	17	40.0k	109.4m	1000P	411C	34L	A	DK	9793064
4»	EXPRESS 4	12450t	19	37.0k	109.0m	1006P	425C	36L	A	DK	9824564
5	FENJA	751t	98	11.5k	49.9m	396P	34C	4L	BA	DK	9189378
6	FRIGG SYDFYEN	1676t	84	13.5k	70.1m	338P	50C	8L	BA	DK	8222824
7	FYNSHAV	3380t	98	14.5k	69.2m	450P	96C	8L	BA	DK	9183025
8	HAMMERSHUS	18500	18	17.7k	158.0m	720P	-	90L	BA	DK	9812107
9	LANGELAND	4500t	12	16.0k	99.9m	600P	122C	36L	BA	DK	9596428
10	LOLLAND	4500t	12	16.0k	99.9m	600P	122C	36L	BA	DK	9594690
11»	MAX	5617t	98	43.0k	91.3m	800P	220C	-	A	DK	9176058
12	MENJA	751t	98	11.5k	49.9m	396P	34C	4L	BA	DK	9189380
13	POVL ANKER	12131t	78	19.5k	121.0m	1500P	262C	26T	BA	DK	7633143
14	SAMSØ	4250t	08	16.0k	91.4m	600P	122C	30L	BA	DK	9548562
15p	SØNDERHO	93t	62	10.0k	26.3m	163P	0C	0L	-	DK	

EXPRESS 1 Incat 112m catamaran built by Incat Tasmania Pty Ltd for *MGC Chartering* of the Irish Republic. Launched as the INCAT 066. On completion, sold to for *MGC Chartering* of the Irish Republic and renamed the MGC 66. In April 2009 chartered to *LD Lines*, renamed the NORMAN ARROW and, in June, placed on the Dover - Boulogne route. In November 2009 withdrawn and laid up for the winter. In April 2010 began operating on the Portsmouth Le Havre - route. In March 2012 chartered to *Mols-Linien* and renamed the KATEXPRESS 1 (Note: in upper and lower case spelt 'KatExpress 1'). Entered service in May 2012. In January 2017 renamed the EXPRESS 1. In September 2018 moved to the *Bornholmslinjen* service.

EXPRESS 2 Incat 112m catamaran built by Incat Tasmania Pty Ltd. Launched as INCAT 067. In March 2013 chartered to *Mols-Linien* and renamed the KATEXPRESS 2 for ten years with a purchase option. (Note: in upper and lower case spelt 'KatExpress 2'). Entered service in May 2013. In March 2017 renamed the EXPRESS 2.

EXPRESS 3 Incat 109m catamaran built by Incat Tasmania Pty Ltd, Hobart, Australia.

EXPRESS 4 Austal 109m catamaran built by Austal Ships, Fremantle, Australia.

FENJA Built by Morsø Værft A/S, Nykøbing Mors, Denmark for *Scandlines Sydfyenske A/S* for the Esbjerg - Nordby service.

FRIGG SYDFYEN Built by Svendborg Skibsværft A/S, Svendborg, Denmark for *Sydfyenske Dampskibsselskab (SFDS)* of Denmark for the service between Spodsbjerg and Tårs. In June 2012 moved to the Fynshav - Bøjden route.

FYNSHAV Built as the KYHOLM by Ørskov Staalskibsværft, Frederikshavn, Denmark for *Samsø Linien* of Denmark. In October 2008 chartered to *Nordic Ferry Services* and in July 2009 sold to them. Used on the Kalundborg - Koby Kås service. In March 2015 renamed the FYNSHAV and moved to the Fynshav - Bøjden service.

HAMMERSHUS Built by Rauma Marine Constructions Oy, Rauma, Finland. Delivered in July 2018. She will operate between Rønne and Køge (Bornholm) and Rønne and Sassnitz from 1st September 2018.

LANGELAND Built by Sietas Werft, Hamburg, Germany for the Spodsbjerg - Tårs route.

LOLLAND Built by Sietas Werft, Hamburg, Germany. She was launched as the SAMSØ and it was intended that she would be operated on the Hou - Sælvig service, being owned by *Samsø Linien* and operated by *Færgen*. However, these plans were dropped and in February 2012 she was renamed the LOLLAND. After delivery in March 2012 she was, in April, placed on the Spodsbjerg - Tårs route.

MAX Incat 91-metre catamaran, built speculatively at Hobart, Tasmania, Australia. In Spring 1998, following *Incat's* acquisition of a 50% share in *Scandlines Cat-Link A/S,* she was sold to that company and named the CAT-LINK IV. In 1999 purchased by *Mols-Linien* and renamed the MAX MOLS. In 2000 chartered to *Marine Atlantic* of Canada to operate between Port aux Basques (Newfoundland) and North Sydney (Nova Scotia). Returned to *Mols-Linien* in Autumn 2000. In Summer 2002 chartered to *Riga Sea Lines* to operate between Riga and Nynäshamn. Returned to *Mols-Linien* in Autumn 2002. In 2004 chartered to *P&O Ferries* to operate between Portsmouth and Caen. Operated under the marketing name 'Caen Express'. In November 2004 returned to *Mols-Linien* and placed on the Århus – Odden route to enhance the service. In June 2017 transferred to the Ebeltoft - Odden route. In January 2019 renamed the MAX. In April transferred to the *Bornholmslinjen* service.

MENJA Built by Morsø Værft A/S, Nykøbing Mors, Denmark for *Scandlines Sydfyenske A/S* for the Esbjerg - Nordby service.

POVL ANKER Built by Aalborg Værft A/S, Denmark for *Bornholmstrafikken*. Used on the Rønne - København (until September 2004), Rønne - Køge (October 2004-date), Rønne - Ystad and Rønne - Sassnitz services. In recent years she has operated between Rønne and Sassnitz and Rønne and Ystad in the peak summer period. In July 2016 sold to *Mols-Linien A/S* and chartered back. Delivered to *Mols-Linien* at the end of August 2018.

SAMSØ Built as the KANHAVE by Frantzis Shipyard, Perama, Greece. Used on the Hou - Sælvig route. In January 2015 transferred to the Kalundborg - Koby Kås (Samsø) service. Later in January 2015 the Samsø terminal was moved to Ballen. In August 2015 renamed the SAMSØ.

SØNDERHO Passenger-only ferry built by Esbjerg Jernstøberi & Maskinfabrik A/S, Esbjerg, Denmark for *Post & Telegrafvæsenet* (Danish Post Office). In 1977 taken over by *DSB*. Used on extra peak sailings and late night and early morning sailings between Esbjerg and Nordby.

REEDEREI NORDEN-FRISIA

THE COMPANY *Aktiengesellschaft Reederei Norden-Frisia* is a German public sector company.

MANAGEMENT President/CEO C U Stegmann, **Managing Director/CFO** Prok. Graw, **Technical Manager** Prok. H Stolle.

ADDRESS Postfach 1262, 26534 Norderney, Germany.

TELEPHONE *Administration* +49 (0)4931 987 0.

FAX *Administration* +49 (0)4931 987 1131.

INTERNET *Email* info@reederei-frisia.de ***Website*** www.reederei-frisia.de *(German)*

Express 1 *(Uwe Jakob)*

Hammershus *(Darren Holdaway)*

Baltivia *(John Bryant)*

Nova Star *(Frank Lose)*

ROUTES OPERATED Car Ferries & Passenger Ferries Norddeich (Germany) - Norderney (German Frisian Islands) (1 hr; ***FRISIA I, FRISIA III, FRISIA IV, FRISIA VI***; up to 15 per day), Norddeich - Juist (German Frisian Islands) (1 hr 20 mins; ***FRISIA II, FRISIA VII***; up to 15 per day). **Excursion Vessels** (***FRISIA IX, FRISIA X, WAPPEN VON NORDENEY***; varies).

1	FRISIA I	1020t	70	12.3k	63.7m	1500P	53C	-	BA	DE	7018604
2	FRISIA II	1125t	78	12.0k	63.3m	1340P	53C	-	BA	DE	7723974
3	FRISIA III	1786t	15	12.0k	74.3m	1342P	58C	-	BA	DE	9732450
4	FRISIA IV	1574t	02	12.0k	71.7m	1342P	58C	-	BA	DE	9246839
5	FRISIA VI	768t	68	12.0k	54.9m	1096P	35C	-	BA	DE	8827179
6F	FRISIA VII	363t	84	12.0k	53.0m	12P	30C	-	BA	DE	8891807
7p	FRISIA IX	571t	80	11.0k	57.0m	785P	0C	-	-	DE	7924310
8p	FRISIA X	187t	72	12.0k	36.3m	290P	0C	-	-	DE	7222308
9p	FRISIA XI	105t	69	12.0k	35.4m	940P	0C	-	-	DE	8137237
10p	WAPPEN VON NORDENEY	154t	67	14.0k	31.1m	200P	0C	-	-	DE	7935395

FRISIA I, FRISIA II, FRISIA VI Built by Jos L Meyer Werft, Papenburg, Germany for *Reederei Norden-Frisia*. Passenger capacities relate to the summer season. Capacity is reduced during the winter.

FRISIA III Built by Cassen-Werft, Emden, Germany.

FRISIA IV Built by Schiffswerft und Maschinenfabrik Cassens GmbH, Emden, Germany for *Reederei Norden-Frisia* to replace the FRISIA VIII.

FRISIA VII Built by Schlömer Werft, Oldersum, Germany for *Reederei Norden-Frisia*. Conveys ro-ro freight to Norderney and Juist.

FRISIA IX, FRISIA X Built by Schiffswerft Julius Diedrich GmbH & Co. KG, Oldersum, Germany for *Reederei Norden-Frisia*. The FRISIA IX was built to convey 9 cars at the bow end but is now used in passenger-only mode. These ships are generally used for excursions.

FRISIA XI Built by Julius Diedrich Schiffswerft, Odersum, Germany as the BALTRUM IV for *Baltrum-Linie* of Germany. In November 1982 sold to *Wyker Dampfschiffs-Reederei* and renamed the RÜM HART. In March 2014 sold to *Reederei Norden-Frisia*. In October renamed the FRISIA XI.

WAPPEN VON NORDENEY Built by Cassens-Werft, Emden, Germany for *Reederei Norden-Frisia*. Used for excursions.

Under Construction

11	FRISIA V	1786t	20	12.0k	74.3m	1338P	58C	-	BA	DE	9886122

FRISIA V Under construction by Pella Sietas Werft, Hamburg. To operate on the Norddeich-Norderney service. A sister vessel of the FRISIA III.

POLFERRIES

THE COMPANY *Polferries* is the trading name of *Polska Zegluga Baltycka SA (Polish Baltic Shipping Company)*, a Polish state-owned company.

MANAGEMENT President Piotr Redmerski.

ADDRESS ul Portowa 41, 78-100 Kolobrzeg, Poland.

TELEPHONE Administration & Reservations *Poland* +48 94 35 52 100, ***Sweden*** +46 (0)8 520 686 60.

INTERNET Email info@polferries.pl **Website** www.polferries.pl *(Polish, Danish, English, German, Swedish)*

ROUTES OPERATED Świnoujście - Ystad (7 hrs; ***BALTIVIA***, ***CRACOVIA, MAZOVIA***; up to 3 per day), Gdańsk - Nynäshamn (Sweden) (18 hrs; ***NOVA STAR, WAWEL***; up to 6 per week.

1	BALTIVIA	17790t	81	19.0k	146.9m	250P	30C	80L	BA	BS	7931997

2	CRACOVIA	25028t	02	22.8k	180.0m	550P	-	150T	BA	BS	9237242
3	MAZOVIA	25996t	96	21.0k	168.0m	200P	-	154T	BA2	BS	9010814
4	NOVA STAR	27744t	11	19.0k	162.0m	1215P	400C	90L	A	BS	9462067
5	WAWEL	25318t	80	19.0k	163.9m	900P	550C	75L	A2	BS	7814462

BALTIVIA Built as the SAGA STAR by Fartygsentreprenader AB, Kalmar, Sweden for *TT-Saga-Line* and, from 1982, used on freight services between Travemünde and Trelleborg/Malmö. (Originally ordered by *Rederi AB Svea* as the SAGALAND). In 1989 sold to *Cie Meridionale* of France, renamed the GIROLATA and used on *SNCM* (later *CMR*) services in the Mediterranean. In 1993 she was chartered back to *TT-Line*, resumed her original name and was used on the Travemünde - Trelleborg service. Following delivery of the ROBIN HOOD and the NILS DACKE in 1995, she was transferred to the Rostock - Trelleborg route. In July 1997 she was purchased by *TT-Line* and in 1998 passenger facilities were completely renovated to full ro-pax format; following the delivery of the TOM SAWYER she was transferred back to the Travemünde - Trelleborg route, operating additional freight sailings. Briefly transferred back to Rostock - Trelleborg when the charter of the TT-TRAVELLER ended. Withdrawn in 2002, sold to *Transmanche Ferries* and renamed the DIEPPE. In 2006 replaced by the SEVEN SISTERS, sold to *Polferries*, renamed the BALTIVIA and, in 2007, placed on the Gdańsk - Nynäshamn route. In February 2013 transferred to the Świnoujście – Ystad service.

CRACOVIA Built as the MURILLO by Astilleros Españoles SA, Seville, Spain for *Trasmediterranea* of Spain. Used mainly on the service between Cadiz and Canary Islands. In June 2014 sold to *Bulgaria West Port* of Bulgaria and renamed the DRUJBA. She operated between Bourgas, Bulgaria, Batumi (Georgia) and Novorossiysk (Russia). In March 2017 sold to *Polferries* and, in June 2017, renamed the CRACOVIA. In September 2017 introduced onto the Świnoujście - Ystad route.

MAZOVIA Built as the GOTLAND by Pt Dok Kodja Bahri, Kodja, Indonesia for *Rederi AB Gotland* for charter. In 1997 briefly chartered to *Tor Line* and then to *Nordic Trucker Line*, to operate between Oxelösund and St Petersburg (a ro-ro freight service). In June 1997 she was chartered to *SeaWind Line*, enabling a twice-daily passenger service to be operated. In late 1997 she was sold to *Finnlines* and renamed the FINNARROW. She started operating twice weekly between Helsinki and Travemünde. During Summer 1998 she was transferred to *FinnLink*; a bow door was fitted and she was modified to allow for two-level loading. In 2003 transferred to *Nordö Link*. In 2005 returned to *FinnLink*. In 2006 transferred to *Finnlines Nordö Link* again. In 2007 chartered to *Stena Line* to operate between Karlskrona and Gdynia. In December 2011 transferred to the Hoek van Holland - Killingholme route. In March 2011 returned to *Finnlines* and placed on the Travemünde - Malmö service. In October 2011 transferred to *FinnLink*. Between January and March 2013 chartered to *Stena Line* to cover Irish Sea routes during the refit period but withdrawn from service prematurely following an accident. In April 2013 chartered to *Grimaldi Line* of Italy for five years and renamed the EUROFERRY BRINDISI. In October 2014 sold to the *Grimaldi Group* of Italy. In November sold to *Polferries* and renamed the MAZOVIA. Entered service in June 2015 on the Świnoujście - Ystad service.

NOVA STAR Built as the NORMAN LEADER by St Marine Shipyard, Singapore for *LD Lines* of France. However, delivery was not taken as she did not meet the design specification. She was registered to *Singapore Technologies Marine* and remained laid up until February 2014 when she was chartered to *Nova Star Cruises* of Canada and renamed the NOVA STAR. She operated between Portland, Maine USA and Yarmouth, Nova Scotia, Canada. In October 2015 she was arrested in Portland Arrested in Maine due to unpaid bills and the service ceased. In February 2016 she was chartered to *Inter Shipping* of Morocco and placed on their Algeciras (Spain) - Tangier Morocco service. In November 2017 chartered to *Polferries* and sub-charted to *Inter Shipping* until February 2018 when she was taken over by *Polferries*. She began operating between Gdańsk and Nynäshamn in September 2018.

WAWEL Built as the SCANDINAVIA by Kockums Varvet AB, Malmö, Sweden for *Rederi AB Nordö* of Sweden. After service in the Mediterranean for *UMEF*, she was, in 1981, sold to *SOMAT* of Bulgaria, renamed the TZAREVETZ and used on *Medlink* services between Bulgaria and the Middle East, later on other routes. In 1986 she was chartered to *Callitzis* of Greece for a service between Italy and Greece. In 1988 she was sold to *Sealink*, re-registered in The Bahamas and renamed the FIESTA. She was then chartered to *OT Africa Line*. During Autumn 1989 she was rebuilt at Bremerhaven to convert her for passenger use and in March 1990 she was renamed the FANTASIA and placed on the Dover - Calais service. Later in 1990 she was renamed the STENA FANTASIA. In 1998 transferred to *P&O Stena Line*. In 1999 she was renamed the P&OSL CANTERBURY. In 2002 renamed the PO CANTERBURY. In Spring 2003 replaced by the PRIDE OF CANTERBURY and laid up at Dunkerque. Later in the year sold to *GA Ferries* and renamed the ALKMINI A. In 2004 moved to Greece and, after a partial rebuild (including the welding up of the bow door) placed on the Igoumenitsa – Brindisi route. Later in 2004 sold to *Polferries* and renamed the WAWEL; rebuilt to increase the number of cabins. In 2005 placed on the Świnoujście – Ystad service. In May 2015 transferred to the Gdańsk - Nynäshamn route.

Under Construction

6	NEWBUILDING	33000	20	18.0k	202.4m-	400P	-	180T	BA2	-	-

NEWBUILDING Under construction by Gryfia Marine Repair Shipyard SA, Szczecin, Poland. Likely to replace the BALTIVIA on the Świnoujście - Ystad route. Dual fuel - diesel and LNG.

PRAAMID

THE COMPANY *Praamid* is the trading name of the ferry operation of the *TS Laevad*, a company owned by the Republic of Estonia. It took over the operation of services to the islands of Hiiumaa and Saaremaa in October 2016.

ADDRESS Sadama 25, Tallinn 15051, Estonia.

TELEPHONE 618 1310.

INTERNET Email info@praamid.ee **Website** www.praamid.ee *(Estonia, English)*

ROUTES OPERATED Kuivastu - Virtsu (Saaremaa) (28 mins; ***PIRET, REGULA, TÕLL***; up to 25 per day), Rohuküla - Heltermaa (Hiiumaa) (1 hr 30 mins; ***LEIGER, TIIU***; up to 11 per day).

1	LEIGER	4012t	16	10.0k	114.0m	700P	150C	-	BA	EE	9762675
2	PIRET	4012t	17	10.0k	114.0m	700P	150C	-	BA	EE	9762663
3	REGULA	3774t	71	14.5k	71.2m	580P	105C	20L	BA2	EE	7051058
4	TIIU	4012t	17	10.0k	114.0m	700P	150C	-	BA	EE	9762687
5	TÕLL	4012t	17	10.0k	114.0m	700P	150C	-	BA	EE	9762651

LEIGER, TIIU Built by Sefine Shipyard, Yalova, Turkey. LNG powered.

PIRET, TÕLL Built by Remontowa Shipyard, Gdańsk, Poland (The PIRET's hull was subcontracted to Irko, Gdańsk, Poland). LNG powered.

REGULA Built by Jos L Meyer, Papenburg, Germany for *Stockholms Rederi AB Svea* of Sweden for the service between Helsingborg and Helsingør operated by *Linjebuss International AB* (a subsidiary company). In 1980 she was sold to *Scandinavian Ferry Lines*. During Winter 1984/85 she was rebuilt to increase vehicle and passenger capacity. In 1991 ownership was transferred to *SweFerry* and operations to *ScandLines* on the Helsingborg - Helsingør service. Ownership later transferred to *Scandlines AB*. In 1997 sold to *Saaremaa Laevakompanii*. In October 2016 chartered to *Praamid*. Following delivery of new vessels, she was retained as spare vessel. However, in summer 2017 she was used on regular service and the MERCANDIA VIII of *HH Ferries* was chartered as spare vessel. In September 2017 purchased by *TS Laevad*.

SAMSØ REDERI

THE COMPANY *Samsø Rederi* is a Danish public sector company owned by the Samsø Municipality.

MANAGEMENT Managing Director Carsten Kruse.

ADDRESS Sælvig 64, 8305 Samsø, Denmark.

TELEPHONE Administration and Reservations + 45 7022 5900.

Hamlet *(Uwe Jakob)*

Copenhagen *(Darren Holdaway)*

INTERNET Email tilsamsoe@samsoe.dk **Website** www.tilsamsoe.dk (Danish, German, English).

ROUTE OPERATED Sælvig (Samsø) - Hou (Jylland) (1 hr; ***PRINSESSE ISABELLA***; up to 7 per day).

1	PRINSESSE ISABELLA	5478t	15	9.9k	100.0m	600P	160C	16T	BA	DK	9692806

PRINSESSE ISABELLA Built as the SAMSØ by Stocznia Remontowa, Gdańsk, Poland. Entered service in March 2015. In June 2015 renamed the PRINSESSE ISABELLA.

SCANDLINES

THE COMPANY In 2007, the owners of *Scandlines AG*, the Danish Ministry of Transport and Energy and Deutsche Bahn AG, decided to sell their shares. The new owner was a consortium of the 3i Group (UK), Allianz Capital Partners GmbH (Germany) (40% of the shares each) and *Deutsche Seereederei GmbH* (Germany) (20% of the shares). The company was subsequently transformed into a private limited company and now trades under the name Scandlines GmbH, uniting the companies *Scandlines Deutschland GmbH* and *Scandlines Danmark A/S*. With *Deutsche Seereederei GmbH* selling its shares in *Scandlines GmbH* in 2010, 3i and Allianz Capital Partners held 50% of the shares each. During 2012 *Stena Line* took over the Travemünde - Ventspils, Travemünde - Liepaja and Nynäshamn - Ventspils routes, took full control of the joint routes - Rostock - Trelleborg and Sassnitz - Trelleborg services and took over the vessels used. The freight-only route between Rostock and Hanko passed to *SOL*. In November 2013 3i Group purchased Allianz Capital Partners' share and now control 100% of the company. In March 2016 3i sold a majority share in the company to First State Investments and Hermes Investment Management.

MANAGEMENT CEO Søren Poulsgaard Jensen, **Managing Director & Chief Customer Officer** Morten Haure-Petersen.

ADDRESS Am Bahnhof 3a, 18119 Rostock, Germany.

TELEPHONE Administration & Reservations *Denmark* +45 33 15 15 15, ***Germany*** +49 (0)381-77 88 77 66.

INTERNET Email servcecenter.germany@scandlines.com **Website** www.scandlines.com *(Danish, German, English)*,

ROUTES OPERATED Rødby (Lolland, Denmark) - Puttgarden (Germany) (45 mins; ***DEUTSCHLAND, HOLGER DANSKE, KRONPRINS FREDERIK, PRINS RICHARD, PRINSESSE BENEDIKTE, SCHLESWIG-HOLSTEIN*** (***HOLGER DANSKE*** *specially for dangerous goods)*; half-hourly train/vehicle ferry + additional road freight-only sailings), Gedser (Falster, Denmark) - Rostock (Germany) (2 hours; ***BERLIN, COPENHAGEN***; every 2 hours).

1	BERLIN	22319t	16	20.5k	169.5m	1300P	460C	96L	BA2	DE	9587855
2	COPENHAGEN	22319t	16	20.5k	169.5m	1300P	460C	96L	BA2	DK	9587867
3	DEUTSCHLAND	15187t	97	18.5k	142.0m	1200P	364C	30Lr	BA2	DE	9151541
4F	HOLGER DANSKE	2779t	76	14.9k	86.8m	12P	-	12L	BA	DK	7432202
5	KRONPRINS FREDERIK	16071t	81	20.5k	152.0m	1082P	210C	46T	BA	DE	7803205
6	PRINS RICHARD	14822t	97	18.5k	142.0m	1100P	364C	36Lr	BA2	DK	9144419
7	PRINSESSE BENEDIKTE	14822t	97	18.5k	142.0m	1100P	364C	36Lr	BA2	DK	9144421
8	SCHLESWIG-HOLSTEIN	15187t	97	18.5k	142.0m	1200P	364C	30Lr	BA2	DE	9151539

BERLIN Partly built by Volkswerft Stralsund, Stralsund, Germany for *Scandlines* to operate on the Gedser - Rostock route. The propulsion system allows for adaption to LNG. Originally due to enter service in Spring 2012, construction was seriously delayed. It was then found that she did not meet the specification and the order was cancelled. She was 90% finished and had undertaken sea trials. In March 2014, purchased by *Scandferries ApS* of Denmark (an associated company) and towed, firstly to Blohm + Voss Shipyards, Hamburg and then to Fayard Shipyard, Odense to be completed with an almost completely new superstructure. Her engines were also modified straight diesel to diesel-electric hybrid. In May 2016 chartered to *Scandlines* and entered service on the Gedser - Rostock route.

COPENHAGEN As the BERLIN except that at the time of purchase by *Scandlines*, she had been launched but was only 50% finished. Entered service in Autumn 2016.

DEUTSCHLAND Train/vehicle ferry built by Van der Giessen-de Noord, Krimpen aan den IJssel, Rotterdam, The Netherlands for *DFO* for the Puttgarden - Rødby service. During Winter 2003/04 a new hoistable deck was added for cars by Neptun Yard Rostock, (Germany).

HOLGER DANSKE Built by Aalborg Værft A/S, Aalborg, Denmark as a train/vehicle ferry for *DSB* for the Helsingør - Helsingborg service. In 1991 transferred to the Kalundborg - Samsø route (no rail facilities). In 1997 transferred to subsidiary *SFDS A/S*. Withdrawn at the end of November 1998 when the service passed to *Samsø Linien*. In 1999 began operating between Rødby and Puttgarden as a road-freight-only vessel, carrying, among others, loads which cannot be conveyed on passenger vessels.

KRONPRINS FREDERIK Train/vehicle ferry built by Nakskov Skibsværft A/S, Nakskov, Denmark for *DSB* for the Nyborg - Korsør service. Withdrawn in 1997. After conversion to a car/lorry ferry, she was transferred to the Gedser - Rostock route (no rail facilities). In March 2017, following modifications, transferred to the Rødby - Puttgarden route to provide extra capacity for lorry traffic. Also serves as reserve vessel on Gedser - Rostock service.

PRINS RICHARD, PRINSESSE BENEDIKTE Train/vehicle ferries, built by Ørskov Christensen Staalskibsværft A/S, Frederikshavn, Denmark for *Scandlines A/S* for the Rødby - Puttgarden service. During Winter 2003/04 a new hoistable deck was added for cars by Neptun Yard Rostock, (Germany).

SCHLESWIG-HOLSTEIN Train/vehicle ferry built by Van der Giessen-de Noord, Krimpen aan den IJssel, Rotterdam, The Netherlands for *DFO* for the Puttgarden - Rødby service. During Winter 2003/04 a new hoistable deck was added for cars by Neptun Yard Rostock, (Germany).

SMYRIL LINE

THE COMPANY *Smyril Line* is a Faroe Islands company.

MANAGEMENT Adm. Director Rúni Vang Poulsen, **Accounting and Department Manager** Nina Djurhuus.

ADDRESS Yviri við Strond 1, 110 Tórshavn, Faroe Islands.

TELEPHONE Administration & Reservations +298-34 59 00.

INTERNET Email office@smyrilline.com **Website** www.smyrilline.com *(English, Danish, Dutch, Faroese, French, German, Icelandic, Norwegian, Swedish)*

ROUTES OPERATED ***Winter/Early Spring*** Tórshavn (Faroes) - Hirtshals (Denmark) (36 hrs; ***NORRÖNA***; 1 per week), ***Spring/Early Summer/Autumn*** Tórshavn - Hirtshals (36 hrs; ***NORRÖNA***; 1 per week), Tórshavn - Seyðisfjördur (Iceland) (19 hrs; ***NORRÖNA***; 1 per week), ***Summer*** Tórshavn - Hirtshals (Denmark) (30 hrs; ***NORRÖNA***; 2 per week), Tórshavn - Seyðisfjördur (Iceland) (19 hrs; ***NORRÖNA***; 2 per week). ***Freight services*** Tórshavn - Hirtshals - St Petersburg (***EYSTNES***, ***HVITANES***), Thorlakshofn (Iceland) - Tórshavn - Rotterdam (***MYKINES***).

1F	EYSTNES	4610t	81	15.0k	102.2m	0P	-	24T	AS	FO	7922166
2F	HVITANES	4636t	80	12.0k	77.3m	0P	-	14T	AS	FO	7915541
3F	MYKINES	18979t	96	20.0k	138.5m	12P	1452C	105T	A2	FO	9121998
4	NORRÖNA	35966t	03	21.0k	164.0m	1482P	800C	134T	BA	FO	9227390

EYSTNES Con-ro vessel (only the main deck can take trailers) built as the COMETA by Fosen Mekaniske Verksteder, Rissa, Norway for *Nor-Cargo*. Until 2010 she operated for *Sea-Cargo* between Norwegian ports and Immingham; afterwards she operated on *Nor-Cargo* Norwegian domestic services. In September 2015 sold to *Smyril Line* and renamed the EYSTNES.

HVITANES Con-ro vessel (only the main deck can take trailers) built as the TANAGER by Bergen Mekaniske Verksteder, Bergen, Norway for *NorCargo* of Norway. In September 2015 sold to *Smyril Line* and renamed the EYSTNES.

MYKINES Built as the TRANSGARD by Umoe Sterkoder, Kristiansund, Norway for *Bror Husell Chartering* of Finland for long-term charter to *Transfennica* and used between Rauma and Antwerpen and Hamina and Lübeck. Later chartered to *Finncarriers*. In 2005 she underwent conversion in Poland to add a garage on top of the original weather deck and was placed on long-term charter to *UECC*. She was generally used on the Baltic or Iberian services. In 2007 renamed AUTO BALTIC. In January 2016 chartered to *Flotta Suardiaz*. In April 2017 sold to *Smyril Line* to inaugurate a new service between Thorlakshofn (Iceland), Tórshavn and Rotterdam and renamed the MYKINES.

NORRÖNA Built by Flender Werft, Lübeck, Germany for *Smyril Line*, to replace the existing NORRÖNA. Originally due to enter service in Summer 2002, start of building was delayed by financing difficulties. She was to have been built at Flensburger Schiffbau-Gesellschaft, Flensburg, Germany, but delays in arranging finance led to change of shipyard.

STENA LINE

THE COMPANY *Stena Line Scandinavia AB* is a Swedish private sector company. During 2012, the operations of subsidiary *Scandlines AB* of Sweden were absorbed and some of the Baltic operations and vessels of *Scandlines GmbH* of Germany were taken over. In *2015 Stena Line Scandinavia's* share in *Scandlines AB* where sold and the route Helsingborg - Helsingør sold to new owners.

MANAGEMENT CEO Niclas Mårtensson, **Chief Operating Officer** Peter Arvidsson.

ADDRESS Danmarksterminalen, 405 19 Göteborg, Sweden.

TELEPHONE Administration +46 (0)31-85 80 00, **Reservations** +46 (0)770 57 57 00.

INTERNET Email info@stenaline.com **Website** www.stenaline.com *(Czech, Danish, Dutch, English, French, German, Latvian, Lithuanian, Norwegian, Polish, Russian, Swedish)*

ROUTES OPERATED Passenger Ferries Göteborg (Sweden) - Frederikshavn (Denmark) (3 hrs 15 mins; ***STENA DANICA, STENA JUTLANDICA, STENA VINGA***; up to 6 per day), Göteborg - Kiel (Germany) (14 hrs; ***STENA GERMANICA, STENA SCANDINAVICA***; 1 per day), Frederikshavn - Oslo (Norway) (8 hrs 45 mins; ***STENA SAGA***; 1 per day), Varberg (Sweden) - Grenaa (Denmark) (4 hrs; ***STENA NAUTICA***; 2 per day), Karlskrona (Sweden) - Gdynia (Poland) (10 hrs 30 mins; ***STENA BALTICA***, ***STENA NORDICA, STENA SPIRIT, STENA VISION***; 3/4 per day), Rostock (Germany) - Trelleborg (Sweden) (7 hrs); ***MECKLENBURG-VORPOMMERN, SASSNITZ, SKÅNE***; 3/4 per day), Sassnitz (Germany) - Trelleborg (4 hrs 15 mins; ***SASSNITZ***; 5 per week), Travemünde (Germany) - Liepaja (Latvia) (27 hrs; ***STENA GOTHICA, URD***; 5 per week), Nynäshamn (Sweden) – Ventspils (Latvia) (12 hrs; ***SCOTTISH VIKING, STENA FLAVIA***; 12 per week).

1	MECKLENBURG-VORPOMMERN	36185t	96	22.0k	199.9m	600P	445C	230Tr	A2	DE	9131797
2	SASSNITZ	21154t	89	18.5k	171.5m	875P	314C	50Tr	BA2	DE	8705383
3	SCOTTISH VIKING	26500t	09	24.0k	186.5m	800P	185C	120L	A	IT	9435454
4	SKÅNE	42705t	98	21.0k	200.2m	600P	520C	240Tr	AS2	SE	9133915
5	STENA BALTICA	22542t	07	23.0k	167.0m	160P	-	140L	BA2	UK	9364978
6»●	STENA CARISMA	8631t	97	40.0k	88.0m	900P	210C	-	A	SE	9127760
7	STENA DANICA	28727t	83	19.5k	154.9m	2274P	555C	120T	BAS2	SE	7907245
8	STENA FLAVIA	26904t	08	24.0k	186.5m	852P	185C	120L	A	DK	9417919
9	STENA GERMANICA	44372t	01	22.0k	240.1m	900P	-	250L	BA	SE	9145176
10F	STENA GOTHICA	13144t	82	18.0k	171.0m	186P	-	104T	AS	SE	7826867
11	STENA JUTLANDICA	29691t	96	21.5k	183.7m	1500P	550C	156T	BAS2	SE	9125944
12	STENA NAUTICA	19504t	86	19.4k	134.0m	700P	330C	70T	BA2	SE	8317954
13	STENA NORDICA	24206t	01	25.7k	169.8m	405P	375C	90L	BA2	BS	9215505
14	STENA SAGA	33750t	81	22.0k	166.1m	2000P	510C	76T	BA	SE	7911545
15	STENA SCANDINAVICA	55050t	03	22.0k	240.1m	900P	-	260L	BA	SE	9235517

16	STENA SPIRIT	39169t	88	20.0k	175.4m	2400P	550C	120T	BAS2	BS	7907661
17	STENA VINGA	13906t	05	18.5k	124.9m	400P	342C	106T	A	SE	9323699
18	STENA VISION	39178t	87	20.0k	175.4m	2400P	550C	120T	BAS2	SE	7907659
19	URD	13144t	81	17.5k	171.0m	186P	-	104T	AS	DK	7826855

MECKLENBURG-VORPOMMERN Train/vehicle ferry built by Schichau Seebeckwerft, Bremerhaven, Germany for *DFO* for the Rostock - Trelleborg service. During Winter 2002/03 modified to increase freight capacity and reduce passenger capacity. In September 2012 sold to *Stena Line*.

SASSNITZ Train/vehicle ferry built by Danyard A/S, Frederikshavn, Denmark for *Deutsche Reichsbahn*. In 1993 ownership transferred to *DFO*. Used on the Sassnitz - Trelleborg service. In September 2012 sold to *Stena Line*. From September 2018 operates twice weekly from Trelleborg to Rostock.

SCOTTISH VIKING Built by CN Visentini, Porto Viro, Italy for *Epic Shipping* of the UK and chartered to *Norfolkline*. Operated between Zeebrugge and Rosyth until December 2010. In January 2010 chartered to *Scandlines* and placed on the Nynäshamn - Ventspils service. In September 2012 charter transferred to *Stena Line*.

SKÅNE Train/vehicle ferry built by Astilleros Españoles, Cadiz, Spain for an American trust and chartered to *Scandlines*. She is used on the Trelleborg - Rostock service.

STENA BALTICA Built as the COTENTIN by STX Finland, Helsinki, Finland for *Brittany Ferries*. Used on freight service from Poole to Cherbourg and Santander. In March 2013 replaced by the BARFLEUR (operating to Cherbourg only). During summer 2013 operated twice weekly from Poole to Bilbao and Santander. In October 2013 sold to *Stena RoRo* and renamed the STENA BALTICA. In November 2013 chartered to *Stena Line* and replaced the STENA ALEGRA on the Karlskrona - Gdynia route.

STENA CARISMA Westamarin HSS 900 craft built at Kristiansand, Norway for *Stena Line* for the Göteborg - Frederikshavn service. Work on a sister vessel, approximately 30% completed, was ceased. She has not operated since 2013.

STENA DANICA Built by Chantiers du Nord et de la Méditerranée, Dunkerque, France for *Stena Line* for the Göteborg - Frederikshavn service.

STENA FLAVIA Built by CN Visentini, Porto Viro, Italy for *Epic Shipping* of the UK. Launched as the WATLING STREET. On delivery, chartered to *ISCOMAR* of Spain and renamed the PILAR DEL MAR. In 2009 laid up until February 2010 when she was chartered to *Acciona Trasmediterranea* of Spain and operated between Barcelona and Tangiers. Later that month, chartered to *T-Link* and resumed the name WATLING STREET. In May 2011 chartered to *Scandlines* and placed on the Travemünde - Ventspils service. In April 2012, sold to *Stena RoRo*; she continued to be chartered to *Scandlines*. In September 2012 charter transferred to *Stena Line*. In April 2013 renamed the STENA FLAVIA. She now operates one weekly roundtrip from Nynäshamn to Liepaja, two roundtrips to Nynäshamn to Ventspils and once weekly Ventspils - Travemünde.

STENA GERMANICA Ro-pax ferry built as the STENA HOLLANDICA by Astilleros Españoles, Cadiz, Spain for *Stena RoRo* and chartered to *Stena Line BV* to operate between Hoek van Holland and Harwich. In 2007 lengthened by 50m at Lloyd Werft, Bremerhaven and passenger capacity increased to 900. Between May and August 2010 refurbished at Gdańsk and had an 100 additional cabins added. At the end of August entered service on the Göteborg - Kiel route, renamed the STENA GERMANICA III. In September, after the previous STENA GERMANICA had been renamed the STENA VISION, she was renamed the STENA GERMANICA.

STENA GOTHICA Built as the LUCKY RIDER by Nuovi Cantieri Apuania S.P.A., Marina De Carrara, Italy, a ro-ro freight ferry, for *Delpa Maritime* of Greece. In 1985 she was acquired by *Stena Line* and renamed the STENA DRIVER. Later that year she was acquired by *Sealink British Ferries* and renamed the SEAFREIGHT FREEWAY to operate freight-only services between Dover and Dunkerque. In 1988 she was sold to *SOMAT* of Bulgaria for use on *Medlink* services in the Mediterranean and renamed the SERDICA. In 1990 she was sold and renamed the

Skåne *(Darren Holdaway*

Sassnitz *(Frank Lose)*

Stena Saga *(Peter Therkildsen)*

Stena Vinga *(Frank Lose)*

NORTHERN HUNTER. In 1991 she was sold to *Blæsbjerg* of Denmark, renamed the ARKA MARINE and chartered to *DSB*. She was then converted into a ro-pax vessel, renamed the ASK and introduced onto the Århus - Kalundborg service. Purchased by *Scandlines A/S* of Denmark in 1997. In 1999 she was, after some modification, transferred to *Scandlines Euroseabridge* and placed on the Travemünde - Klaipėda route. In 2000 she was transferred to the Rostock - Liepaja route. Lengthened by 20m in 2001 and, in late 2001, chartered to *Nordö Link* to operate between Travemünde and Malmö. In late 2002 replaced by the FINNARROW and returned to *Scandlines*. She was transferred to the Rostock - Trelleborg route whilst the MECKLENBURG-VORPOMMERN was being rebuilt. She was then transferred to the Kiel - Klaipėda route. In 2003 chartered to *Scandlines AB* to operate on the Trelleborg - Travemünde route. In April 2005 the charter ended and she returned to *Scandlines AG*. Initially she was due to replace the FELLOW on the Nynäshamn – Ventspils route during her annual refit. In Autumn 2005 moved to the Rostock - Ventspils route. In January 2009 moved to the Nynäshamn – Ventspils route. In January 2011 moved to the Travemünde - Liepaja route. In May 2011 laid up. In November introduced as second vessel. In September 2012 sold to *Stena Line*. In September 2015 moved to the Göteborg - Frederikshavn freight service and renamed the STENA GOTHICA. In September to be 2018 moved to the Travemünde - Liepaja route.

STENA JUTLANDICA Train/vehicle 'ro-pax' vessel built by Van der Giessen-de Noord, Krimpen aan den IJssel, Rotterdam, The Netherlands for *Stena Line* to operate between Göteborg and Frederikshavn. She was launched as the STENA JUTLANDICA III and renamed on entry into service.

STENA NAUTICA Built as the NIELS KLIM by Nakskov Skibsværft A/S, Nakskov, Denmark for *DSB (Danish State Railways)* for their service between Århus (Jylland) and Kalundborg (Sjælland). In 1990 she was purchased by *Stena Rederi* of Sweden and renamed the STENA NAUTICA. In 1992 she was chartered to *B&I Line*, renamed the ISLE OF INNISFREE and introduced onto the Rosslare - Pembroke Dock service, replacing the MUNSTER (8093t, 1970). In 1993 she was transferred to the Dublin - Holyhead service. In early 1995 she was chartered to *Lion Ferry*. She was renamed the LION KING. In 1996 she was replaced by a new LION KING and renamed the STENA NAUTICA. During Summer 1996 she was chartered to *Transmediterranea* of Spain but returned to *Stena RoRo* in the autumn and remained laid up during 1997. In December 1997 she was chartered to *Stena Line* and placed on the Halmstad - Grenaa route. This route ended on 31st January 1999 and she was transferred to the Varberg - Grenaa route. During Winter 2001/02 she was rebuilt to heighten the upper vehicle deck and allow separate loading of vehicle decks; passenger capacity was reduced. On 16th February 2004 she was hit by the coaster JOANNA and holed. Returned to service at the end of May 2004 after repairs at Göteborg and Gdańsk.

STENA NORDICA Built as the EUROPEAN AMBASSADOR by Mitsubishi Heavy Industries, Shimonoseki, Japan for *P&O Irish Sea* for their Liverpool - Dublin service. Service transferred to from Liverpool to Mostyn in November 2001. Also operated between Dublin and Cherbourg once a week. In 2004 the Mostyn route closed and she was sold to *Stena RoRo*. Chartered to *Stena Line* to operate between Karlskrona and Gdynia and renamed the STENA NORDICA. In 2008 transferred to the Holyhead - Dublin service. In February 2015 replaced by the STENA SUPERFAST X and chartered to *DFDS Seaways*. She was renamed the MALO SEAWAYS and, in April 2015, placed on the Dover - Calais route. Withdrawn from traffic in February 2016 and laid up. In June 2016 charter ended. Renamed the STENA NORDICA and chartered to *GNV* of Italy to operate between Sicily and the Italian mainland. In January 2017 chartered to *Stena Line* and performed refit relief duties in the Irish Sea. In April placed on the Travemünde - Liepāja service. In October 2018 to be moved back to the Karlskrona - Gdynia route. In March 2019 replaced the STENA EUROPE on the Fishguard - Rosslare route for six months.

STENA SAGA Built as the SILVIA REGINA by Oy Wärtsilä Ab, Turku, Finland for *Stockholms Rederi AB Svea* of Sweden. She was registered with subsidiary company *Svea Line* of Turku, Finland and was used on *Silja Line* services between Stockholm and Helsinki. In 1981 she was sold to *Johnson Line* and in 1984 sold to a Finnish Bank and chartered back. In 1990 she was purchased by *Stena RoRo* of Sweden for delivery in 1991. In 1991 she was renamed the STENA BRITANNICA and took up service on the Hoek van Holland - Harwich service for Dutch subsidiary *Stena Line BV*, operating with a British crew. In 1994 she was transferred to the Oslo - Frederikshavn route and renamed the STENA SAGA. During Winter 2002/03 rebuilt to increase passenger capacity by 200.

STENA SCANDINAVICA Ro-pax vessel built by Hyundai Heavy Industries, Ulsan, South Korea, for *Stena RoRo*. Launched and delivered in January 2003 as the STENA BRITANNICA II. Chartered to *Stena Line* for use on the Hoek van Holland - Harwich service, replacing the 2000-built STENA BRITANNICA, now the FINNFELLOW of *FinnLink*. In March 2003 renamed the STENA BRITANNICA. In 2007 lengthened at Lloyd Werft, Bremerhaven. In September 2010 renamed the BRITANNICA. Between October 2010 and April 2011 refurbished and had 100 additional cabins added at Gdańsk. In April 2011 renamed the STENA SCANDINAVICA IV and entered service on the Göteborg - Kiel route. In May, after the previous STENA SCANDINAVICA had been renamed the STENA SPIRIT, she was renamed the STENA SCANDINAVICA.

STENA SPIRIT Built as the STENA SCANDINAVICA by Stocznia i Komuni Paryski, Gdynia, Poland for *Stena Line* for the Göteborg - Kiel service (launched as the STENA GERMANICA and names swapped with sister vessel before delivery). There were originally intended to be four vessels. Only two were delivered to *Stena Line*. The third (due to be called the STENA POLONICA) was sold by the builders as an unfinished hull to *Fred. Olsen Lines* of Norway and then resold to *ANEK* of Greece who had her completed at Perama and delivered as EL VENIZELOS for service between Greece and Italy. The fourth hull (due to be called the STENA BALTICA) was sold to *A Lelakis* of Greece and was to be rebuilt as a cruise ship to be called REGENT SKY; however, the project was never completed. The hull was broken up in 2004. During the summer period on some days, the vessel arriving in Göteborg overnight from Kiel operates a round trip to Frederikshavn before departing for Kiel the following evening. During Winter 1998/99 she was modified to increase freight capacity and reduce the number of cabins. In April 2011 replaced by the former STENA BRITANNICA (renamed the STENA SCANDINAVICA IV) and entered CityVarvet in Göteborg for refurbishment. In June 2011 she was renamed the STENA SPIRIT and, in July 2011, transferred to the Karlskrona - Gydnia route.

STENA VINGA Built as the HAMMERODDE by Merwede Shipyard, Hardinxveld-Giessendam, The Netherlands for *Bornholmstrafikken*. In Winter 2010 an additional vehicle deck was added for freight and some additional cabins. In November 2017 sold to *Stena RoRo* and chartered back. In September 2018 delivered to *Stena Line*, renamed the STENA VINGA and placed on the Göteborg - Frederikshavn service, replacing the STENA GOTHICA.

STENA VISION Built as the STENA GERMANICA by Stocznia im Lenina, Gdańsk, Poland for *Stena Line* for the Göteborg - Kiel service. During the summer period on some days, the vessel arriving in Göteborg overnight from Kiel operates a round trip to Frederikshavn before departing for Kiel the following evening. During Winter 1998/99 modified to increase freight capacity and reduce the number of cabins. In August 2010 replaced by the former STENA HOLLANDICA (renamed the STENA GERMANICA III initially) and entered CityVarvet in Göteborg for refurbishment. In September she was renamed the STENA VISION and, in November, transferred to the Karlskrona - Gydnia route.

URD Built as the EASY RIDER by Nouvi Cantieri Aquania SpA, Venice, Italy, a ro-ro freight ferry, for *Delpa Maritime* of Greece and used on Mediterranean services. In 1985 she was acquired by *Sealink British Ferries* and renamed the SEAFREIGHT HIGHWAY to operate a freight-only service between Dover and Dunkerque. In 1988 she was sold to *SOMAT* of Bulgaria for use on *Medlink* services in the Mediterranean and renamed the BOYANA. In 1990 she was sold to *Blæsbjerg* of Denmark, renamed the AKTIV MARINE and chartered to *DSB*. In 1991 she was converted into a ro-pax vessel, renamed the URD and introduced onto the Århus - Kalundborg service. Purchased by *Scandlines* in 1997. Withdrawn at the end of May 1999 and, after modification, transferred to the *Balticum Seaways* (later *Scandlines Balticum Seaways*) Århus - Aabenraa - Klaipėda route. In 2001 lengthened and moved to the Rostock - Liepaja route. In Autumn 2005 this route became Rostock - Ventspils. Withdrawn from Rostock - Ventspils in November 2009. Vessel inaugurated new service Travemünde - Ventspils in January 2010. Replaced by the WATLING STREET in May 2011 and moved to the Travemünde - Liepaja route. In October 2012 sold to *Sol Dru A/S* (a subsidiary of *Swedish Orient Line*) and chartered to *Stena Line*. In August 2013 sold to *Stena Line*.

Note The Stena 'E-flexers' under construction in Nanjing are all listed in Section 1 as the first six will all be deployed in UK waters (three for *Stena Line*, three on charter). A further two have been ordered but their deployment is currently unknown and they may operate in the Baltic.

STRANDFARASKIP LANDSINS

THE COMPANY *Strandfaraskip Landsins* is owned by the Faroe Islands Government.

ADDRESS Sjógøta 5, Postsmoga 30, 810 Tvøroyri, Faroe Islands.

TELEPHONE Administration & Reservations +298 34 30 00.

FAX Administration & Reservations +298 34 30 01.

INTERNET Email firstssl.fo **Website** www.ssl.fo *(Faroese)*

ROUTES OPERATED Passenger and Car Ferries Tórshavn (Streymoy) - Tvøroyri (Suduroy) (1 hr 50 mins; ***SMYRIL***; up to 3 per day), Klaksvík - Sydradali (20 min; ***SAM***; up to 6 per day), Skopun – Gamlarætt (30 mins; ***TEISTIN***; up to 9 per day). **Passenger-only Ferries** Sørvágur - Mykines (1 hr 15 mins; ***JÒSUP (chartered ship)***; up to 3 per day, May to August only), Hvannasund - Svínoy (40 mins) - Kirkja (20 mins) - Hattarvik (10 mins) - Svínoy (30 mins; ***RITAN***; up to 4 per day), Sandur - Skúvoy (35 mins; ***SILDBERIN***; up to 5 per day), Tórshavn - Nólsoy (25 mins; ***TERNAN***; up to 5 per day.

1p	RITAN	81t	71	10.5k	22.1m	125P	0C	0L	-	FO	
2	SAM	217t	75	9.7k	30.2m	115P	17C	-	A	FO	7602168
3p	SILDBERIN	34t	79	7.5k	11.2m	30P	0C	0L	-	FO	
4	SMYRIL	12670t	05	21.0k	135.0m	976P	200C	32L	A	FO	9275218
5p	SÚLAN	11t	87	-	12.0m	40P	0C	0L	-	FO	
6	TEISTIN	1260t	01	11.0k	45.0m	288P	33C	2L	BA	FO	9226102
7	TERNAN	927t	80	12.0k	39.7m	319P	0C	0L	BA	FO	7947154

RITAN Built by Monnickenda, Volendam, The Netherlands. Used on the Hvannasund – Svínoy-Kirkja- Hattarvik service.

SAM Built by Blaalid Slip & Mek Verksted, Raudeberg, Norway. Used on the Klaksvik - Syòradali route and the Leirvik - Syòradali route.

SILDBERIN Built at Tvøroyri, Faroe Islands. Used on the Sandur - Skúvoy route.

SMYRIL Built by IZAR, San Fernando, Spain for *Strandfaraskip Landsins*. Operates on the Tórshavn – Tvøroyri service.

SÚLAN Built by Faaborg Værft A/S, Faaborg, Denmark. Used on the Sørvágur - Mykines service. Now conveys freight to Skúvoy.

TEISTIN Built by P/F Skipasmidjan a Skala, Skala, Faroe Islands for *Strandfaraskip Landsins*. Used on the Skopun – Gamlarætt service.

TERNAN Built by Tórshavnar Skipasmidja P/f, Tórshavn, Faroe Islands for *Strandfaraskip Landsins*. Used on the Tórshavn – Nólsoy service.

SYLTFÄHRE

THE COMPANY *Syltfähre* (*Syltfærge* in Danish) is the trading name of *Römö-Sylt Linie GmbH & Co. KG*, a German private sector company, a subsidiary of *FRS (Förde Reederei Seetouristik)* of Flensburg.

MANAGEMENT Managing Director RSL Birte Dettmers, Tim Kunstmann.

ADDRESS *Germany* Am Fähranleger 3, 25992 List, Germany, ***Denmark*** Kilebryggen, 6792 Rømø, Denmark.

TELEPHONE Administration +49 (0)461 864 0, **Reservations *Germany*** +49 (0)461 864 601, ***Denmark*** +49 461 864 601.

INTERNET Email info@rsl.de **Website** www.syltfaehre.de *(Danish, English, German)*

ROUTE OPERATED List auf Sylt (Sylt, Germany) - Havneby (Rømø, Denmark) (approx. 40 mins; ***SYLT EXPRESS***; variable - approx two-hourly). **Note**: The Danish island of Rømø is linked to the Danish mainland by a toll-free road causeway; the German island of Sylt is linked to the German mainland by the Hindenburgdamm, a rail-only causeway on which cars are conveyed on shuttle wagons.

1	SYLT EXPRESS	3650t	05	16.0k	88.2m	600P	80C	10L	BA	CY	9321823

SYLT EXPRESS Built by Fiskerstrand Verft A/S, Aalesund, Norway for *Römö-Sylt Linie*.

To be introduced in November 2019

2	TRESFJORD	3423t	91	15.0k	96.95m	345P	127C	-	BA	CY	9008794

TRESFJORD Built by Fiskerstrand Verft A/S of Norway for *Møre og Romsdal Fylkesbåtar AS (MRF)* of Molde, Norway. In 2005 transferred to *Fjord1 MRF AS* of Molde, Norway. In October 2012 transferred to *Fjord 1 AS* of Florø, Norway. Until 2010 operated between Molde and Vestnes. She was then converted to LNG propulsion. Between February 2011 and January 2019 operated between Flakk and Rørvik. In January 2019 became a reserve vessel on the Molde and Vestnes route. In November 2019 to be operated for *Römö-Sylt Linie* whilst the Hindenburgdamm is closed during the week for track maintenance. After this work is completed, she will be retained to provide additional capacity during the summer. She may be renamed.

TALLINK/SILJA LINE

THE COMPANY *AS Tallink Grupp* is an Estonian private sector company. *Tallink Silja Oy* is a Finnish subsidiary, *Tallink Silja AB* is a Swedish subsidiary.

MANAGEMENT *AS Tallink Grupp:* Chairman of Management Board Paavo Nõgene, **Communications Director** Katri Link, ***Tallink Silja Oy* Managing Director** Margus Schults, ***Tallink Silja AB* Managing Director** Marcus Risberg.

ADDRESSES *AS Tallink Grupp* Sadama 5/7, Tallinn 10111, Estonia, ***Tallink Silja Oy*** P.O. Box 100, 00181 Helsinki, Finland, ***Tallink Silja AB*** Box 27295, 10253 Stockholm, Sweden.

TELEPHONE *AS Tallink Grupp* +372 (0)640 9800, ***Tallink Silja Oy* Administration** +358 (0)9 18041, **Reservations** +49 (0)40 547 541 222.

FAX *AS Tallink Grupp* Administration + 372 (0)640 9810, ***Tallink Silja Oy* Administration** +358 (0)9 180 4262.

INTERNETEmail info@tallink.ee **Websites** www.tallinksilja.com *(17 languages, see the internet page)*, www.tallink.com (corporate site) *(English)*

ROUTES OPERATED Tallink branded services *Passenger Ferries* Helsinki - Tallinn: ***Shuttle*** (2 hrs; ***MEGASTAR, STAR***; up to 6 per day), ***Cruise Ferries*** (3 hrs 30 - 4hrs 30 mins; ***SILJA EUROPA***; normally 2 per day), Stockholm - Mariehamn (Åland) - Tallinn (14 hrs; ***BALTIC QUEEN, VICTORIA I***; daily), Stockholm - Riga (Latvia) (16 hrs; ***ISABELLE, ROMANTIKA***; daily). ***Freight and Car Passengers Ferry*** Helsinki (Vuosaari) - Tallinn (Muuga) (3 hrs 30 mins; ***SEA WIND***; 2 per day). ***Freight-only Ferry*** Kapellskär - Paldiski (9 hrs - 11 hrs; ***REGAL STAR***; alternate days (round trip on Sunday)),

Silja Line branded services Helsinki (Finland) - Mariehamn (Åland) - Stockholm (Sweden) (16 hrs; ***SILJA SERENADE, SILJA SYMPHONY***; 1 per day), Turku (Finland) - Mariehamn (Åland) (day)/Långnäs (Åland) (night) - Stockholm (11 hrs; ***BALTIC PRINCESS***, ***GALAXY***; 2 per day).

1	ATLANTIC VISION	30285t	02	27.9k	203.3m	728P	695C	110L	BA2	CA	9211509
2	BALTIC PRINCESS	48300t	08	24.5k	212.0m	2800P	300C	82T	BA	FI	9354284
3	BALTIC QUEEN	48300t	09	24.5k	212.0m	2800P	300C	82T	BA	EE	9443255
4	GALAXY	48915t	06	22.0k	212.0m	2800P	300C	82T	BA	SE	9333694
5	ISABELLE	35154t	89	21.5k	170.9m	2420P	364C	30T	BA	LV	8700723
6	MEGASTAR	49000t	16	27.0k	212m	2800P	-	-	BA2	EE	9773064
7F	REGAL STAR	15281t	00	17.5k	156.6m	100P	-	120T	A	EE	9087116

8	ROMANTIKA	40803t	02	22.0k	193.8m	2178P	300C	82T	BA	EE	9237589
9F	SEA WIND	15879t	72	17.5k	154.4m	260P	55C	88T	BAS	EE	7128332
10	SILJA EUROPA	59912t	93	21.5k	201.8m	3000P	400C	68T	BA	EE	8919805
11	SILJA SERENADE	58376t	90	21.0k	203.0m	2800P	410C	70T	BA	FI	8715259
12	SILJA SYMPHONY	58377t	91	21.0k	203.0m	2800P	410C	70T	BA	SE	8803769
13	STAR	36249t	07	27.5k	185.0m	1900P	450C	120L	BA2	EE	9364722
14	VICTORIA I	40975t	04	22.0k	193.8m	2500P	300C	82T	BA	EE	9281281

ATLANTIC VISION Built as the SUPERFAST IX by Howaldtswerke Deutsche Werft AG, Kiel, Germany for *Attica Enterprises* for use by *Superfast Ferries*. She operated between Rostock and Södertälje from January until April 2002. In May 2002 she began operating between Rosyth and Zeebrugge (with the SUPERFAST X (now the STENA SUPERFAST X)). In 2004 fitted with additional cabins and conference/seating areas. In 2005 transferred to the Rostock - Hanko (later Helsinki) route. In 2006 sold to *Tallink*. In October 2008 chartered to *Marine Atlantic* of Canada to operate on the North Sydney-Port aux Basques service and renamed the ATLANTIC VISION.

BALTIC PRINCESS Built by Aker Yards, Helsinki. A large part of the hull was built at St Nazaire, France. In August 2008 replaced the GALAXY on the Tallinn - Helsinki route. In February 2013 transferred to the Stockholm - Turku service.

BALTIC QUEEN Built by STX Europe, Rauma, Finland. Currently operates between Stockholm and Tallinn.

GALAXY Built by Aker Yards, Rauma, Finland to operate as a cruise ferry on the Tallinn - Helsinki route. In July 2008 transferred to the Stockholm - Turku route and rebranded as a *Silja Line* vessel.

ISABELLE Built as the ISABELLA by Brodogradevna Industrija, Split, Yugoslavia for *SF Line*. Used on the *Viking Line* Stockholm - Naantali service until 1992 when she was switched to operating 24-hour cruises from Helsinki and in 1995 she was transferred to the Stockholm - Helsinki route. During 1996 she additionally operated day cruises to Muuga in Estonia during the 'layover' period in Helsinki. In 1997 she was transferred to the Stockholm - Turku route. in January 2013 she was replaced by the VIKING GRACE. After covering for the AMORELLA during her refit period she was laid up. In April 2013 sold to *Hansa Link Limited*, a subsidiary of *AS Tallink Grupp* and renamed the ISABELLE. In May placed on the Stockholm - Riga service, replacing the SILJA FESTIVAL.

MEGASTAR Built by Meyer Turku, Turku, Finland to operate on the Tallinn - Helsinki Shuttle. She is LNG/diesel dual powered. An option on a second vessel was allowed to lapse in March 2016.

REGAL STAR Partly built by Sudostroitelnyy Zavod Severnaya Verf, St Petersburg. Work started in 1993 (as a deep-sea ro-ro) but was never completed. In 1999 the vessel was purchased, taken to Palumba SpA, Naples and completed as a short-sea ro-ro with accommodation for 80 drivers. In 2000 she was delivered to *MCL* of Italy and placed on a route between Savona and Catania. In September of that year she was chartered to *Grimaldi Ferries* and operated on a route Salerno – Palermo – Valencia. In late 2003 she was sold to *Hansatee Shipping* of Estonia and, in 2004, placed on the Kapellskär – Paldiski route, replacing the KAPELLA. From February 2006 she was transferred to the Helsinki – Tallinn service, replacing the KAPELLA due to the hard ice conditions. She continued in this service for the summer, but the returned to the Paldiski – Kapellskär service. In June 2010 moved to the *SeaWind Line* Stockholm – Turku service for the summer seasons and returned to the Kapellskär - Paldiski route in the autumn.

ROMANTIKA Built by Aker Finnyards, Rauma, Finland for *Tallink Grupp* to operate for *Tallink* between Tallinn and Helsinki. Currently operating between Stockholm and Riga.

SEA WIND Train/vehicle ferry built as the SVEALAND by Helsingørs Skipsværft, Helsingør, Denmark for *Stockholms Rederi AB Svea* and used on the *Trave Line* Helsingborg (Sweden) - København (Tuborg Havn) - Travemünde freight service. In 1981 she was sold to *TT-Saga Line* and operated between Travemünde and Malmö. In 1984 she was rebuilt to increase capacity and renamed the SAGA WIND. In 1989 she was acquired by *Silja Line* subsidiary *SeaWind Line*, renamed the SEA WIND and inaugurated a combined rail freight, trailer and lower-priced passenger service between Stockholm and Turku. This route later became freight-only. In January 2015 transferred to the Tallinn - Helsinki freight service.

SILJA EUROPA Built by Jos L Meyer, Papenburg, Germany. Ordered by *Rederi AB Slite* of Sweden for *Viking Line* service between Stockholm and Helsinki and due to be called EUROPA. In 1993, shortly before delivery was due, *Rederi AB Slite* went into liquidation and the order was cancelled. A charter agreement with her builders was then signed by *Silja Line* and she was introduced onto the Stockholm - Helsinki route as SILJA EUROPA. In early 1995 she was transferred to the Stockholm - Turku service. In January 2013 she was transferred to the Helsinki - Tallinn route. In August 2014 chartered to an Australian company as an accommodation vessel. In March 2016 joined the BALTIC PRINCESS as second vessel on the Helsinki - Tallinn 'Cruise' service. In December 2016 resumed the role of sole cruise vessel on the route.

SILJA SERENADE, SILJA SYMPHONY Built by Masa-Yards Oy, Turku, Finland for *Silja Line* for the Stockholm - Helsinki service. In 1993, SILJA SERENADE was transferred to the Stockholm - Turku service but in early 1995 she was transferred back to the Helsinki route.

STAR Built by Aker Yards, Helsinki, Finland for *Tallink* to operate on the Tallinn - Helsinki route. In January 2017 modified at Vene Balti Shipyard, Tallinn to allow for two deck loading.

VICTORIA I Built by Aker Finnyards, Rauma, Finland for *Tallink*. Operates between Tallinn and Stockholm.

Under Construction

15	NEWBUILDING	49000t	22	27.0k	212.0m	2800P	-	-	BA2	EE	-

NEWBUILDING Under construction by Rauma Marine Constructions of Finland to operate on the Helsinki - Tallinn 'Shuttle' service.

TESO

THE COMPANY *TESO (Texels Eigen Stoomboot Onderneming)* is a Dutch private company, with most shares owned by inhabitants of Texel.

MANAGEMENT Managing Director Cees de Waal.

ADDRESS Pontweg 1, 1797 SN Den Hoorn, The Netherlands.

TELEPHONE Administration +31 (0)222 36 96 00, **Reservations** Not applicable.

INTERNET Email info@teso.nl **Website** www.teso.nl *(Dutch, English, German)*

ROUTE OPERATED Den Helder (The Netherlands) - Texel (Dutch Frisian Islands) (20 minutes; ***DOKTER WAGEMAKER***, ***TEXELSTROOM***; hourly).

1	DOKTER WAGEMAKER	13256t	05	15.6k	130.4m	1750P	320C	44L	BA2	NL	9294070
2	TEXELSTROOM	16400t	16	15.0k	135.4m	1750P	350C	44L	BA2	NL	9741918

DOKTER WAGEMAKER Built at Galatz, Romania (hull and superstructure) and Royal Schelde, Vlissingen (fitting out) for *TESO*.

TEXELSTROOM Built by La Naval Shipyard, Sestao, Spain.

TT-LINE

THE COMPANY *TT-Line GmbH & Co KG* is a German private sector company.

MANAGEMENT Managing Directors Hanns Heinrich Conzen & Jens Aurel Scharner, **Sales Manager** Dirk Lifke.

ADDRESS Zum Hafenplatz 1, 23570, Lübeck-Travemünde, Germany.

TELEPHONE +49 (0)4502 801-82.

INTERNET Email info@ttline.com **Website** www.ttline.com *(English, German, Lithuanian, Polish, Swedish)*

Victoria I *(Uwe Jakob)*

Megastar *(Darren Holdaway)*

ROUTES OPERATED *Passenger Ferries* Travemünde (Germany) - Trelleborg (Sweden) (8 hrs 30 mins/9 hrs 30 mins; ***NILS HOLGERSSON, PETER PAN***; 2 per day). ***Ro-pax Ferries*** Travemünde (Germany) - Trelleborg (Sweden) (7 hrs 30 mins/8 hrs 15 mins; ***ROBIN HOOD***; 1 per day), Rostock (Germany) - Trelleborg (Sweden) (5 hrs 30 mins/6 hrs 30 mins/7 hrs 30 mins; ***HUCKLEBERRY FINN, TOM SAWYER***; 3 per day, Świnoujście (Poland) - Trelleborg (Sweden) (7 hrs; ***NILS DACKE***; 1 per day), Świnoujście (Poland) - Rønne (Bornholm, Denmark) (5 hrs (day), 6 hrs 30 mins (night); ***NILS DACKE***; 1 per week) (summer only), Trelleborg - Klaipėda (Lithuania) (15 hrs; ***ROBIN HOOD, TOM SAWYER***, 1 per week).

1	BARBARA KRAHULIK	14398t	93	19.0k	150.3m	130P	-	130T	A2	IT	9019080
2	HUCKLEBERRY FINN	26391t	88	18.0k	177.2m	400P	280C	121T	BAS2	SE	8618358
3	NILS DACKE	26796t	95	18.5k	179.7m	300P	-	157T	BA	CY	9087465
4	NILS HOLGERSSON	36468t	01	18.0k	190.8m	744P	-	171T	BAS2	DE	9217230
5	PETER PAN	44245t	01	18.0k	220.0m	744P	-	210T	BAS2	SE	9217242
6	ROBIN HOOD	26790t	95	18.5k	179.7m	317P	-	157T	BA	DE	9087477
7	TOM SAWYER	26478t	89	18.0k	177.2m	400P	280C	121T	BAS2	DE	8703232

BARBARA KRAHULIK Built as the VIA IONIO by van der Gissen de Noord, Krimpen-a d Ijssel, Netherlands at their Welgelegen shipyard for *Viamare di Navigazione SpA* of Italy. Between April and August 1993 chartered to *TT-Line* and operated between Travemünde and Trelleborg. In August, placed on Mediterranean service. In April 1994 sold to *Adriatica di Navigazione SpA* of Italy and renamed the ESPRESSO RAVENNA. Operated between Ravenna - Catania. In July 2012 sold to *Compagnia Italiana Di Navigaz* of Italy and in January 2017 renamed the BARBARA KRAHULIK. In July 2019 sold to *TT-Line* and chartered back. Operated for *Tirenna* of Italy, mainly between Naples and Catania To be delivered in late October or early November. She will be renamed. Usage not yet known.

HUCKLEBERRY FINN Built as the NILS DACKE by Schichau Seebeckwerft AG, Bremerhaven, Germany, as a ro-pax vessel. During Summer 1993 rebuilt to transform her into a passenger/car ferry and renamed the PETER PAN, replacing a similarly named vessel (31356t, 1986). On arrival of the new PETER PAN in Autumn 2001 she was renamed the PETER PAN IV. She was then converted back to ro-pax format, renamed the HUCKLEBERRY FINN and, in early 2002, transferred to the Rostock -Trelleborg route.

NILS DACKE, Ro-pax vessels built as the ROBIN HOOD by Finnyards, Rauma, Finland. She operated on the Travemünde - Trelleborg and Travemünde - Helsingborg routes. In December 2014 she was renamed the NILS DACKE and transferred to Cypriot registry. Moved to the Trelleborg - Świnoujście route.

NILS HOLGERSSON, PETER PAN Built by SSW Fähr und Spezialschiffbau GmbH, Bremerhaven, Germany for the Travemünde - Trelleborg route. In January and February 2018 the PETER PAN was lengthened at MWB Motorenwerke Bremerhaven AG, Germany by 30 metres.

TOM SAWYER Built as the ROBIN HOOD by Schichau Seebeckwerft AG, Bremerhaven, Germany, as a ro-pax vessel. During Winter 1992/93 rebuilt to transform her into a passenger/car ferry and renamed the NILS HOLGERSSON, replacing a similarly named vessel (31395t, 1987) which had been sold to *Brittany Ferries* and renamed the VAL DE LOIRE. In 2001 converted back to ro-pax format and renamed the TOM SAWYER. Transferred to the Rostock - Trelleborg route.

ROBIN HOOD Ro-pax vessels built as the NILS DACKE, by Finnyards, Rauma, Finland. She operated on the Travemünde - Trelleborg and Travemünde - Helsingborg routes. In January 2014, she was transferred to a new Trelleborg - Świnoujście service and changed to Polish registry. In December 2014 she was renamed the ROBIN HOOD and transferred German Registry. Moved to the Travemünde - Trelleborg route.

Under Construction

8	NEWBUILDING 1	24500	22	-	177.0m	900P	-	160T	BAS2	-	-
9	NEWBUILDING 2	24500	22	-	177.0m	900P	-	160T	BAS2	-	-

NEWBUILDING1, NEWBUILDING 2 Under construction by the Jinling Shipyard, China. It is likely that they will replace the HUCKLEBERRY FINN and TOM SAWYER.

UNITY LINE

THE COMPANY *Unity Line* is a Polish company owned by *Polish Steamship Company (Polsteam)*. The operator manages seven ferries on two routes: Świnoujście – Ystad and Świnoujście – Trelleborg. Three ships are owned by *Euroafrica Shipping* which was previously a partner in the company; the ships continue to be operationally managed by to *Unity Line*.

MANAGEMENT Managing Director Jarosław Kotarski.

ADDRESS Plac Rodla 8, 70-419 Szczecin, Poland.

TELEPHONE Administration& Reservations +48 (0)91 88 02 909.

FAX Administration +48 91 35 95 885.

INTERNET Email rezerwacje@unityline.pl **Website** www.unityline.pl *(English, German, Polish, Swedish)*

ROUTES OPERATED Passenger Service Świnoujście (Poland) - Ystad (Sweden) (6 hrs 30 mins (day), 9 hrs (night); ***POLONIA, SKANIA***; 2 per day). **Freight Services** Świnoujście (Poland) - Ystad (Sweden) (8 hrs (day), 9 hrs (night); ***JAN ŚNIADECKI***; 1 per day), Świnoujście (Poland) - Trelleborg (Sweden) (6 hrs 30 mins (day), 9 hrs (night); ***COPERNICUS, GALILEUSZ, GRYF, WOLIN***; 4 per day).

1F+	COPERNICUS	14398t	96	19.0k	150.4m	50P	-	122T	A	CY	9031703
2F+	GALILEUSZ	15848t	92	17.0k	150.4m	160P	-	115L	A	CY	9019078
3F+	GRYF	18653t	90	16.0k	158.0m	180P	-	125L	BA	BS	8818300
4F+	JAN ŚNIADECKI	14417t	88	17.0k	155.1m	57P	-	70Lr	SA2	CY	8604711
5	POLONIA	29875t	95	17.2k	169.9m	920P	440C	145Lr	SA2	BS	9108350
6	SKANIA	23933t	95	22.5k	173.7m	1400P	430C	140L	BA	BS	9086588
7F+	WOLIN	22874t	86	17.5k	188.9m	370P	-	110Lr	SA	BS	8420842

COPERNICUS Built as the PUGLIA by Fincantieri-Cantieri Navali Italiani SpA, Ancona, Italy for *Tirrenia di Navigazione SpA.* of Italy. In 2016 rebranded as *Moby Cargo*. In December 2017 sold to *Euroafrica Shipping,* renamed the COPERNICUS and, in September 2018, placed on the Świnoujście - Trelleborg route.

GALILEUSZ Built as the VIA TIRRENO by Van der Giessen-de Noord, Krimpen aan den IJssel, The Netherlands for *Viamare di Navigazione SpA* of Italy. Initially operated between Voltri and Termini Imerese. In 1998 transferred to the Génova - Termini Imerese route and in 2001 to the Génova - Palermo route. In 2006 sold to *Euroafrica Shipping*, renamed the GALILEUSZ and in November introduced onto the *Unity Line* Świnoujście - Ystad service. In February 2007 transferred to the new Świnoujście - Trelleborg route.

GRYF Built as the KAPTAN BURHANETTIN ISIM by Fosen Mekaniske Verksteder, Fevag, Norway for *Turkish Cargo Lines* of Turkey to operate between Trieste (Italy) and Derince (Turkey). In 2002 chartered to *Latlines* to operate between Lübeck and Riga (Latvia). In 2003 chartered to *VentLines* to inaugurate a new service between Travemünde and Ventspils. In 2004 sold to *Polsteam*, managed by *Unity Line* and renamed the GRYF. Entered service in 2005. In February 2007 transferred to the new Świnoujście - Trelleborg route.

JAN ŚNIADECKI Built by Falkenbergs Varv AB, Falkenberg, Sweden for *Polish Ocean Lines* to operate between Świnoujście and Ystad. Now operates for *Unity Line* on this route.

POLONIA Train/vehicle ferry built by Langsten Slip & Båtbyggeri A/S, Tomrefjord, Norway for *Polonia Line Ltd* and managed by *Unity Line*.

SKANIA Built as the SUPERFAST I by Schichau Seebeckwerft, Bremerhaven, Germany for *Superfast Ferries* of Greece. Operated between Patras and Ancona (Italy). In 1998 transferred to the Patras - Igoumenitsa (Greece) - Bari (Italy) route. In 2004 sold to a subsidiary of *Grimaldi Lines*, renamed the EUROSTAR ROMA and placed on the Civitavecchia (Italy) -

Barcelona (Spain) service. In 2008 sold to *Polsteam* and renamed the SKANIA. After modifications, she was placed on the *Unity Line* Świnoujście - Ystad service as second passenger vessel. In during the peak summer period in 2010 operated a round trip between Ystad and Rønne for *Bornholmstrafikken*.

WOLIN Train/vehicle ferry built as the ÖRESUND by Moss Rosenberg Værft, Moss, Norway for *Statens Järnvägar* (*Swedish State Railways*) for the 'DanLink' service between Helsingborg and København. Has 817 metres of rail track. Service ceased in July 2000 and vessel laid up. In 2001 sold to *Sea Containers Ferries* and in 2002 converted at Gdańsk, Poland to a passenger ferry. She was chartered to *SeaWind Line*, renamed the SKY WIND and in Autumn 2002 replaced the STAR WIND on the Stockholm - Turku service. In 2007 sold to *Polsteam*, renamed the WOLIN and placed on the *Unity Line* Świnoujście - Trelleborg service.

VIKING LINE

THE COMPANY *Viking Line Abp* is a Finnish company Listed on the Helsinki Stock Exchange since 1995.

MANAGEMENT President & CEO Jan Hanses, **Executive Vice President/Deputy CEO and Chief Financial Officer at Viking Line Abp** Mats Engblom.

ADDRESS Box 166, AX-22100 Mariehamn, Åland, Finland.

TELEPHONE Administration +358 (0)18 27000, **Reservations** +358 (0)600 41577.

INTERNET Email international.sales@vikingline.com **Websites** www.vikingline.com *(English)* www.vikingline.fi *(Finnish)* www.vikingline.se *(Swedish)* www.vikingline.ee *(Estonian)* www.vikingline.de *(German)*

ROUTES OPERATED *Conventional Ferries - all year* Stockholm (Sweden) - Mariehamn (Åland) - Helsinki (Finland) (14 hrs; ***GABRIELLA, MARIELLA***; 1 per day), Stockholm - Mariehamn (day)/Långnäs (Åland) (night) - Turku (Finland) (9 hrs 10 mins; ***AMORELLA, VIKING GRACE***; 2 per day), Kapellskär (Sweden) - Mariehamn (Åland) (2 hrs 15 mins; ***ROSELLA***; up to 3 per day), Helsinki - Tallinn (2 hrs 30 mins; ***VIKING XPRS***; 2 per day), Cruises from Stockholm to Mariehamn (21 hrs - 24 hrs round trip (most 22 hrs 30 mins); ***VIKING CINDERELLA***; 1 per day),

1	AMORELLA	34384t	88	21.5k	169.4m	2450P	450C	53T	BA	FI	8601915
2	GABRIELLA	35492t	92	21.5k	171.2m	2420P	400C	50T	BA	FI	8917601
3	MARIELLA	37799t	85	22.0k	176.9m	2500P	400C	60T	BA	FI	8320573
4	ROSELLA	16850t	80	21.3k	136.0m	1700P	340C	40T	BA	AL	7901265
5	VIKING CINDERELLA	46398t	89	21.5k	191.0m	2500P	100C	-	BA	SE	8719188
6	VIKING GRACE	57000t	13	23.0k	214.0m	2800P	556C	90L	BA	FI	9606900
7	VIKING XPRS	34000t	08	25.0k	185.0m	2500P	250C	60L	BA	EE	9375654

AMORELLA Built by Brodogradevna Industrija, Split, Yugoslavia for *SF Line* for the Stockholm - Mariehamn - Turku service.

GABRIELLA Built as the FRANS SUELL by Brodogradiliste Industrija, Split, Croatia for *Sea-Link AB* of Sweden to operate for subsidiary company *Euroway AB*, who established a service between Lübeck, Travemünde and Malmö. In 1994 this service ceased and she was chartered to *Silja Line*, renamed the SILJA SCANDINAVIA and transferred to the Stockholm - Turku service. In 1997 she was sold to *Viking Line* to operate between Stockholm and Helsinki. She was renamed the GABRIELLA. In 2014, a daytime sailing during summer from Helsinki to Tallinn was introduced.

MARIELLA Built by Oy Wärtsilä Ab, Turku, Finland for *SF Line*. Used on the Stockholm - Helsinki service. During 1996 additionally operated short cruises to Muuga in Estonia during the 'layover' period in Helsinki. In 2014, a daytime sailing during summer from Helsinki to Tallinn was introduced.

ROSELLA Built by Oy Wärtsilä Ab, Turku, Finland for *SF Line*. Used mainly on the Stockholm - Turku and Kapellskär - Naantali services until 1997. From 1997 operated 21 to 24-hour cruises

Galileusz *(Frank Lose)*

Jan Śniadecki *(Uwe Jakob)*

Gabriella *(Uwe Jakob)*

Mariella *(Uwe Jakob)*

from Stockholm to Mariehamn under the marketing name 'The Dancing Queen', except in the peak summer period when she operated between Kapellskär and Turku. In Autumn 2003 transferred to a new twice-daily Helsinki - Tallinn ferry service. In May 2008 placed on the Mariehamn - Kapellskär route under the Swedish flag. In 2011 she was extensively rebuilt at Balti Laevaremondi Tehas in Tallinn, Estonia. Cabin capacity was lowered from 1184 to 418 and the restaurant and shop areas were increased. In January 2014 placed under the Finnish flag.

VIKING CINDERELLA Built as the CINDERELLA by Wärtsilä Marine Ab, Turku, Finland for *SF Line*. Until 1993 provided additional capacity between Stockholm and Helsinki and undertook weekend cruises from Helsinki. In 1993 she replaced the OLYMPIA (a sister vessel of the MARIELLA) as the main Stockholm - Helsinki vessel after the OLYMPIA had been chartered to *P&O European Ferries* and renamed the PRIDE OF BILBAO. In 1995 switched to operating 20-hour cruises from Helsinki to Estonia in the off peak and the Stockholm - Mariehamn - Turku service during the peak summer period (end of May to end of August). From 1997 she remained cruising throughout the year. In Autumn 2003 she was transferred to the Swedish flag, renamed the VIKING CINDERELLA and transferred to Stockholm - Mariehamn cruises. She operates these cruises all year round.

VIKING GRACE Built by STX Europe, Turku, Finland. She operates between Stockholm and Turku. She is powered by LNG. Entered service in January 2013.

VIKING XPRS Built by Aker Yards, Helsinki to operate between Helsinki and Tallinn. In January 2014 placed under the Estonian flag.

Under construction

8	VIKING GLORY	63800t	20	23.0k	225.5m	2800P	556C	90L	BA	FI

VIKING GLORY Under construction by Xiamen Shipbuilding Industry Co. Ltd, Xiamen, China. She will be LNG powered and will replace the AMORELLA on the Stockholm - Mariehamn - Turku service.

WAGENBORG

THE COMPANY *Wagenborg Passagiersdiensten BV* is a Dutch private sector company.

MANAGEMENT Managing Director Ger van Langen.

ADDRESS Reeweg 4, 9163 ZM Nes, Ameland, The Netherlands.

TELEPHONE Administration & Reservations *International* +31 88 1031000, ***Netherlands*** 0900 9238.

INTERNET Email info@wpd.nl **Website** www.wpd.nl *(Dutch, English, German)*

ROUTES OPERATED *Car Ferries* Holwerd (The Netherlands) - Ameland (Frisian Islands) (45 minutes; ***OERD, SIER***; up to 14 per day), Lauwersoog (The Netherlands) - Schiermonnikoog (Frisian Islands) (45 minutes; ***MONNIK, ROTTUM***; up to 6 per day).

1	MONNIK	1121t	85	12.2k	58.0m	1000P	46C	9L	BA	NL	8408961
2	OERD	2286t	03	11.2k	73.2m	1200P	72C	22L	BA	NL	9269673
3	ROTTUM	1121t	85	12.2k	58.0m	1000P	46C	9L	BA	NL	8408959
4	SIER	2286t	95	11.2k	73.2m	1200P	72C	22L	BA	NL	9075761

MONNIK Built by Scheepswerf Hoogezand, Hoogezand, The Netherlands for *Wagenborg Passagiersdiensten BV* as the OERD. In 2003, on delivery of the new OERD, she was renamed the MONNIK. Used on the Lauwersoog - Schiermonnikoog route.

OERD Built by Scheepswerf Bijlsma Lemmer, Lemmer, The Netherlands for *Wagenborg Passagiersdiensten BV*. Used on the Ameland - Holwerd route.

ROTTUM Built as the SIER by Scheepswerf Hoogezand, Hoogezand, The Netherlands for *Wagenborg Passagiersdiensten BV* and used on the Holwerd - Ameland route. In 1995 renamed the ROTTUM and transferred to the Lauwersoog - Schiermonnikoog route.

SIER Built by Shipyard Bijlsma, Wartena, The Netherlands for *Wagenborg Passagiersdiensten BV*. Used on the Ameland - Holwerd route.

WASALINE

THE COMPANY *Wasaline* is the trading name of *NLC Ferry Oy Ab*, a Finnish company, jointly owned by the cities of Vaasa and Umeå.

MANAGEMENT Managing Director Peter Ståhlberg.

ADDRESS *Finland* Skeppsredaregatan 3, 65170 Vasa, Finland ***Sweden*** Blå Vägen 4, 91322 Holmsund, Sweden.

TELEPHONE Administration & Reservations *Finland* +358 (0)207 716 810, ***Sweden*** +46 (0)90 185 200.

INTERNET *Email* info@wasaline.com ***Website*** www.wasaline.com *(English, Finnish, Swedish)*

ROUTE OPERATED Vaasa (Finland) - Umeå (Sweden) (4 hrs; ***WASA EXPRESS***; 1/2 per day).

1	WASA EXPRESS	17053t	81	17.0k	140.8m	1100P	450C	84T	BAS2	FI	8000226

WASA EXPRESS Built by Oy Wärtsilä AB, Helsinki, Finland as the TRAVEMÜNDE for *Gedser-Travemünde Ruten* of Denmark for their service between Gedser (Denmark) and Travemünde (Germany). In 1986 the company's trading name was changed to *GT Linien* and in 1987, following the takeover by *Sea-Link AB* of Sweden, it was further changed to *GT Link*. The vessel's name was changed to the TRAVEMÜNDE LINK. In 1988 she was purchased by *Rederi AB Gotland* of Sweden, although remaining in service with *GT Link*. Later in 1988 she was chartered to *Sally Ferries* and entered service in December on the Ramsgate - Dunkerque service. She was renamed the SALLY STAR. In 1997 she was transferred to *Silja Line* to operate between Vaasa and Umeå during the summer period, under the marketing name WASA EXPRESS (although not renamed). She returned to *Rederi AB Gotland* in Autumn 1997, was renamed the THJELVAR and entered service with *Destination Gotland* in January 1998. Withdrawn and laid up in December 2003. In 2004 chartered to *Color Line* to inaugurate a new service between Larvik and Hirtshals. Renamed the COLOR TRAVELLER. Operated in reduced passenger mode on this service but in summer peak period operated between Frederikshavn and Larvik in full passenger mode. In December 2006 returned to *Rederi AB Gotland*. In 2007 renamed the THJELVAR, chartered to *Scandlines* and placed on the Gedser - Rostock route. Renamed the ROSTOCK. In Autumn 2008 withdrawn and laid up. In June 2009 sub-chartered to *Comarit* of Morocco for two months. In September she resumed the name THJELVAR. In August 2008 she was chartered to *Fred. Olsen SA* of Spain, renamed the BETANCURIA and placed on the Las Palmas - Puerto del Rosario - Arrecife service. In September 2012 laid up. In October 2012 purchased by *NLC Ferry Oy Ab* and, in November, renamed the WASA EXPRESS. Entered service in January 2013.

Under Construction

2	NEWBUILDING	24300t	21	20.0k	150.0m	800P	-	105T	-	FI	-

NEWBUILDING Under construction by Rauma Marine Constructions, Rauma, Finland.

WYKER DAMPFSCHIFFS-REEDEREI

THE COMPANY *Wyker Dampfschiffs-Reederei* is a German company.

MANAGEMENT CEO Axel Meynköhn.

ADDRESS PO Box 1540, 25933 Wyk auf Föhr, Germany.

TELEPHONE Administration & Reservations +49 (0)4681 800.

INTERNET *Email* info@faehre.de ***Website*** www.faehre.de *(Danish, English, German)*

ROUTES OPERATED Dagebüll - Föhr (50min; ***NORDERAUE, NORDFRIESLAND, RUNGHOLT***; ***SCHLESWIG-HOLSTEIN, UTHLANDE***; up to 14 per day), Dagebüll - Amrun (90 min (120 min via Föhr); ***NORDERAUE, NORDFRIESLAND, RUNGHOLT, SCHLESWIG-HOLSTEIN***,

UTHLANDE; 7 per day), Föhr - Amrum (1 hr; ***NORDERAUE, NORDFRIESLAND, RUNGHOLT***; ***SCHLESWIG-HOLSTEIN, UTHLANDE***; up to 4 per day), Schlüttsiel - Hooge - Langeness (2 hrs; ***HILLIGENLEI***; up to 2 per day).

1	HILLIGENLEI	467t	85	19.0k	38.3m	200P	22C	-	BA	DE	8411217
2	NORDERAUE	3250t	18	12.0k	75.9m	1200P	75C	-	BA	DE	9796121
3	NORDFRIESLAND	2287t	95	12.0k	67.0m	1200P	55C	-	BA	DE	9102758
4	RUNGHOLT	2268t	92	12.5k	67.9m	975P	55C	-	BA	DE	9038660.
5	SCHLESWIG-HOLSTEIN	3202t	11	12.0k	75.9m	1200P	75C	-	BA	DE	9604378
6	UTHLANDE	1960t	10	12.0k	75.9m	1200P	75C	-	BA	DE	9548407

HILLIGENLEI Built as the PELLWORM by Husumer Schiffswerft, Husum, Germany for *Neue Pellwormer Dampfschiffahrtsgesellschaft* of Germany and operated between Pellworm and Strucklahnungshörn. In 1996 sold to Sven Paulsen, Altwarp, Germany and renamed the ADLER POLONIA. Operated between Altwarp and Novo Warpno (Poland). In 2002 sold to *Wyker Dampfschiffsreederei* and renamed the HILLIGENLEI I. In February 2010 renamed the HILLIGENLEI.

NORDERAUE Built by Neptun Werft GmbH, Rostock, Germany for *Wyker Dampfschiffsreederei*.

NORDFRIESLAND, RUNGHOLT Built by Husumer Schiffswerft, Husum, Germany for *Wyker Dampfschiffsreederei*.

SCHLESWIG-HOLSTEIN Built by Neptun Werft GmbH, Rostock, Germany for *Wyker Dampfschiffsreederei*.

UTHLANDE Built by J.J. Sietas GmbH & Co KG, Hamburg, Germany for *Wyker Dampfschiffsreederei*.

SECTION 8 - OTHER VESSELS

The following passenger vessels are, at the time of going to print, not operating and are owned by companies which do not currently operate services or are used on freight -only services. They are therefore available for possible re-deployment, either in the area covered by this book or elsewhere. Passenger vessels operating freight-only services outside the scope of this book are also included here. Exceptionally we have included two freight-only vessels possibly to be chartered to an operator serving the UK. Withdrawn vessels not yet disposed of and owned by operating companies are shown under the appropriate company and marked '●'.

Rederi AB Gotland

1	GUTE	7616t	79	15.0k	138.8m	88P	-	60T	A	SE	7802794

GUTE Built as the GUTE by Falkenbergs Varv AB, Falkenberg, Sweden for *Rederi AB Gotland* of Sweden. Used on service between Gotland and the Swedish mainland. In 1988 chartered to *Brambles Shipping* of Australia and used between Port Melbourne (Victoria) and Burnie (Tasmania). In 1992 she was renamed the SALLY SUN and chartered to *Sally Ferries*, operating between Ramsgate and Dunkerque. In 1994 she inaugurated a Ramsgate - Vlissingen service, which was later changed to Dartford - Vlissingen. In 1995 she was chartered to *SeaWind Line*, renamed the SEAWIND II and operated between Stockholm and Turku. In 1997 she was chartered to *Nordic Trucker Line* for the Oxelösund - St Petersburg service and in 1998 she returned to *SeaWind Line*. In 1998, after *Rederi AB Gotland*-owned *Destination Gotland* regained the franchise to operate to Gotland, she was renamed the GUTE and resumed her summer role of providing summer freight back-up to the passenger vessels, but with a number of short charters during the winter. In Autumn 2002 chartered to *Amber Lines* for the Karlshamn - Liepaja service. In February 2003 chartered to *NATO* for the Iraq crisis. Returned to *Destination Gotland* in Summer 2003. In Autumn 2003 chartered to *Scandlines Amber Lines* to operate between Karlshamn and Liepaja. In 2004 lengthened by 20.3m by Nauta Shiprepair, Gdynia, Poland. In Autumn 2004 chartered to *Riga Sea Line* to inaugurate a freight service between Riga and Nynäshamn. In Autumn 2005 the service ended and the vessel was laid up. In January 2006 chartered to *Lisco* and placed on the Klaipėda - Karlshamn route, also undertaking two trips from Klaipėda to Baltiysk. In May 2006 chartered to *SeaWind Line*. In

March 2007 chartered to *Baltic Scandinavian Line*. Charter ended September 2007. Apart from a trip to Cameroon, conveying Swedish UN Troops for Chad, she remained laid up until October 2008 when she was chartered to *Baltic Scandinavian Line* to operate between Härnösand and Kaskinen. In 2009 this service closed and she was laid up. At the end of March 2015 she was chartered to *Færgen* to operate between Køge and Rønne covering for the HAMMERODDE. She returned to layup in May. In August 2017 chartered to *Stena Line* to operate as fourth ship on the Karlskrona - Gdynia route. In September 2018 replaced by the STENA NORDICA and the charter ended. In July 2019 replaced the PETER PAN of *TT Line* following a fire.

Saaremaa Laevakompanii (Estonia)

1	HARILAID	1028t	85	9.9k	49.9m	120P	35C	5L	BA	EE	8727367
2	KÖRGELAID	1028t	87	9.9k	49.9m	190P	35C	5L	BA	EE	8725577

HARILAID, KÖRGELAID Built by Riga Shiprepair Yard, Riga, Latvia (USSR) for *ESCO* of Estonia. In 1994 transferred to *Saaremaa Laevakompanii*. In October 2016 transferred to *Praamid* until new vessels were delivered. Then laid up in Tallinn.

9 - SISTERS – A LIST OF SISTER (OR NEAR SISTER) VESSELS IN THIS BOOK

The following vessels are sisters or near sisters. This refers to 'as built' condition; some ships will subsequently have been modified and become different from their sister vessels.

ÆRØSKØBING, MARSTAL *(Ærøfærgerne)*

AMORELLA, GABRIELLA *(Viking Line)*, ISABELLE *(Tallink Silja Line)*, CROWN OF SCANDINAVIA *(DFDS Seaways)*.

ARGYLE, BUTE *(Caledonian MacBrayne)*.

ATLANTIC VISION *(Tallink)*, STENA SUPERFAST VII, STENA SUPERFAST VIII, STENA SUPERFAST X *(Stena Line)*.

AURORA AF HELSINGBORG, HAMLET, TYCHO BRAHE *(ForSea)*.

BALTIC QUEEN, BALTIC PRINCESS, GALAXY *(Tallink Silja Line)*.

BASTØ I, BASTØ II *(Bastø Fosen)*.

BASTØ IV, BASTØ V, BASTØ VI *(Bastø Fosen)*.

BEN-MY-CHREE *(Isle of Man Steam Packet Company)*, COMMODORE CLIPPER *(Condor Ferries)*, STENA VINGA *(Stena Line)* (Near sisters).

BEN WOOLLACOTT, DAME VERA LYNN *(Woolwich Free Ferry)*.

BERGENSFJORD, STAVANGERFJORD *(Fjord Line)*.

BERLIN, COPENHAGEN *(Scandlines)*.

CANNA *(Arranmore Fast Ferries)*, CLEW BAY QUEEN *(Clare Island Ferry Company)*, COLL *(Arranmore Island Ferries)*, EIGG *(Clare Island Ferry Company)*, MORVERN *(Arranmore Fast Ferries)*, RAASAY *(Inishbofin Island Discovery)*, RHUM *(Arranmore Island Ferries)*.

CARRIGALOE, GLENBROOK *(Cross River Ferries)*.

CATRIONA, HALLAIG, LOCHINVAR *(Caledonian MacBrayne)*

COLOR FANTASY, COLOR MAGIC *(Color Line)*.

COLOR VIKING *(Color Line)*, STENA NAUTICA *(Stena Line)*.

CONNEMARA *(Brittany Ferries)*, EPSILON *(Irish Ferries)*, ETRETAT, KERRY *(Brittany Ferries)*, SCOTTISH VIKING, STENA HORIZON, STENA LAGAN, STENA MERSEY, STENA FLAVIA *(Stena Line)*.

CÔTE D'ALBATRE, SEVEN SISTERS *(DFDS Seaways)*.

CÔTE DES DUNES, CÔTE DES FLANDRES *(DFDS Seaways).*

DAGALIEN, DAGGRI *(Shetland Islands Council).*

DELFT SEAWAYS, DOVER SEAWAYS, DUNKERQUE SEAWAYS *(DFDS Seaways).*

DEUTSCHLAND, SCHLESWIG-HOLSTEIN *(Scandlines).*

EARL SIGURD, EARL THORFINN *(Orkney Ferries).*

ECKERÖ *(Eckerö Linjen)*, POVL ANKER *(Molslinjen).*

EUROPEAN CAUSEWAY, EUROPEAN HIGHLANDER *(P&O Ferries).*

FENJA, MENJA *(Molslinjen).*

FINNCLIPPER, FINNEAGLE, FINNFELLOW *(Finnlines)*, STENA GERMANICA *(Stena Line).*

FINNLADY, FINNMAID, FINNSTAR, FINNSWAN *(Finnlines).*

FINNPARTNER, FINNTRADER *(Finnlines).*

GALICIA, SALAMANCA *(Brittany Ferries).*

GOTLAND, VISBY *(Destination Gotland).*

HJALTLAND, HROSSEY *(NorthLink Ferries).*

HUCKLEBERRY FINN, TOM SAWYER *(TT-Line).*

KING SEAWAYS, PRINCESS SEAWAYS *(DFDS Seaways).*

KONG HARALD, NORDLYS, RICHARD WITH *(Hurtigruten).*

LANGELAND, LOLLAND *(Molslinjen).*

LOCH DUNVEGAN, LOCH FYNE *(Caledonian MacBrayne).*

LOCH LINNHE, LOCH RANZA, LOCH RIDDON, LOCH STRIVEN *(Caledonian MacBrayne).*

LYNHER II, PLYM II, TAMAR II *(Torpoint Ferries).*

MARIELLA *(Viking Line)*, SPL PRINCESS ANASTASIA *(Moby SPL).*

MERCANDIA IV, MERCANDIA VIII *(Scandlines - Helsingør - Helsingborg).*

MIDNATSOL, TROLLFJORD *(Hurtigruten).*

MIDSLAND, WESTFALEN *(Rederij Doeksen).*

MONNIK, ROTTUM *(Wagenborg).*

MÜNSTERLAND, OSTFRIESLAND *(AG Ems).*

NILS DACKE, ROBIN HOOD *(TT-Line).*

NILS HOLGERSSON, PETER PAN *(TT-Line).*

NORBANK, NORBAY *(P&O Ferries).*

NORDKAPP, NORDNORGE, POLARLYS *(Hurtigruten).*

OERD, SIER *(Wagenborg).*

OILEAN NA H-OIGE, SANCTA MARIA *(Bere Island Ferries).*

PRIDE OF BRUGES, PRIDE OF YORK *(P&O Ferries).*

PRIDE OF CANTERBURY, PRIDE OF KENT *(P&O Ferries).*

PRIDE OF HULL, PRIDE OF ROTTERDAM *(P&O Ferries).*

PRINS RICHARD, PRINSESSE BENEDIKTE *(Scandlines).*

RED EAGLE, RED FALCON, RED OSPREY *(Red Funnel Ferries).*

RENFREW ROSE *(Highland Ferries)*, YOKER SWAN *(Sherkin Island Ferry)*.

ROMANTIKA, VICTORIA I *(Tallink Silja Line)*.

SILJA SERENADE, SILJA SYMPHONY *(Tallink Silja Line)*.

SOUND OF SCARBA, SOUND OF SHUNA *(Western Ferries)*.

SOUND OF SEIL, SOUND OF SOAY *(Western Ferries)*.

SPIRIT OF BRITAIN, SPIRIT OF FRANCE *(P&O Ferries)*.

STENA ADVENTURER, STENA SCANDINAVICA *(Stena Line)*.

STENA BRITANNICA, STENA HOLLANDICA *(Stena Line)*.

STENA GOTHICA, URD *(Stena Line)*.

STENA SPIRIT, STENA VISION *(Stena Line)*.

SUPERSPEED 1, SUPERSPEED 2 *(Color Line)*.

WIGHT LIGHT, WIGHT SKY, WIGHT SUN *(Wightlink)*.

Fast Ferries

EXPRESS 1, EXPRESS 2, EXPRESS 3 *(Molslinjen)*.

RED JET 6, RED JET 7 *(Red Funnel Ferries)*.

WIGHT RYDER I, WIGHT RYDER II *(Wightlink)*.

Freight Ferries

ADELINE *(CLdN/Cobelfret Ferries)*, WILHELMINE *(Stena Line)*.

AMANDINE, OPALINE *(CLdN/Cobelfret Ferries)*.

ANVIL POINT, EDDYSTONE *(Foreland Shipping)*, FINNMERCHANT *(Finnlines)*, HARTLAND POINT, HURST POINT*(Foreland Shipping)*.

ARROW *(Isle of Man Steam Packet)*, CLIPPER RANGER *(Seatruck Ferries)*, HELLIAR, HILDASAY *(NorthLink Ferries)*.

BORE BANK *(Transfennica)*, MYKINES (*Smyril Line*)

AUTO ECO, AUTO ENERGY *(UECC)*

AUTOPREMIER, AUTOPRESTIGE, AUTOPRIDE, AUTOPROGRESS *(UECC)*.

AUTOSKY, AUTOSTAR, AUTOSUN *(UECC)*.

BALTICBORG, BOTHNIABORG *(Smurfit Kappa Group)*.

BARBARA KRAHULIK *(TT-Line)*, COPERNICUS, GALILEUSZ *(Unity Line)*

BEGONIA SEAWAYS, FICARIA SEAWAYS, FREESIA SEAWAYS, PRIMULA SEAWAYS *(DFDS Seaways)*.

BOTNIA SEAWAYS, FINLANDIA SEAWAYS *(DFDS Seaways)*, FINNHAWK, FINNKRAFT *(Finnlines)*.

BRITANNIA SEAWAYS, SELANDIA SEAWAYS, SUECIA SEAWAYS *(DFDS Seaways)*.

CAPUCINE, SEVERINE (*CLdN/Cobelfret Ferries*).

CELANDINE, CELESTINE, CLEMENTINE, MELUSINE, VALENTINE, VICTORINE *(CLdN/Cobelfret Ferries)*.

CELINE, DELPHINE *(CLdN/Cobelfret Ferries)*.

CLIPPER PENNANT, CLIPPER POINT, SEATRUCK PACE, SEATRUCK PANORAMA *(Seatruck Ferries)*.

COLOR CARRIER *(Color Line)*, FINNMASTER *(Finnlines)*, MN PELICAN *(Brittany Ferries)*, SC CONNECTOR *(Sea-Cargo)*.

CORONA SEA *(Transfennica)*, FINNBREEZE, FINNMILL, FINNPULP, FINNSEA, FINNSKY, FINNSUN, FINNTIDE, FINNWAVE *(Finnlines)*, FIONIA SEAWAYS *(DFDS Seaways)*. HAFNIA SEA *(Transfennica)*, JUTLANDIA SEAWAYS *(DFDS Seaways)*.

CYMBELINE, UNDINE *(CLdN/Cobelfret Ferries)*.

GARDENIA SEAWAYS *(DFDS Seaways)*, MELEQ *(CLdN/Cobelfret Ferries)*, TULIPA SEAWAYS *(DFDS Seaways)*.

GENCA, KRAFTCA, PLYCA, PULPCA, TIMCA, TRICA *(Transfennica)*.

HERMINE, LAURELINE, SIXTINE, YSALINE *(CLdN/Cobelfret Ferries)*.

MAGNOLIA SEAWAYS, PETUNIA SEAWAYS *(DFDS Seaways)*.

MAZARINE, PALATINE, PEREGRINE, VESPERTINE *(CLdN/Cobelfret Ferries)*.

MISANA, MISIDA *(Stena Line)*.

MISTRAL *(P&O Ferries)*, SEAGARD *(Transfennica)*.

NORSKY, NORSTREAM *(P&O Ferries)*.

PAULINE, YASMINE *(CLdN/Cobelfret Ferries)*.

SCA OBBOLA, SCA ORTVIKEN, SCA ÖSTRAND *(SCA Transforest)*.

BELGIA SEAWAYS, GOTHIA SEAWAYS *(DFDS Seaways)*, SOMERSET *(Stena Line)*.

SEATRUCK PERFORMANCE, SEATRUCK POWER, SEATRUCK PRECISION, SEATRUCK PROGRESS *(Seatruck Ferries)*.

STENA FORECASTER, STENA FORERUNNER *(Stena Line)*, STENA FORETELLER *(DFDS Seaways)*.

STENA TRANSIT, STENA TRANSPORTER *(Stena Line)*.

SECTION 10 - CHANGES SINCE FERRIES 2019 - BRITISH ISLES AND NORTHERN EUROPE

DISPOSALS

The following vessels, listed in *Ferries 2019 - British Isles and Northern Europe* have been disposed of - either to other companies listed in this book or others. Company names are as used in that publication.

AEGEAN BREEZE *(UECC)* In February 2018 scrapped in Alagia, Turkey.

ANGLIA SEAWAYS *(DFDS Seaways)* In June 2019 sold to *Attica Group* of Greece and renamed the BLUE CARRIER 1.

ARABIAN BREEZE *(UECC)* In January 2019 scrapped in Alagia, Turkey.

ASIAN BREEZE *(UECC)* In April 2018 scrapped in Alagia, Turkey.

BALTIC BREEZE *(UECC)* In January 2019 scrapped in Alagia, Turkey.

BOHUS *(Color Line)* In August 2019 sold to a subsidiary of *Northbay Transportes Maritimos*, Madeira, Portugal.

BORE BAY *(Stena Line - Section 7)* In August 2918 charter ended.

BRUERNISH *(Humphrey O'Leary, Clare Island)* Now operates as a fish farm service vessel on Clare Island.

CANNA *(Humphrey O'Leary, Clare Island)* In 2018 chartered to *Arranmore Fast Ferries*.

CHIEFTAIN *(Clyde Cruises)* In October 2019 to be chartered to *Caledonian MacBrayne*. Continues on the Gourock-Kilkreggan route.

CROMARTY QUEEN *(Cromarty Ferry Company*) In 2018 sold to *Summer Isles Enterprises Limited* and used as a work boat for restoration project on the isle of Tanera Mòr.

ERNEST BEVIN *(Woolwich Free Ferry)* In October 2018 scrapped.

EUROPEAN ENDEAVOUR *(P&O Ferries)* In May 2019 sold to *Rederi AB Eckerö*. Renamed the FINBO CARGO and provides freight and car passenger services between Helsinki and Tallinn for *Eckerö Line.*

FINNCARRIER *(Finnlines)* . In July 2018 sold to *Color Line* and chartered back to *Finnlines*. In January 2019 delivered to *Color Line* and renamed the COLOR CARRIER.

GRETE *(Conmar Shipping)* In September 2018 sold to the *Woodward Group* of Canada. Renamed the QAJAQ W.

HIIUMAA *(Conmar Shipping)* In September 2018 sold to the *Woodward Group* of Canada.

JAMES NEWMAN *(Woolwich Free Ferry)* In October 2018 scrapped.

JOHN BURNS *(Woolwich Free Ferry)* In October 2018 scrapped.

JONATHAN SWIFT *(Irish Ferries*) In January 2019 sold to *Baleària* of Spain, renamed the CECILIA PAYNE and, in June, entered service between Denia and Ibiza and Mallorca.

KIRSTY M *(Bere Island Ferries)* Withdrawn from service. Although not actually scrapped she is being allowed to rust away on Bere Island.

KOPERNIK *(Unity Line)* In March 2019 sold to unknown Greek owners for scrapping. In June 2019 re-sold to *Levante Ferries* of Greece to operate between Smyrni and Thessaloniki. Renamed SMYRNA

OSCAR WILDE *(Irish Ferries)* In March 2019 sold (bareboat charter/hire purchase arrangement) to *Mediterranean Shipping Company SA* of Italy. Renamed the GNV ALLEGRA and used by subsidiary *GNV* on their Genova - Olbia service.

RAASAY *(Humphrey O'Leary, Clare Island)* In 2018 sold to *Inishbofin Island Discovery.*

RED JET 3 *(Red Funnel Ferries)* In March 2019 sold to *Adriatic Fast Ferries* of Croatia. Renamed the ADRIATIC EXPRESS. She operates between Split Airport, Bol and Stari Grad, on the islands of Brac and Hvar.

ROYAL DAFFODIL *(Mersey Ferries)* In 2019 sold to *Liverpool City Sights Ltd* for use as a static leisure attraction.

SAAREMAA *(Conmar Shipping)* In April 2019 sold to the *Société des traversiers du Québec* of Canada. In May renamed the SAAREMAA 1.

SCHULPENGAT *(TESO)* In October 2018 scrapped.

SCHIEBORG *(SOL Continent Line)* In June 2019 sold to *DFDS Seaways* and renamed the GOTHIA SEAWAYS.

SLINGEBORG *(SOL Continent Line)* In June 2019 sold to *DFDS Seaways* and renamed the BELGIA SEAWAYS.

ST CECILIA *(WightLink)* In January 2019 sold to *Delcomar* of Italy to sail between Isola di San Pietro and Sant'Antioco. She was renamed the NANDO MURRAU.

STENA CARRIER *(P&O Ferries)* In August 2018 charter ended. Vessel sold to *Baja Ferries* of Mexico and renamed the MEXICO STAR.

TAVASTLAND *(SOL Continent Line)* No longer operates to the UK.

GNV Allegra (ex Oscar Wilde) *(Frank Lose)*

European Endeavour *(Matt Davies)*

VESSELS RENAMED

The following vessels have been renamed since the publication of *Ferries 2019 - British Isles and Northern Europe* without change of owner or operator.

FBD TINTERN *(Frazer Ferries)* In 2018 renamed the FRAZER TINTERN.

GOTHIA SEAWAYS *(DFDS Seaways)* In March 2019 renamed the EPHESUS SEAWAYS and diverted to *DFDS Seaways'* Mediterranean operation instead of Gent - Göteborg as previously planned.

MAX MOLS *(Molslinjen)* In January 2019 renamed the MAX.

COMPANY CHANGES

Argyle Ferries In January 2019 all activities were transferred to sister company *Caledonian MacBrayne.*

Clyde Cruises This company has ceased passenger activities. The CRUISER is to be chartered to *Caledonian MacBrayne* and the rest of the fleet laid up.

David MacBrayne Ltd All vessels now listed under *Caledonian MacBrayne.*

SCA Transforest Company now trades as *SCA.*

Scandlines Helsingør - Helsingborg Now trades as *ForSea*.

LATE NEWS

Hurtigruten. In 2021 the FINNMARKEN, MIDNATSOL and TROLLFJORD will be converted to hybrid operation (with shore-side power supply) and will become full time cruise vessels, renamed the OTTO SVERDRUP, EIRIK RAUDE and MAUD respectively.

Finnmarken *(Agurtxane Concellon / Hurtigruten)*

FERRIES ILLUSTRATED

INDEX

NEW BOOKS FROM FERRY PUBLICATIONS

SUPERFAST

The publication looks at the development and introduction of the Superfast ships. The distinctive and slick Superfast vessels built in Germany and Finland transformed the Greek ferry business from the mid-1990s. The book contains unique first-hand accounts of the design development, construction and operations of the Superfast fleet and the development of the Blue Star Ferries brand. A fascinating insight into the contemporary Greek Ferry Industry. 120 pages. Price £18.95 plus p&p.

BRETAGNE

Narrative in both English and French this book covers the history of the distinctive 30 year old ship, which has served the Santander and the St.Malo principally. The title also features the distinctive art work of Alexander Goudi and his commission by Brittany Ferries to fulfil the art onboard the ship. Over 160 photos including construction views and plans of the ship. A4 Style. 112 pages. Price £18.00 plus p&p.

IN DEEP WATER

Following on from Robert Lloyd's *All At Sea* publication this new publication brings a further stunning collection of technically accurate paintings from his portfolio of the last nine years. The paintings subjects are varied from ferries to liners, super tankers to supply vessels, and coasters to sailing ships all of which are set in interesting locations. Images will include: ***W.B Yeats***, HMS ***Agamemnon***, the cruise ship ***Marina***, New York harbour with nine cruise ships afloat, the ***Goelo*** and the ***Viking Venturer***. A4 Style. 140 pages. Price £22.50 plus p&p

FERRIES FROM THE BRITISH ISLES TO IBERIA

This book looks at the development of the ferry services from Britain to Spain from the 1960's and includes the pioneering companies of Swedish Lloyd, Southern Ferries, Aznar Line and Brittany Ferries who have successfully developed and expanded the routes over the last 40 years. 144 pages. Price £19.50 plus p&p.

BRITTANY FERRIES - THE FLEET

This illustrated fleet publication encompasses the entire fleet of Brittany Ferries from the ***Kerisnel*** to the companies latest ship currently under construction in Germany, the ***Honfleur***. Detail information is given for each of the fleet, accompanied by a photograph or an illustration.The principal ships are illustrated by specially commissioned drawing by Marc-Antoine Bombail, who did all the detailed illustrations in Cunard – The Fleet and Townsend Thoresen – The Fleet Book. The book also includes ships of the former fleet in their new waters since their sail. 96 pages. Price £16.95 plus p&p.

FERRIES 2020

The 2020 edition of Ferries focus' on ***W. B.Yeats*** Irish Ferries new continental ferry, Stena Line new Holyhead Ferry – ***Stena Estrid***, Hurtigruten's hybrid explorer ship the ***Roald Amundsen***, Steam Packet new tonnage on the horizon and Red Funnel's new ***Red Kestrel***. The publication also includes comprehensive coverage of all British and European Ferry operations and full fleet listings. Price £19.00 plus p&p.

HYTHE PIER & FERRY

Hythe is a charming village fronting onto Southampton Water. Over the centuries much has changed, yet the links between the big city and the backwater village are still very much alive. Ferry passengers make the quarter of an hour crossing from Hythe's Victorian pier, the pier is the seventh longest in Britain. The story of the Hythe-Southampton ferry passage is a rich tapestry across the Southampton water. A4 Style. 140 pages. Price £16.95 plus p&p

Order online from
www.ferrypubs.co.uk
By telephone on
+44 (0)1624 898446
By post from
PO Box 33, Ramsey, Isle of Man IM99 4LP
Please telephone or email for current postage costs.